INTRODUCTORY GEOMETRIES

by
Larry Wiley, Ph. D.

TRILLIUM PRESS
New York

Acknowledgement

Preparation and publication of this book have been partially supported by a grant from the Geraldine R. Dodge Foundation in keeping with its commitment to the development of innovative educational programs and materials. The Foundation has been notably patient during the many unexpected delays caused by extensive revision and rewriting of major parts of the text.

We are most grateful for the Foundation's support and forebearance.

L.D.W.

Trillium Press, Inc.
PO Box 209
Monroe, New York 10950

Printed in the United States of America
ISBN: 0-89824-065-4

Table of Contents

Dedication

This book is dedicated to my wife Susan, to my son, Christopher, and to my daughter, Laura, for their love and patient understanding during the *many* long hours consumed in its creation.

Grateful thanks are also due to the many young women, my students, who cheerfully worked through versions of the manuscript in my Honors Geometry class at The Nightingale-Bamford School. I am especially grateful for the enthusiasm of   Jennifer Levin
Wendy Lader
Jennifer Mah
Debbie Mayer
Pammie Staab
Caroline Corbin
Marina Rustow
and Leslie Wolff.

L.D.W.

To the Reader

This book—unlike most mathematics texts—has been written with the intention that you will *read* it. With pen in hand, ponder and answer the exercises.

Ideally, very little of your class time will be spent listening to lectures. Instead, devote most of the time to discussing what you have read, clearing up inevitable confusions and misunderstandings, and sharing insights with your classmates and teachers.

All of you will find some of the material difficult, but keep at it both in and out of class! Sustained diligent effort should enable you to master the material and to develop an appreciation for the spirit of living mathematics.

Valeas qui legis quod scripsi!

L.D.W.

Unit I

God eternally geometrizes.

Plato

Let no one ignorant of geometry enter this door.

Plato's Academy

Well, why *should* you study geometry? It is difficult to answer that question; many questions which seem simple are really so complex that they either have no easy answers or lack answers entirely. This is particularly vexing for those who demand quick, simple answers to all questions. I believe that this question is one for which neither I nor anyone else could possibly have a simple answer. We cannot magically wish complexity or difficulty away. Einstein urged us to try to make everything as simple as possible, but not more so. In that spirit, I will try to give you some of the many reasons for studying mathematics and, in particular, geometry. I hope that soon you will be able to think of your own reasons for doing so.

Of course, if you stop to think about it, you will realize that you are surrounded by—indeed, you are part of—things geometrical. Bend your arm or leg, and you form an angle of a sort. Take a short cut at a corner, and you show a good intuitive grasp of the triangle inequality (i.e., that the length of one side of a triangle is less than the sum of the lengths of its other two sides). Consider why it is vital for many classes of objects to be made up of items which are all "identical" in size and shape, and you're thinking about a basic geometric relationship called *congruence*.

Intuitive Notion: We say two objects are *congruent* if and only if they are:
          1) the same size, and
          2) the same shape.

You may think of it as stretching the notion a bit to say that any object is congruent to itself, but it is standard to do so in geometry.

There are, in fact, people whose job it is to set standards for things just to make sure that they will be congruent. You might like to investigate the work of such organizations as the National Bureau of Standards or the American National Standards Institute to learn about how they function and of what value it is for society to have such organizations. (Hint: If you've ever been to England and encountered the bewildering variety of electrical plugs and sockets there, you may have a glimmer of why congruence can be of enormous value and importance.)

1. Can you think of some examples of congruent objects? List them. Explain briefly why their congruence is necessary or desirable. Is it necessary (or even physically possible) for distinct *real* objects to be absolutely and perfectly congruent to one another? Discuss and explain the implications for congruence of real objects.

If you drop the "same size" restriction for congruence, but insist that objects be related to one another by having the same shape—e.g., a small circle and a large one—then this "relaxed" requirement of having the same shape but *perhaps* not the same size characterizes the basic relationship between things in most of the geometry you'll be learning in this course. This relationship is called *similarity*, and objects so related to one another are said to be *similar* to one another

---

Intuitive Notion: We say two objects are *similar* if and only if they are the same shape.

It is standard in geometry to consider each object to be similar to itself.

We shall see that the assumption that the size of an object can vary without affecting its shape is a very big assumption indeed and has consequences most important for your thinking about geometry.

2. Must similar objects necessarily be of different sizes? Explain. Can you think of some examples of similar objects? List them; be sure to include examples of similar but non-congruent objects. Explain briefly why their similarity is necessary or desirable. It is necessary (or even physically possible) for distinct *real* objects to be absolutely and perfectly similar to one another? Discuss and explain the implications for similarity of real objects.

Because the relations of congruence and similarity are basic to everything you will study in this geometry course, you must have very clear intuitive notions of both. Later on in the course, you will supplement your intuitive notions with very formal, abstract ideas of both congruence and similarity.

3. Were you surprised or puzzled to think that it might not be possible, even in theory, to change the size of an object without changing its shape? If so, you should ponder what would happen if the object were, say, any triangle drawn on the surface of a sphere. If you draw a bigger triangle, by doubling the length of each side of the original triangle on that same sphere, would the new triangle be exactly the same shape as (i.e., similar to) the original triangle? Think very carefully about this. Try an experiment by drawing a triangle on the surface of a globe or basketball; then "double" the triangle on the same surface and determine whether or not the two triangles are similar. (Hint: Use a protractor to measure the angles in the triangles, and record what you find.) What is your conclusion?

4. By the way, if size is allowed to vary, just what *is* it about things that makes them the same shape? There is no easy answer here.

5. Now that you've thought about the ideas of congruence and similarity for a while, answer the following questions:
   a) If two objects are congruent to one another, are they *necessarily* similar to one another? Explain.
   b) If two objects are similar to one another, are they *necessarily* congruent to one another? Explain. *Could* they be congruent to one another? Explain.

6. a) Does it make sense to say that an object is congruent to itself? How about saying that an object is similar to itself? Briefly explain your answers.
   b) If you know that object 1 is congruent to object 2, does it follow that object 2 is congruent to object 1? If you know that object 1 is similar to object 2, does it follow that object 2 is similar to object 1? Explain.
   c) If you know that object 1 is congruent to object 2 and also that object 2 is congruent to object 3, does it follow that object 1 is congruent to object 3? How about the same sort of question for similar objects? Briefly explain your answers.

Because of the importance of the relations of congruence and similarity, we shall expand briefly on the idea of a relation. In particular, we concern ourselves with the so-called *binary* relations, i.e., relations between *two* objects.

If you stop to think about it, you will realize that you already have a good intuitive notion of many binary relations. For example, given a certain collection of people, you could examine how they are related to one another under various binary relations:

> 1. "Is the same sex as"
> 2. "Is taller than"
> 3. "Weighs less than"
> 4. "Is the brother of", etc.

Thus, for any two individuals in the given collection, say John and Mary, you could decide the truth or falsity of such statements as:

> 1. John is the same sex as Mary.
> 2. John is taller than Mary.
> 3. Mary weighs less than John.
> 4. John is the brother of Mary, etc.

Such decisions are usually easy to make for familiar relations on well-known collections. The fact that you could make such decisions easily is evidence for the knowledge you already have of binary relations.

In mathematics, we want to be able to consider very general relations on arbitrary collections (sets) which may consist of numbers, geometric figures, or any other items of interest. Hence, the definition of a binary relation must necessarily be quite general and abstract.

Definition: A *binary relation,* R, on a set, S, is *any set of ordered pairs of elements of S.*

Remarks:

1. You probably already know that in a reasonably elementary approach to sets one simply regards a *set* as a definite collection of things which are called *elements* of the set. For example, we might wish to consider the set, S, of integers from 1 to 10. We would write S = $\{1,2,3,4,5,6,7,8,9,10\}$ or S = $\{1,2,3, \ldots ,10\}$ to specify the set S. The *elements* of S are the indicated integers. To signify that a particular integer, say 4, is an element of S, we write 4 ∈ S. The Greek letter epsilon, ∈, is to be read as, "is an element of," or, "belongs to," or, "is in."

2. An *ordered pair* of elements is simply a pair of elements in which we specify that one element is *first* and the other is *second*. For example, from the set S above we could choose the ordered pair of elements having 6 first and 2 second. We denote this ordered pair by (6,2). In your study of algebra, you have probably seen ordered pairs that represented the coordinates of points in the the plane, and so you are well aware of how important it is to distinguish between (6,2) and (2,6).

3. You should be sure to note that, given a set S, you can *arbitrarily* specify a binary relation, R, on S simply by listing *any* set of ordered pairs of elements of S and declaring it to be R. Of course, most arbitrary relations will be of no great interest, but the freedom to choose arbitrarily is there. For example, using the set S above, we could define binary relations on S by:

R_1 = $\{(1,2), (5,9)\}$, R_2 = $\{(1,1)\}$, etc.

If we use the set T = $\{a, b, c\}$, we could define binary relations on T by:

R_1 = $\{(a,a), (b,b), (c,c)\}$,
R_2 = $\{(a,b), (b,a)\}$,
R_3 = $\{(a,b), (b,a), (a,a), (b,b)\}$, etc.

To indicate that two elements are related to one another, e.g., 1 and 2 in the relation R_1 on the set S above, we usually write 1 R_1 2 (sometimes we write (1,2) ∈ R_1—but only rarely). Note carefully that 1 R_1 2 does *not* necessarily mean that 2 R_1 1—the *order* is important!

Remark: We read a R b as "a is R-related to b," or more simply, as "a is related to b."

When you answered question 6 (page 3), you had to think about various *properties* of the relations of "congruence" and "similarity." Relations which have the properties considered in exercise 6 are very special indeed and are of great general interest in mathematics. To save on the labor of writing about congruence and similarity, let's introduce the standard symbols used to denote these relations.

The symbol for "is congruent to" is ≅; thus, we would translate "A is congruent to B" into symbols as "A ≅ B."

The symbol for "is similar to" is ∼; thus, we would translate "A is similar to B" into symbols as "A ∼ B."

To negate any of the relational symbols we write a slash through it. Thus, for example, we would translate "A is *not* congruent to B" into symbols as "A ≇ B."

The properties of relations considered in exercise 6 have fancy, technical names which we learn, once and for all, now:

Reflexivity: If a relation R on a set S is such that every element of S is related to itself under R, i.e., if for every element x of S we have x R x (just as every element *equals* itself, or *is congruent to* itself, or *is similar to* itself), we say that the relation R is *reflexive* or that it has the property of *reflexivity*. Thus, for example, the relations $=$, $\cong$, and $\sim$ are all reflexive. A relation which is *not* reflexive is said to be *irreflexive*. For example, the relation "is less than" on the set of real numbers is irreflexive since no number is less than itself.

Note carefully that a relation R on a set S is reflexive if and only if x R x for *every* element x of S.

7.   Choose your own set S and give at least one new example of a relation on it which is reflexive and another relation on it which is irreflexive. (Hint: Use a set S with few elements.)

Symmetry: If a relation R on a set S is such that whenever x R y is true for two elements x and y of S, it is also true that y R x, then we say that R is a *symmetric* relation, or that it has the property of *symmetry*. For example, $=$, $\cong$, and $\sim$ are symmetric relations. A relation which is *not* symmetric is called *asymmetric*. For example, the relation "is less than" on the set of real numbers is asymmetric.

8.   Choose your own set S and give at least one new example of a relation on it which is symmetric and another relation on it which is asymmetric.

Transitivity: If a relation R on a set S is such that whenever x R y and y R z are true for elements x, y, z of S it is also true that x R z, then we say that R is a *transitive* relation or that it has the property of *transitivity*. For example, $=$, $\cong$, and $\sim$ are all transitive relations. A relation which is *not* transitive is called *intransitive*. For example, the relation "is the mother of" on the set of human beings is intransitive.

9.   Choose your own set S and give at least one new example of a relation on it which is transitive and another relation on it which is intransitive.

Equivalence: Any relation R on a set S which has *all three* of the above properties is called an *equivalence* relation, i.e., an equivalence relation is one which is reflexive, symmetric, and transitive.

10.   Give at least three examples of equivalence relations.

The following is a brief way of remembering the various properties discussed above:

For all x,y,z in S:
  Reflexivity: x R x.
  Symmetry: If x R y, then y R x.
  Transitivity: If x R y and y R z, then x R z.

Geometric forms—natural and man-made—spread throughout the world. Thus, it should seem reasonable to you that your study of geometry should improve your ability to describe and understand reality. In fact, geometry is the principal means by which we can translate reality into terms with which we can deal. Thus, it can help us attain a deep feeling for the "inscape" of reality. (Read some of the poetry of Gerard Manley Hopkins to discover the significance of "inscape.")

We are always immersed in—and even part of—the geometry of the real world. Have you ever wondered why most road intersections form right angles? Why do the big nuts on top of fire hydrants all share a special, unusual shape? Why are manhole covers round? Why does the triangle occur so often as a basic architectural form? (Read about the geodesic domes of R. Buckminster Fuller.)

1. Try to answer the questions above. Can you think of some other interesting examples of geometry or its use in the real world? List a few and be prepared to discuss them.

Of course, a firm grasp of geometry will also serve to increase your intellectual power by equipping you with various paradigms (patterns or models) for organizing your knowledge. It is the systematic organization of information which raises us above the crude level of amassing unrelated scraps of knowledge. Geometry provides us with a systematic organizational tool and goes far toward giving us a clear insight into the nature of precise, orderly thinking.

Let's go on to seek some insight into the origins, importance, and structure of geometry.

Most of the geometry studied in a beginning course owes its existence to the astonishing richness of the explosive cultural development of ancient Greece. For various reasons, not entirely understood, Greek culture, beginning around the eighth century BC, experienced a flowering of such supreme magnificence that it is no exaggeration to say that it formed the basis of most of Western civilization. From the veritable flood of brilliant intellectual activity that flowed from Greek geniuses issued the well-springs of a very great variety of disciplines; among the most important were philosophy, literature, drama, politics, art, and (supremely important for us) mathematics! I think that one of the important reasons to study geometry is that we are thereby put in touch with one of the fountainheads of our Western intellectual heritage.

Extra-Credit Project:
>Try to discover some possible reasons for the explosive cultural growth in ancient Greece. Write a brief essay which reflects the results of your research. Use your best essay form, cite your sources, etc.

Mathematics, however, did not originate with the Greeks. Mathematics had long existed in the civilizations of Babylonia, Egypt, and China, but it was the creative spirit of the Greeks which breathed life into mathematics as we know it today. Prior to falling under the happy influence of the Greeks, mathematics had generally played a workaday role in solving practical problems which confronted land surveyors (indeed, the very word geometry comes from GE (earth) + METREIN (measure)), artisans, inventory keepers, etc. For example, each year before the building of the Aswan dam, the Nile river flooded the major croplands of Egypt and deposited a rich, alluvial soil. These same floods doubtless eroded some fields and obliterated some boundaries. Since the taxes paid by landholders were based upon, among other things, the size of their lands, it was most important to be able to survey fields accurately to determine their extent and to resolve any boundary disputes. Moreover, you may well appreciate that the artisans and builders of colossal projects—ziggurats, pyramids, palaces, temples, etc.—needed to know a great deal about practical, applied mathematics. However, despite the magnificent precision which characterizes the best work of these master builders (read, for example, about the construction of the pyramids), many of the rules which guided their calculations were, at best, only approximately correct and, at worst, simply wrong.

There were also some very important uses of mathematics which might not occur to you. For example, mathematics was crucial for interpreting the very accurate, ingenious astronomical observations made by the ancients. The information gleaned from these observations was used for purposes ranging from the practical—determining the optimal time to plant crops—to the mystical—delving into the dark mysteries of astrology. The Babylonians were particularly adept astrologers; their mathematics seems to have been notably superior to that of the Egyptians. However, despite the existence of masses of what we might call mathematical rules-of-thumb or procedures (some correct and some not) for doing various things, there was no unifying, underlying "theme" to tie mathematics together and thereby endow it with the vastly superior power which flows from coherence, consistency, and systematic organization. The diagram below should help you grasp some of the great changes wrought by the ancient Greeks in the nature of mathematical activity:

Contrasts Between Pre-Greek and Greek Mathematics

Most of Pre-Greek Mathematics was:	Most of Greek Mathematics was:
1. Concrete	1. Abstract
2. Practical	2. Theoretical
3. Disorganized	3. Systematic
4. Procedures	4. Proved results
5. Devoted to very specific problems	5. Devoted to general, logical development.

2. Using at least two different sources (one of which should be a good, high-powered encyclopedia, the other perhaps a history of mathematics—see the sources at the end of Unit I for some possible ideas), write an essay of one page or more on the ancient Greek influence on the development of mathematics. In particular, discuss *Euclid*, (the geometer not the philosopher) and his *Elements*—what is known of the man and his work and why it was of such great importance. You may improve your essay by following up on the related references you will discover in doing your basic research.

Section 3

There was creative mathematical genius present in great abundance before the advent of the Greeks, but unbridled creative impulse based on intuitive insight alone can lead to grievous error (it was not too long ago that everyone "knew" that the sun moved around the earth, which was the center of the universe). Ancient, pre-Greek mathematicians were often "guilty" of putting their trust in unverified, false procedures. How is one to "prove," i.e. *test*, the products of creative genius to ensure their correctness and thus maintain the robust health of mathematics? Read on and see.

It took the Greek genius to capture the missing component of the abstract essence of mathematics, namely the hypothetico-deductive or *axiomatic method*. Dimly foreshadowed in the sixth century BC writings of Thales, a wealthy, wily, much-travelled Greek businessman who perceived a logical connection among several of the then-known geometric results, it is this *method* which I hope you will begin to understand and, perhaps, to appreciate as a result of your study of geometry. It would be difficult (but not at all impossible) to overemphasize the importance of the axiomatic method in the growth of mathematics. However, one must never forget that the driving impulse of *creativity* is the origin of the results which are kept in good order by the application of the axiomatic method.

Once formulated, the idea of the axiomatic method captured the imagination of Western thinkers and became the paradigm of excellence in many realms of intellectual endeavor. Lest you think that its influence was strictly confined to mathematical areas, you should know about the axiomatic approach taken by the philosopher Spinoza in his approach both to ethics and to a psychology of the emotions.

1. Look up Spinoza, Benedictus (or Baruch) in an encyclopedia and find out about the *Ethica Ordine Geometrico Demonstrativa* (i.e., Ethics Demonstrated in the Geometric Way) and his ideas on the psychology of the emotions.

The axiomatic method is an organizational tool of fantastic power and economy of thought. Thus, the Greeks were able to tease out the deductive structure of mathematics and thereby draw order out of chaos and replace a hodge-podge of procedures with an elegantly beautiful pattern of proven results. This feat has been regarded as one of the greatest achievements of the human mind for well over two thousand years!

Because of its crucial importance for all of modern mathematics and not just for geometry, I shall try to give you an elementary but accurate idea of the nature of the axiomatic method. Very roughly, the method begins with some *undefined* terms concerning which one must *assume* certain statements which are so obviously self-evident (whatever that may mean!) as to be acceptable to all as a basis from which to work. Then, by "right reasoning" one goes on to *deduce* as inescapable conclusions other statements which may not be at all obvious. It sounds ridiculously simple in outline, but the simplicity is a major part of the power and elegant beauty of the axiomatic method.

2. Among the statements assumed true by Euclid were some called "common notions" or *axioms* and others called *postulates*. Look up these nouns and record what you find. In particular, try to determine the difference between an <u>axiom</u> and a <u>postulate</u>. (Hint: one was a "global" assumption and the other was a "local" assumption.) Do modern mathematicians continue to distinguish between axioms and postulates? If

you've not already done so, try to find and record at least some of the statements which were Euclidean axioms or postulates.

3. The "right reasoning" mentioned in the rough description of the axiomatic method is usually called *logic*. Look up this term and record what you find.

4. The statements which are derived by right reasoning are called *theorems*. Look up this term and record what you find.

5. The process of deducing theorems is called *proving*. Look up the verb *prove* and record the meanings you find. What does your source say a *proof* is? What about *rigor*?

Now, for obvious reasons, if one is trying to do a careful axiomatic development of geometry, it would *seem* necessary to define carefully *all* the terms one wished to use, e.g., what *is* a "point?" What *is* a "line?" However, if you think about it, you will realize that it is *absolutely impossible* to define *everything* rigorously. We are not sure, but we believe that Euclid may not have fully realized this basic impossibility. He began his *Elements* with a long list of "definitions," such as: "A point is that which has no part." Does that make sense? In order to understand it, wouldn't you need to know what a "part" is and also what it means to "have" a part? So, for example, you might try to define "part." But to do that, you'd have to use yet more terms needing further definition and so on. . . forever! Thus, one is *forced* to do one of two things. One may fall into the logical error of defining a term by using that same term in the definition, e.g., "a basilisk is a basilisk." This circularity in definition may indicate the truth—although it is scarcely helpful—but it is severely frowned upon. Or, one may *accept some basic undefined terms* and hope that their "meaning" will become clear from the way in which they are used. "The true meaning of a term is to be found by observing what a man does with it, not by what he says about it" (P. W. Bridgman). Further definitions may then employ either the basic, undefined terms or other terms which have been previously defined. Ultimately, however, one cannot escape the fact that the axiomatic treatment of a subject is based on *undefined* terms. This is why mathematics has been jokingly described by Lord Bertrand Russell as a subject in which we never know what we are talking about.

6. Try to find an example of circularity in definition. Look up "life" or "alive" in a dictionary and, if necessary, keep looking up the definitions of the terms used until you find a circularity. Record your findings. Try another word, such as "line." Do you begin to appreciate the problem involved here?

The acceptable rules of logic for an axiomatic system are almost never explicitly stated, but if you look up "Aristotelian logic" or "formal axiomatic method" in an encyclopedia, you will get some idea of the "logical rules of the game."

7. Look up the terms quoted just above and record your findings. (*The World of Mathematics*, edited by J. R. Newman, Simon and Schuster, NY, 1956, is an excellent reference. Check the index in Vol. 4.)

Although I am trying to keep this introductory discussion on a very intuitive level, I want to try to make a point about logic to help you refrain from falling into the most common logical errors.

First, I must introduce some new ideas, terminology, and notation. A *statement* is an assertion which is either true (valid) or false (invalid)—there is no third possibility. The assumption that there is no alternative to a statement's truth or falsity is known as the *Law of the Excluded Middle*. (There *are* systems of logic—multi-valued logics—in which a statement may be something other than simply true or false. In fact, there are logics in which a statement may have any one of an *infinite* number of "truth values"!) We shall assume that the Law of the Excluded Middle is part of our logic for geometry.

Examples

    i) "2 is an even number" is a true statement.

    ii) "6 is a prime integer" is a false statement.

    iii) "Spinach tastes worse than liver" is *not* a statement—it is an expression of opinion.

8.   Give other examples of statements, both true and false, and of assertions which fail to be statements. Explain your examples.

Suppose P is the statement, "2 is an odd integer." Since P is obviously not valid, we would surely like to have a way of *denying* P. We can do so by asserting the *negation* of P, denoted by $\rightarrow$P; in this case, $\rightarrow$P is the statement, "2 is *not* an odd integer."

Since $\rightarrow$P is the denial of P, it is easy to see that we would want both:

    i) $\rightarrow$P is true if and only if P is false, and

    ii) $\rightarrow$P is false if and only if P is true.

We may also say that $\rightarrow$ P is the logical opposite of P.

---

9.   i) Give other examples of statements and their negations.

    ii) Is "a < b" the negation of "b < a"? (Careful!) Explain your answer.

As an example of a statement, we might take the plea of a defendant in a trial: "Not guilty." This statement is obviously the negation of the statement: "Guilty." Let P be the statement, "guilty." Then, the defendant claims $\rightarrow$P while the prosecutor may be thought of as trying to prove either P or $\rightarrow\rightarrow$P. You probably assume that the statements P and $\rightarrow\rightarrow$P are equivalent for any statement P. Not all mathematicians would agree to such an equivalence in general. We, however, shall assume that for all P, P and $\rightarrow\rightarrow$P are equivalent in the logic we shall use for geometry.

Now, many of the theorems of mathematics (and *most* of those in geometry) are (or could be rephrased so as to be) in the so-called *conditional* form: "If P, then Q" (in symbols, "P$\Rightarrow$Q"), where P and Q are statements. (In English, one often finds a conditional stated in the form, "Q if P" e.g., "I can go out if I do my math first." Beware of confusing the form "Q if P" with 'Q$\Rightarrow$P;" in fact, "Q if P" means the same thing as "if P, then Q.") When we say that a conditional statement with *hypothesis* (given, data) P and *conclusion* Q (i.e., P$\Rightarrow$Q) is valid, we intuitively understand that the "truth" of P implies the "truth" of Q, i.e., that it is utterly impossible for P to be true and Q to be false at the same time.

Let us suppose, for example, that we are talking about a triangle. Let P be the statement, "two sides of the triangle are congruent." Let Q be the statement, "two angles of the triangle are congruent." Consider the two statements:

i) If P, then Q (i.e., $P \Rightarrow Q$).
ii) If Q, then P (i.e., $Q \Rightarrow P$).

(Both of these statements are valid theorems in geometry.) Each of the conditional statements i) and ii) is said to be the *converse* of the other. The *converse* of a conditional statement is another conditional statement arrived at by interchanging the hypothesis and the conclusion of the original conditional. When—and only when— both of the converses are valid—as in our example—we can roll the two conditionals into one *biconditional* of the form "P if and only if Q" (in symbols, "$P \Leftrightarrow Q$" or "P iff Q").

Now, it's not always the case that both a conditional and its converse are true, and that's a crucial fact to keep in mind! For example, let P be the statement, "It's raining outside." Let Q be the statement, "The street is wet." The conditional, $P \Rightarrow Q$, is true, but the converse, $Q \Rightarrow P$ is *not* always true, e.g., an open fire hydrant could have flooded the street on a sunny, hot, rainless day. The error which you must guard against (called "affirming the consequent") amounts to confusing the conditional with its converse. E.g., suppose you know that $P \Rightarrow Q$ is true and you also know that Q is true. Does it follow that P must be true? *No!* Avoid this classic error of logic!

If you are interested in learning more about logic ("the grammar of mathematics"), a good place to start is in *The World of Mathematics* (see exercise 7). For extra credit, you could write an essay on symbolic logic and truth tables, or on the uses of implication (so called because "$P \Rightarrow Q$" is read as "P implies Q") in mathematics, or on some other related topic which you find interesting.

There is no universal agreement on the laws of mathematical logic. In fact, there is a deep and sometimes heated disagreement among mathematicians of differing philosophies concerning what procedures and mathematical "laws" of logic are generally acceptable. For example, the noted Intuitionist L.E.J. Brouwer wrote a paper with the thought-provoking title, "The Untrustworthiness of the Principles of Logic." In general, Intuitionists and Constructivists oppose the unrestricted use of either the Law of the Excluded Middle or the method of proof by contradiction (See Section 4 for a discussion of proof by contradiction). On the contrary, Formalists and Logicists would be happy with unrestricted use of both of these mathematical principles.

You may wish to investigate this philosophical dispute among mathematicians. If so, search for information on the philosophy and foundations of mathematics. There are many sources.

For our purposes, however, "right reasoning" should be understood as the sort of reasoning which "makes sense." There are limits to this idea, of course, since an argument which seems entirely convincing to one mathematician may not even be comprehensible to another. We shall regard as "good" a proof which is "clearly understandable," and in which each step is seen to follow logically from previous steps, theorems, or definitions. There should *not* remain, in a good proof, any unremovable shadow of doubt about its certainty. You must be prepared either to justify every step or at least to convince your intended audience that such a justification *could* be given. If you can't do this, then your "proof" is faulty and must be repaired. Remember that "a good proof is one which makes us wiser!"

To help fix the important ideas in your mind, do the following exercises on conditionals:

10. i) Does every statement have a converse?
    ii) Does every conditional statement have a converse?
    iii) If a conditional statement such as $P \Rightarrow Q$ is true, is its converse necessarily also
    true? Give an example (not cited in the text) to illustrate your answer.

11. What is the converse of the statement: "I will do well in geometry if I study hard and never fail to do my homework."? (Careful!)

12. Rephrase the following statement into conditional form: "Two triangles congruent to the same triangle are congruent to each other." Is the conditional true? Is its converse true? Explain.

13. Suppose you know that $P \Rightarrow Q$ is true and that $\rightarrow P$ is true. Does it necessarily follow that $\rightarrow Q$ is true? (Hint: Refer back to the example about rain and wet streets if necessary.) Explain.

That last exercise points out yet another logical error for you to avoid, viz., $P \Rightarrow Q$ and $\rightarrow P$ do *not* yield $\rightarrow Q$! (You may wish to investigate what the *inverse* and *contrapositive* of a conditional statement are and how they are related logically to the conditional and its converse. You could write up your investigation for presentation as a minor extra credit project.)

Let's end this section by studying a diagram which should help you remember the essential components of the axiomatic method. Roughly speaking, each component in the diagram is dependent on those found below it:

The Components of the Axiomatic Method

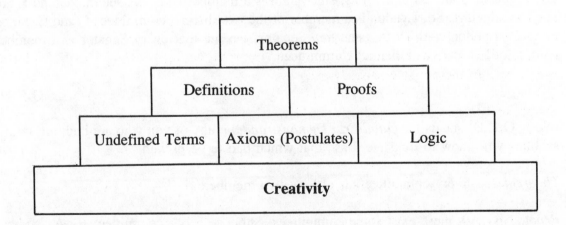

Section 4.

Now, at last, let's look at a very small example of the axiomatic method in action. Let's suppose we are studying the committee structure of the Senate in the far-away city of Foggy Bottom. Our basic undefined terms and relation will be: "Senator," "Committee," and, "is a member of." You are perfectly free to imagine your own model of the following system as long as your model satisfies the axioms we state. (As S.I. Hayakawa says, "Whenever two or more human beings can communicate with each other, they can, by agreement, make anything stand for anything.") We assume the five axioms which follow:

A0. There exist some Senators and some committees.

A1. For each committee there is at least one Senator who is a member.

A2. Every Senator is a member of at least one committee.

A3. For every pair of Senators there is one and only one committee of which both are members.

Definition: We say two committees are *disjoint* if there is no Senator who is a member of both of them.

A4. For every committee there is one and only one committee disjoint from it.

Definition: We say two committees are *distinct* if there is at least one Senator who is a member of one but not of the other.

Theorem 1. Every Senator is a member of at least two distinct committees.

Proof: By A0, there exist some Senators. Suppose Lyndon is a Senator.
By A2, Lyndon is a member of at least one committee, say C.
By A4, there is a unique committee D which is disjoint from C.
By A1, there is a Senator, say Sam, who is a member of D.
By A3, there is a unique committee E of which both Lyndon and Sam are members. Now, Sam is not a member of C since he is a member of D, and D and C are disjoint. Thus, since Sam is a member of E, we see that C and E are distinct. So, Lyndon is a member of the two distinct committees C and E. Since Lyndon could have been *any* Senator, we see that every Senator is a member of at least two distinct Committees.

Q.E.D.

(Note: Q.E.D. stands for *Quod Erat Demonstrandum*; any of you who are budding Latin scholars will know to translate it as "that which had to be proved.")

Theorem 2. Every committee has at least two members.

Proof: By A0, there exist some committees. Suppose F is a committee. By A1, F has at least one member, say Strom. Now suppose F has only one member, namely Strom. (Remark: this supposition will lead to an impossible situation, and so it must be wrong. Thus, it follows that every committee has at least two members, as we are trying to prove.) By Theorem 1, there is another committee G, distinct from F, of which Strom is a member. Now, there must be a Senator, say Teddy, who is also a member of G. Otherwise, Strom would be the only member of F and G, and they wouldn't be distinct committees. By A4, there is a unique committee H which is disjoint from G. Now H is also disjoint from F since we have supposed that F is a one-man committee with Strom as its sole member; since Strom is a member of G, and H is disjoint from G, Strom can't be a member of H. So, we have two distinct committees, F and G, which are disjoint from H. But A4 forbids this situation. Thus, our supposition that F has only one member has led to an impossible situation. Hence, it must be that F has at least two members. Since F could have been *any* committee, every committee has at least two members.

Q.E.D.

I have given proofs of the two theorems above in a boringly complete form to help you see the basic structure of a good proof. Proofs which you make up will differ from these two examples. However, the basic idea is that a proof should be a "little story" which *completely* convinces the reader or listener of the validity of the theorem being proved.

Carefully note the special technique of proof which was used in proving Theorem 2. It is a method of proof called "proof by contradiction." (*Reductio ad absurdum* (RAA) is the Latin name for it.) The method seems to involve high risk, since one begins with the supposition that the thing to be proved is false. If it were really false, the task of proof would be hopeless. One hopes to be led by the original supposition to an impossible conclusion, a contradiction of something already known to be valid. If one can arrive correctly at such an impossible conclusion, then the supposition itself must be false. Thus, the desired conclusion must be true since it is false that it is false! In this regard you may enjoy the following quotes:

"I contradict myself. I am large. I contain multitudes."

—Walt Whitman—

"There's no use trying," said Alice: "one can't believe impossible things."
"I dare say you haven't had much practice," said the Queen. "When I was your age I always did it for half an hour a day. Why sometimes I've believed as many as six impossible things before breakfast."

—Lewis Carroll—

Of course, these quotes, while amusing, do not embody the mathematical certitude of proof by contradiction.

1. Look up *reductio ad absurdum* or proof by contradiction and record what you find. (Use a large, unabridged dictionary.)

Let's extend our study of committees a bit more.

Theorem 3. There are at least four Senators.

Proof: We saw in the proof of Theorem 1 that there must be at least two Senators, Lyndon and Sam. By A3, there must be a unique committee of which both Lyndon and Sam are members. Call this committee E. By A4, there is a unique committee I which is disjoint from E. By Theorem 2, there are at least two member Senators on Committee I, say Strom and Teddy, different from Lyndon and Sam. Thus, there are at least four Senators.

Q.E.D.

One could go on making up and proving theorems, but this should be enough to give you a rough but correct idea of how the axiomatic method works.

2. Prove: There are at least six committees.

3. (*Very* difficult—extra credit) Prove or Disprove: No committee has more than two members.

Note that in the previous example of the axiomatic method we could simply replace every occurrence of the words Senator and committee by the words point and line, respectively, and everything would still follow logically. This demonstrates the power of the abstractness of the axiomatic method. One may interpret the undefined terms in many ways and get different models in which all the theorems are satisfied.

4. Rewrite the axioms and definitions of the committee example but replace each instance of the word Senator with the word point and each instance of the word committee with the word line. Do the axioms and definitions still seem obvious? Read the theorems and proofs again, making the same word replacement (mentally) as described above, and see if the theorems and proofs still make logical sense. Do they?

5. Can you think of other substitutions for the basic undefined terms which will yield a model of the axioms which makes sense to you? If so, explain.

It is absolutely necessary for a useful axiomatic system to be *consistent*, i.e., non-contradictory. One must be quite certain that it is impossible to deduce from the axioms that a statement P and its logical opposite $\rightarrow P$ are both simultaneously valid—a blatant absurdity! Failure to be consistent is the worst possible disaster which can befall an axiomatic system, because it makes *every* statement, whether true or false, a theorem of the system!

How then may one guarantee that a given axiomatic system is consistent? Unfortunately, one may do so only in a relative sense. By providing a *model* for an axiomatic system (i.e., an interpretation of the undefined terms such that all the axioms are satisfied), one shows that the axiomatic system is *consistent relative to* the system in which the interpretation is formulated.

For example, we can give two different models of the system of Senators and committees axiomatized in this section:

Model 1. In this model each Senator is represented by a large dot; each committee consists of exactly two Senators, and the fact that two Senators are on a committee is indicated by joining two large dots with a straight line segment. This model is diagrammed below:

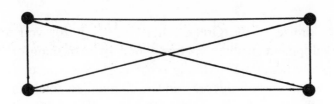

Model 2. In this model, each Senator is represented by a letter from the set
{A, B, C, D}. The committees are pairs of Senators, viz., {A, B}, {A, C},
{A, D}, {B, C}, {B, D}, and {C, D}.

6. Examine each of the models above and convince yourself that each of the Senator-committee axioms is valid when interpreted in terms of the model.

You probably see clearly the underlying sameness of the two models above. There could be, however, models very different from these two. It is well beyond our scope to try to determine whether or not every model of the Senator-committee axioms is essentially the same as these two. Indeed, there are axiomatic systems (e.g., those for the real numbers) for which every model is essentially the same as any other model.

To give yet other examples of how one can give such a relative consistency proof, I point out that the algebra with which you are slightly acquainted may be axiomatized. The resulting axiomatic system can be modelled in arithmetic. Hence, one knows that algebra is consistent *provided* that arithmetic is consistent, i.e., that algebra is consistent relative to arithmetic. Later in this book, we shall see something of a model (called analytic geometry) of Euclidean geometry formulated within the system of algebra. The fact that such a model exists means that Euclidean geometry is consistent relative to algebra. Thus, if arithmetic is consistent, so are algebra and Euclidean geometry. But *is* arithmetic consistent? Alas, no one knows absolutely for certain. It is a curious and perverse twist in mathematics that it seems impossible for us to assure ourselves *absolutely* that our axiomatic systems are consistent. Some mathematicians jokingly say that we know God exists because we *know* arithmetic is consistent, and we know that Satan exists because we can't *prove* that it is consistent!

Later in this book, we'll discuss the properties of completeness and independence of axiomatic systems. These properties, unlike consistency, are not essential properties of all axiomatic systems but are sometimes desirable. One may say, roughly, that an axiomatic system is *complete* if it contains all the axioms needed for us to be able to prove all the theorems about the structure being axiomatized. Moreover, one may say, again roughly, that an axiomatic system is *independent* if it doesn't contain any unnecessary (extra, deducible from the others) axioms.

Why do you suppose the axiomatic method was so fascinating to the ancient Greeks as well as to many of the later great thinkers? Certainly it gave the Greeks an orderly way of extracting from the collection of Egyptian and Babylonian procedures those results which were correct and could be proved; thus, the method was a powerful organizational tool. But more than this, perhaps the Greeks were convinced that by starting from what they felt were self-evident beginnings they could carefully reason their way to an absolutely certain knowledge of the nature, workings, and properties of the *real* world! Surely those who could do so were like unto gods. We shall see later to what extent they succeeded in their "divine quest"—and that we have have never completely abandoned this "quest."

Despite my lavish praise of the Greeks, it is only fair for you to know that their influence on the development of mathematics—their overstressing of the geometric approach—was not entirely beneficial. Among other negative aspects, it severely retarded the growth of what we now call algebra, and it channelled mathematical thought into narrowly restricted paths of research and development. (If you're interested in this sort of thing, why not read up on the history of mathematics? Use the references at the end of this Unit.) So, while the achievements of the Greeks were undeniably great, they also warped the development of mathematics in an unfortunate way.

7. Some say that the development of the axiomatic method was not a slow *evolution* through the work of various thinkers such as Thales, Pythagoras, Democritus, Theaetetus, Eudoxus, and Euclid, but that it was a product of necessity, produced by the *revolution* stemming from the Pythagoreans' discovery of the existence of incommensurable magnitudes (or irrational numbers). Using your library resources, write the story of the Pythagoreans and what their discovery of irrationals involved. Be prepared to discuss; know what rational and irrational numbers are, and be able to give examples of each type of number. A possible research project for you would be to show *why* $\sqrt{2}$ is irrational. The proof is in many mathematics books. You might try looking at the top of page 89 of the first volume of *The World of Mathematics*. This set of four volumes should be in your library. It is an excellent and interesting source for many insights into mathematics.

Section 5.

Among the important reasons for studying geometry, we must mention that it is almost universally required in the schools, and that it is regarded as a gateway to further mathematics courses. In fact, a well-developed geometrical intuition and the ability to use pictures to help yourself think are among the most valuable tools you can use to gain insight into mathematics. These tools are crucial in almost all mathematical disciplines, particularly in topology (which is a mathematical generalization of geometry). The mathematician M. Kline says, ". . . pictures should be used whenever possible to illuminate all mathematics, and synthetic geometry provides training in the effective use of pictures."

1. Look up topology and see what you can find out about it. Note your findings for discussion.

"In our increasingly complex technological society, a reasonable grasp of mathematics is an absolute necessity in a very wide variety of careers."

2. Do you believe the claim in the preceding sentence? Ask your parents or friends how they use mathematics in their careers. Ask yourself what is your own honest view of mathematics so far as you know it now. For example, do you find it dull, depressing, monotonous, useless? Or do you find it interesting, stimulating, varied, useful, maybe even fun? Be prepared to discuss your answers to this rather long question.

You should study as much mathematics as you can in order to hold open as many career options as possible; women, especially, since they are often discouraged from studying mathematics for one or another preposterously silly reason (e.g., "math is for boys, not girls;" "math is unladylike;" "boys won't like you if you're good at math;" "women just don't have a head for figures;" etc.!) should take great care to pursue their studies in mathematics to the fullest possible extent.

Reproduced below, you will find a list published by the Mathematical Association of America which indicates how many years of high-school mathematics you should have taken prior to beginning college study in the various career programs. *Caution:* do not be misled by anyone (including school guidance counselors) into thinking that you can drop out of mathematics because it is not required for college entrance. It is true that, due to a lamentable lowering of standards at many (even of "the best") colleges and universities, you may need little mathematics to get in; you will almost surely need it (and perhaps a lot of it) to get out successfully. Check college catalogs and department advisors to be sure of the requirements for your proposed major in college.

Proposed Major	Years H.S. Math			
Agriculture:		**Medicine:**		
Agricultural economics	3	Allied medicine	3	
Entomology	3	Dental hygiene	3	
Environmental sciences	4	Dentistry	4	
Food sciences	3	Medical technology	4	
Forestry	3	Nursing	3	
Genetics	3	Optometry	4	
Landscape architecture	3	Physical therapy	3	
Plant pathology	3	Pre-med	4	
Rural sociology	3	Public health	3	
Wildlife ecology	3			
Other areas of agriculture	2	Music	2	
Architecture	3	Pharmacy	4	
Art	2	Philosophy	2	
Business:		**Physical sciences:**		
Accounting	3	Astronomy	4	
Economics	4	Chemistry	4	
Management	4	Geology	4	
		Physics	4	
Communications	2			
		Social sciences:		
Education:		Anthropology	2	
Elementary	3	Asian Studies	2	
Child Development and Preschool	3	Black Studies	3	
		Geography	3	
Engineering	4	Political Science	3	
		Psychology	4	
History	2	Social welfare	2	
		Sociology	3	
Language and Literature	2	Theater	2	
Law	3			
Life sciences:				
Biology	4			
Bacteriology	4			
Biochemistry	4			
Linguistics	3			
Mathematical sciences				
Mathematics	4			
Statistics	4			
Actuarial sciences	4			
Computer sciences	4			

Besides the obvious, practical reasons for studying geometry (a year of which is included in *every one* of the above MAA recommendations), there are a few less obvious advantages that you may accrue as a result of your study of mathematics in general:

1. You will find that in geometry, as in all mathematics, we must exercise extreme precision in our use of vocabulary and language. Practice in this may benefit you in both your mathematics and your non-mathematics classes, e.g., in writing themes for English or history. You will, I hope, come to appreciate the intimate relationship which exists between clarity and precision of expression.

2. The extensive practice you get in using various problem-solving techniques in mathematics may improve the naive, intuitive approach to problem solving you have been almost wholly dependent upon up to now.

3. A good grasp of mathematics will enable you to think more precisely and generally by freeing you from the shackles of purely qualitative thinking.

4. You will, I hope, begin to see the power of logic as a tool for eliminating chaos and drawing order out of disorder. Logic can be helpful in weighing the merits of opposing arguments and establishing priorities for the expenditure of your time and energies. However, please note that I am *not* advancing logic as the cure-all for life's problems and predicaments. Learn to couple your intuition and creative insight with logic in mastering the challenges which you will encounter in mathematics: It is in the joyous interplay of creative intuition and therapeutic logic that you may find your greatest satisfaction in problem solving and in mathematics.

5. Your exposure to the methods of mathematics should help to convince you of the validity of the assertion that reason and order *should* triumph over unreason and disorder; that same exposure should also equip you with some valuable tools to assist you in making your contribution to the cultivated discourse of a civilized society.

6. You may come to value a bit of the austere beauty of mathematics and to appreciate the fact that, as John Muir said, "You must work for beauty as well as for bread."

7. Of course, you probably already know that knowledge and understanding of mathematics can give you a pleasurable feeling of power, and perhaps some status and prestige in a world generally overawed by mathematics. Perhaps someday you will share with the Greeks that heady feeling of being like unto the gods.

8. Lastly, I hope that you will derive from your experience of studying mathematics some of the joy which comes from grappling with many problems; that you experience the gratification of ingenuity, insight, deftness, persistent application, and the sheer force of your own mind as you overcome most of those problems. The delightful game of mathematics, if you come to appreciate it, is one of the richest sources of sheer fun there ever will be.

References

Bell, E.T., *Men of Mathematics*. New York: Simon and Schuster, 1937.

Boyer, C.B., *A History of Mathematics*. New York: John Wiley & Sons, 1968.

Heath, T.L., *Euclid—The Thirteen Books of the Elements*, (3 vols.). New York: Dover Publications, Inc., 1956.

Jones, B.W., "Miniature Geometries." *The Mathematics Teacher* 52 (1959) pp. 66–71.

Kline, M., *Mathematical Thought from Ancient to Modern Times*. New York: Oxford University Press, 1972.

Mathematics—The Loss of Certainty. New York: Oxford University Press, 1980.

Perl, T., *Math Equals—Biographies of Women Mathematicians & Related Activities*. Reading, MA: Addison-Wesley Publishing Co., 1978.

Struik, D., *A Concise History of Mathematics*, rev. ed. New York: Dover Publications, Inc., 1967.

van der Warden, B.L., *Science Awakening*. New York: Oxford University Press, 1963.

Wilder, R.L. (ed.), *The World of Mathematics (4vols.)*. New York: Simon and Schuster, 1956.

Unit I: Review Topics

1. Congruence: The intuitive notion and illustrative examples.

2. Similarity: The intuitive notion and illustrative examples.

3. How are congruence and similarity related?

4. Binary relations and their properties: Reflexivity, symmetry, and transitivity; equivalence relations.

5. Greek influence on the development of mathematics and the contrasts between pre-Greek and Greek mathematics.

6. Euclid and his *Elements*: The man's life, work, its importance, etc.

7. The axiomatic method: Its essential elements and how it works.

8. Statement, Law of the Excluded Middle, negation, equivalence of P and $\rightarrow\rightarrow$P, conditional statement, hypothesis, conclusion, converse, biconditional statement, errors of logic.

9. Axiomatic systems and their properties, e.g., consistency, completeness, independence; model of axiomatic system.

10. Proof: Characteristics of a good proof; *reductio ad absurdum* (RAA): What it is and how it works, including examples of its use.

11. Various reasons for studying mathematics.

Unit II
Symmetry: An Introduction to Ornamental Groups

The chief forms of beauty are order and symmetry and precision which the mathematical sciences demonstrate in a special degree.

—Aristotle

You boil it in sawdust; you salt it in glue
You condense it with locusts and tape
Still keeping one principal object in view—
To preserve its symmetrical shape.

—Lewis Carroll

This Unit and the next are devoted to a brief investigation of a very recent approach to geometry motivated by a study of the symmetry of certain special types of artistic ornaments. It cannot have escaped your attention that people are fond of decorating things. One of the principal devices used in art and architecture to promote aesthetic enjoyment is a harmonious balance of design which we may call *symmetry*. We usually say an object has symmetry of some sort if it can be split up into at least two "essentially identical" parts.

1. Look up *symmetry* in an encyclopedia or dictionary and reflect upon what you find. List several examples of symmetry. Try to include examples of more than one type of symmetry (e.g., bilateral and point symmetry). Bring in some objects which have symmetry (e.g., drawings, pictures, etc.) and be prepared to show them to the class and to explain their symmetry.

Besides the uses of symmetry in architecture, there are examples of it in art, e.g., in the composition of paintings and sculpture as well as in the rhyme schemes and melodic structures of poetry and music. Moreover, there are many examples of symmetry in nature: the outwardly apparent structure of the human body and in the arrangement of some of our internal organs. Other examples of natural symmetry may be found in the structure of starfish, flowers, leaves, crystals, etc. Indeed, the processes of growth and art seem so predisposed to producing symmetric forms that it is the lack of symmetry rather than its presence which is unexpected.

2. What types of symmetry are found in the specific examples listed above? Record them and be prepared to discuss them in class. Can you find examples of other types of symmetry? For example, what sort of symmetry is to be found in the shell of a chambered nautilus?

In a sense, the entire observable universe is "uniform" or symmetric—no matter where one looks one sees much the same structure of superclusters of galaxies. At the other end of the size scale, we may find symmetry displayed in nature in the "balancing" of elementary particles of matter with oppositely charged particles of anti-matter. The existence of this amazing symmetry was first predicted by the theoretical physicist P.A.M. Dirac who was bold enough to interpret a negative sign in certain equations as implying the existence of "negative mass." As a result, he forecast the discovery of the positron, the antimatter twin of the electron. Now physicists believe that subatomic space is aswarm with charmed and colorful quarks, antiquarks, and other oddities and antioddities. Moreover, investigations of symmetry and asymmetry have led to some vitally important discoveries in physics, neuropsychology, etc. For example, the downfall of the so-called "Law of Parity" was due to the discovery of a lack of symmetry among certain atomic particles. In addition, observations of asymmetry in the functions performed by the two hemispheres of the brain have given rise to on-going studies of the distinct roles played by the right (so-called "intuitive") and left (so called "rational, analytic") halves of the human brain.

It may surprise you to learn that there exists an extensive mathematical theory of symmetry and that we may employ some of the concepts and results of that theory to clarify our understanding of the essence of geometry. Such is the purpose of this Unit.

Among the crucial roles played by the mathematical theory of symmetry is its use in classifying groups of elementary particles of matter. Theoretical work along those lines underlay the study which earned the 1979 Nobel Prize in physics. It is no exaggeration to say that the modern theory of elementary particles would not exist if there were no mathematical theory to capture the elegant essence of symmetry. The ideas of symmetry are absolutely essential in crystallography and very useful in spectroscopy. These ideas have played vital roles in the design of codes which are efficient, error-correcting, and basically unbreakable. The theory of symmetry made it possible for the scientists Rosalind Franklin, James Watson, and Francis Crick to decipher the structure of the DNA molecule, a basic building block of living matter. Other researchers have used ideas about symmetry to crack the problem of the structure of the molecules of various proteins and polymers.

3. If you are interested in applications of symmetry in physics, read *The Key to the Universe* by N. Calder (Penguin Books, NY, 1980). Find out how the "pattern-makers" among the particle physicists were led to predict the discovery of the omega minus particle. You may also wish to investigate other ideas such as the Pauli exclusion principle, the eight-fold way, the invariance of physical laws under translation in time or space, etc. For more information on the neuropsychological asymmetry of the human brain see: *Left Brain, Right Brain* by Springer and Deutsch (Freeman, San Francisco, 1981). To find out more about geometry and symmetry in nature, you might like to consult *Patterns in Nature* by Stevens (Atlantic-Little, Brown, Boston, 1974) or *On Growth and Form* by Thompson (Cambridge University Press, Cambridge, 1961 (Abridged Edition)). Be prepared to discuss situations in which symmetry or asymmetry is vitally important.

Let's begin our study of symmetry by considering a very old symbol, found in the art of the ancient Greeks: the triskelion.

4. Look up *triskelion* in a dictionary and record your findings. Just below you will see an example of an ancient Greek triskelion and a modern business logo having the same sort of symmetry.

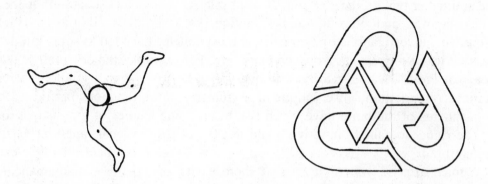

For ease of drawing, let's consider the simplified version of the triskelion which appears just below:

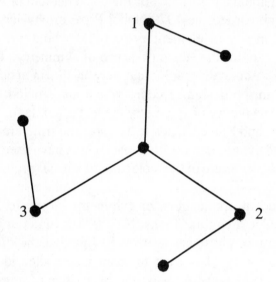

5. On very thin paper, make a tracing of the triskelion above (numbering the legs as shown for convenience) and, before reading beyond this question, investigate how you can move the tracing so that it will coincide with the original. (Hint: try rotation.) Describe the results of your investigations. (Note: the numbers are not part of the triskelion.)

You should have discovered in your investigations in 5 that a 1/3 turn clockwise causes the tracing to coincide with the original. Let's call *this* basic symmetry motion R (for *Rotation*). Note that after you do R to the tracing, the numbers on it no longer lie atop their equals on the original; in fact, 1 is atop 2, 2 is atop 3, and 3 is atop 1. We can denote R by 1⤳2, 2⤳3, 3⤳1, or more simply by $\begin{pmatrix} 1 & 2 & 3 \\ 2 & 3 & 1 \end{pmatrix}$

Note that the key to discussing and symbolizing motions such as this is to ignore any intermediate positions of the tracing and pay attention only to the beginning and ending positions. Thus, we are talking, somewhat paradoxically, about "motion without movement."

6. What motions are represented by the following symbols?

$$\text{a. } \begin{pmatrix} 1 & 2 & 3 \\ 3 & 1 & 2 \end{pmatrix} \qquad \text{b. } \begin{pmatrix} 1 & 2 & 3 \\ 1 & 2 & 3 \end{pmatrix}$$

7. Do you find any motions other than the three above which cause the tracing to coincide with the original? Explain.

8. Is the motion represented by $\begin{pmatrix} 1 & 2 & 3 \\ 3 & 2 & 1 \end{pmatrix}$ a motion which causes the tracing to coincide with the original? (I.e, is this motion an *allowable symmetry motion?*) Explain.

Your answers to 7 and 8 should have been *no*. Just as R, a 1/3 turn clockwise works, so does a 2/3 turn clockwise, i.e., $\begin{pmatrix} 1 & 2 & 3 \\ 3 & 1 & 2 \end{pmatrix}$

which is R followed by another R. We denote this 2/3 turn by R $\circ$ R or R^2. Of course, another allowable symmetry motion is a full turn clockwise, i.e.,

$$R \circ R \circ R = R^3 = \begin{pmatrix} 1 & 2 & 3 \\ 1 & 2 & 3 \end{pmatrix}$$

Do you see that such a full turn is equivalent to doing nothing to the tracing? After this motion, the tracing is *identical* to the original. Hence, we call such a motion I (for *Identity* motion). So, the symmetry motions found for the triskelion are: R, R^2, and R^3 or I.

9. What motion is R $\circ$ R $\circ$ R $\circ$ R? If you continue to do even more R's do you get any *new* motions?

10. What if you turn the tracing counterclockwise? Suppose S is a 1/3 turn counter-clockwise. Fill in the blanks in the symbol $\begin{pmatrix} 1 & 2 & 3 \\ \_ & \_ & \_ \end{pmatrix}$ to represent S. Is S a new symmetry motion or have you already considered S under another name? Explain.

11. Fill in the blanks in $\begin{pmatrix} 1 & 2 & 3 \\ \_ & \_ & \_ \end{pmatrix}$ to represent S $\circ$ S = S^2. Is S^2 a new symmetry motion or have you already considered it under another name? What about S^3? What if you go on and do even more S's? Explain.

Your answers to 10 and 11 should have convinced you that the only distinct symmetry motions for the triskelion (we were using the tracing only for convenience) are I, R, and R^2.

The three symmetry motions which you have found for the triskelion form what is called a group.

A group is a set of elements which can be combined by an operation (in this case, "do one motion and then do the next") in such a way that the resulting element is always in the set and such that the combining operation has certain nice properties. (See below for the full definition of group.) By using such groups of symmetry motions we can capture the essence of symmetry and classify various symmetry types. Thus the title of this Unit—An Introduction to Ornamental Groups.

In the table below you can see the "structure" of the symmetry group of the triskelion:

first→		I	R	R^2	←second
	I	I	R	R^2	
	R	R	R^2	I	
	R^2	R^2	I	R	

This table is to be thought of as though it were a "multiplication" table. Each tabular entry shows the result of *first* doing the motion in the *left border* of the entry row and *then* doing the motion in the *heading of* the entry *column*.

Latin Square Property

Note that each possible symmetry motion appears once and only once in each row and column of the table; such a table is called a Latin Square.

The Latin Square Property is an essential property for a group structure table; a "multiplication" table without this property *cannot* be the table of a group! We shall prove and make frequent use of this fact in the future. But first, let's look at some more examples of groups.

Some of you may have studied so-called "clock arithmetic" before. In any case, you are all familiar with the usual 12 hour clock. If it is 11 o'clock and two hours pass, what time is it then? Obviously you said 1 o'clock and not 13 o'clock. How did you get the answer? One way to think of it is that you *divide* 13 by 12 and use the remainder as your answer. When you do this, you are doing what is properly called "addition modulo 12" or "addition mod 12." Suppose you had a special three-hour clock like this:

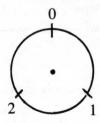

Suppose it reads 1 o'clock and two hours pass. What time does this clock then read? You should see that it would then say 0 o'clock: $1 + 2$ is 0 in mod 3 addition. You can represent mod 3 addition as in the table below:

+	0	1	2
0	0	1	2
1	1	2	0
2	2	0	1

Note the similarity of this table to the table of the symmetry group of the triskelion. We'll learn later that these two tables represent the "same" group.

1. Fill in the missing entries in the following table of addition mod 4. (Hint: to compute the tabular entries you just add, divide the sum by 4, and take the remainder. E.g., $3 + 2 = 1$ mod 4.)

+	0	1	2	3
0				
1				
2				
3		1		

Having seen several examples of groups, let's look at the general, abstract definition of a group:

MEMORIZE

Definition: A group, G, is a non-empty set of elements equipped with a binary operation denoted by ∘. This binary operation must satisfy the following requirements:

1. *Closure:* For any x and y in G, $x \circ y$ is also in G;

2. *Associativity:* For any x, y, and z in G, $x \circ (y \circ z) = (x \circ y) \circ z$;

3. *Existence of Identity:* There is an element e in G such that $e \circ x = x \circ e = x$ for any x in G;

4. *Existence of Inverses:* For each element x in G, there is an element y in G such that $x \circ y = y \circ x = e$, where e is the identity of G.

Remark: The *set* of elements of a group is called the *underlying* set of the group. So, a group is an underlying set of elements equipped with a binary operation satisfying the four axioms in the definition.

In the definition of group, to say that the operation for combining the elements is *binary* simply means that the elements are combined *two*-at-a-time, as is the case with adding or multiplying numbers.

The axiom of closure simply guarantees that there will be no surprise answers outside of G produced by combining elements in G; for example, the sum of any two integers is another integer, but the quotient of two integers is almost never an integer: closure holds for addition of integers but fails to hold for division of integers.

The axiom of associativity is hard to explain verbally. Basically, it says that if you take any three elements, x, y, and z and combine them using the group operation, a certain equality must hold. Since the operation is binary, elements can be combined only two-at-a-time. If you combine x and y to get an element of G called x $\circ$ y, then you can combine that element with z to get an element of G called (x $\circ$ y) $\circ$ z. On the other hand, you might first combine y and z to get an element of G called y $\circ$ z; then you can combine that element with x to get the element x $\circ$ (y $\circ$ z). The associative axiom says that the results of these two different ways of combining the elements should be the same.

The axiom guaranteeing the existence of an identity says that the system should contain an element e which, like 0 for addition or 1 for multiplication, is *neutral* for the operation of the group. The combination of e with anything in the group does not change that thing.

The axiom that guarantees that each element of the group has an inverse in the group is intended to provide elements like negatives or reciprocals in systems with operations of addition or multiplication, respectively. The inverse of an element x is usually denoted by x^{-1} (read "x inverse"). This notation is intended to show the intimate relationship of x and its inverse. *Warning:* The symbol x^{-1} does *not* mean 1/x as it does in algebra! The symbol x^{-1} is simply a *name* for the inverse of x. You may find it helpful to think of x^{-1} as being the element which "wipes out" x when it is combined with x, i.e., $x \circ x^{-1} = x^{-1} \circ x = e$, where e is the identity.

2. Verify that the triskelion group or the group of integers mod 3 is a group, i.e., show that it satisfies the requirements of the definition of group. (The most tedious part of such a verification usually consists of testing to make sure that the operation is associative. How many cases would you have to check to show the associativity even in as small a group as this?)

3. To point out the importance of the associativity of the operation in a system, consider the five-element system given by the structure table below:

$\circ$	I	A	B	C	D
I	I	A	B	C	D
A	A	I	C	D	B
B	B	D	I	A	C
C	C	B	D	I	A
D	D	C	A	B	I

a. Does this system satisfy the axiom of closure?
b. Does this system satisfy the axiom of associativity?
c. Does this system have an identity?
d. Does each element of this system have an inverse?
e. Is this system a group? Explain.

You are already quite familiar with many particular examples of groups. For example, the additive group of integers. The underlying set of elements consists of *all* integers and the binary operation is $+$. This group is denoted by $(\mathbb{Z}, +)$; recall that

$$\mathbb{Z} = \Big\{ \ldots, -2, -1, 0, 1, 2, \ldots \Big\}.$$

4. Verify that $(\mathbb{Z}, +)$ is a group; you may assume all the usual properties of the arithmetic of the integers.

Yet another example of a familiar group is the multiplicative group of non-zero rational numbers. The underlying set is the set of *all non-zero* fractions while the binary operation is ordinary multiplication. This group is denoted by $(\mathbb{Q}^*, \cdot)$.

5. Verify that $(\mathbb{Q}^*, \cdot)$ is a group; you may assume the usual properties of the multiplication of fractions.

6. What if we use the entire set of rational numbers as the underlying set and use multiplication as the operation? Is the resulting system a group? Explain.

7. Can you think of an operation which could be used with the underlying set of *all* rational numbers to yield a group? Explain.

8. Suppose the underlying set is the set of all integers $\mathbb{Z}$, and the binary operation is usual multiplication. Is this system a group? Explain.

9. Using the Latin Square Property, try to fill in the blanks in the structure table of a group with only two elements, I and R.

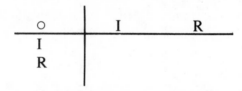

What sort of ornament would have such a group as its symmetry group? (Hint: what do you suppose a "duoskelion" would look like?) Sketch such an ornament.

10. Using the Latin Square Property, display the structure table for a symmetry group with only one element I. What sort of ornament would have this as its symmetry group? Sketch it.

11. Ponder the results of exercises 9, 10, and what you know about the symmetry group of the triskelion. Do you see how to give an example of a group with 4 elements, or with 5, or 6, or . . .? Given any particular order (i.e., number of elements) n, describe an ornament which would have as its symmetry group a group of the given order, n. Explain why this implies that there is a group of any particular finite order.

The groups you should have discovered in answering exercise 11 constitute the class of finite *cyclic* groups, a most important family of groups.

Definition: A group $(\mathbf{G}, \circ)$ is called *cyclic* if there is an element x in **G** such that *any element of* **G** is a "product" of x's or x^{-1}'s. Such an element is called a *generator* of the cyclic group.

For example, the basic rotation R in any of the symmetry groups of the skelia is a generator of the group. Note that a cyclic group may have several elements which can serve as generators.

12. You know that R is a generator for the symmetry group of the triskelion. Can you find another generator? Explain.

13. Can you give an example of an infinite cyclic group? What element(s) could be taken as generators? Explain. (Hint: Think about the additive group of integers $(\mathbb{Z}, +)$. There are two different possible choices for a generator.)

Let's continue our investigation of symmetry by erasing the "bent extensions" on the legs of a triskelion. The resulting figure is called a three-pointed star or tristar (one is shown below). Let's turn our attention to finding out about the allowable symmetry motions for this sort of figure.

1. Using very thin paper, trace the tristar (for convenience, number the three points as shown) and investigate the motions you can perform on the tracing to cause it to coincide with the original. (Hint: motions other than simple rotations will work!) Complete this investigation before you read on.

You should have found *six* motions under which the tristar coincides with itself as desired. If you did not, go back and look again. If R denotes a 1/3 turn clockwise, then (just as for the triskelion) we have symmetry motions I, R, and R^2. How do the other three motions arise? Try flipping your tracing and placing the 1-point atop the 1-point of the original. Eureka! Here is a symmetry motion for the tristar which leaves the 1-point fixed. We shall call this motion F_1 to indicate a "flip" around the "line" labelled 1. Now what do you suppose the two remaining symmetry motions for the tristar are? Of course, F_2 and F_3. It should be easy for you to convince yourself that these six are the only symmetry motions for the tristar.

2. If we use the notation for motions established during our study of the triskelion, we may say that

$$I = \begin{pmatrix} 1 & 2 & 3 \\ 1 & 2 & 3 \end{pmatrix} \quad R = \begin{pmatrix} 1 & 2 & 3 \\ 2 & 3 & 1 \end{pmatrix} \quad R^2 = \begin{pmatrix} 1 & 2 & 3 \\ 3 & 1 & 2 \end{pmatrix}$$

Using this notation, fill in the blanks to represent the three flips:

$$F_1 = \begin{pmatrix} 1 & 2 & 3 \\ \_ & \_ & \_ \end{pmatrix} \quad F_2 = \begin{pmatrix} 1 & 2 & 3 \\ \_ & \_ & \_ \end{pmatrix} \quad F_3 = \begin{pmatrix} 1 & 2 & 3 \\ \_ & \_ & \_ \end{pmatrix}$$

3. Let ○ represent the usual operation on motions (the notation here will perhaps seem backwards), e.g., $R \circ F_1$ stands for first do F_1, and then do R. Now, do you suppose that the underlying set $\{I, R, R^2, F_1, F_2, F_3\}$ with the binary operation ○ forms a group? How could you test it out? Explain.

There is an easy, clever way to compute the result of composing, i.e., combining with ○, two symmetry motions. We can use the notation we have developed to help us. For example, $R \circ F_1 = \begin{pmatrix} 1 & 2 & 3 \\ 2 & 3 & 1 \end{pmatrix} \circ \begin{pmatrix} 1 & 2 & 3 \\ 1 & 3 & 2 \end{pmatrix}$ so we can "chase" elements to

see what happens to them under the action of the composite motion $R \circ F_1$.

$$
\begin{array}{lll}
 & F_1 \quad R & \\
\text{First,} & 1 \rightsquigarrow 1 \rightsquigarrow 2 & \text{so} \quad 1 \rightsquigarrow\!\!\!\longrightarrow 2. \\
\text{Second,} & 2 \rightsquigarrow 3 \rightsquigarrow 1 & \text{so} \quad 2 \rightsquigarrow\!\!\!\longrightarrow 1. \\
\text{Third,} & 3 \rightsquigarrow 2 \rightsquigarrow 3 & \text{so} \quad 3 \rightsquigarrow\!\!\!\longrightarrow 3.
\end{array}
$$

Hence, $R \circ F_1 = \begin{pmatrix} 1 & 2 & 3 \\ 2 & 1 & 3 \end{pmatrix} = F_3$.

With a bit of practice at chasing elements you can compute the result of a composition of motions without writing all the steps. You will get such practice as you do the next exercise.

4. Using the way of computing products explained above (or by using your tracing if necessary), complete a structure table for the symmetry group of the tristar. Recall that we already know $R \circ F_1 = F_3$. The Latin Square property will also help you work in completing the table.

$\circ$	I	R	R^2	F_1	F_2	F_3
I						
R						
R^2						
F_1		F_3				
F_2						
F_3						

5. Verify that the table you constructed in exercise 4 is the structure table of a *group*. You may assume that the associative axiom is satisfied (provided you did the table right). So, you must verify the other axioms in the definition of a group.

You have now computed the structure tables for the symmetry groups of two different ornaments: the triskelion and the tristar. Place these tables side-by-side in front of you.

6. On the basis of these tables would you say that the two ornaments have the *same* symmetry? Explain.

Simply on the basis of the number of elements in each of the symmetry groups, we can clearly see that they do not have the same structure. Thus, we say that the ornaments do not have the same symmetry. In order for two symmetry groups to be structurally equivalent it is neccesary, but *not* sufficient, for the two groups to have the same number of elements. (Note that there are groups having the same number of elements which are *not* structurally equivalent. We shall see an example of this phenomenon a bit later.) Since the number of elements in a group is, thus, of some significance for us in studying symmetry groups, we make the following definition:

Definition: The number of elements in the underlying set of any group G is called the *order* of G and denoted by #G.

Remark: Let G and H be two groups. If #G ≠ #H, then G and H can't be structurally equivalent. Or, another way of saying the same thing, if two groups G and are structurally equivalent, we must have #G = #H. *Caution: #G = #H* is *not* enough to guarantee that G and H are structurally equivalent groups!

While you have the two group tables together before you, let's make a few more observations about them:

Observation: Draw a diagonal line in each table (going from the upper-left-hand entry to the lower-right-hand entry). Do you notice anything interesting about the arrangement of the entries in the triskelion table with respect to this so-called "main diagonal"? Isn't it as though the triangular block:
$R \quad R^2$
I
had simply been flipped in the main diagonal to give: R
$\qquad\qquad\qquad R^2 \quad I$

Definition: We say that such a table is *symmetric with respect to its main diagonal.*

7.   Is the structure table for the tristar symmetric with respect to its main diagonal? Explain.

Obviously, your answer to exercise 7 was no. Here is another difference in the structure of the two groups! Even if these two groups had the same order, the lack of main diagonal symmetry in the structure table of one as contrasted with its presence in the structure table of the other would tip us off to the fact that they were not structurally equivalent.

8.   Complete a structure table for the symmetry group of each of the following ornaments; represent your basic symmetry motions using the $\begin{pmatrix} 1 & 2 & 3 & 4 \\ \_ & \_ & \_ & \_ \end{pmatrix}$ notation and, by

chasing elements, compute all the products to fill in your tables.

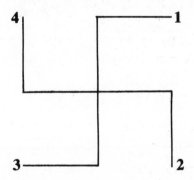
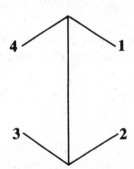

   a. What are the orders of the two symmetry groups? (Hint: they should be of equal order.)

   b. Examine the tables and decide whether these symmetry groups are structurally equivalent or not; explain your answer as fully as you can. (Hint: think about *all* the structural properties known to you which can be used to classify and distinguish groups.)

-35-

Remark: In exercise 8, you were confronted with two groups of order 4. Moreover, both structure tables were symmetric with respect to the main diagonal. You may, nevertheless, have felt (and rightly so) that the two groups should not be structurally equivalent because the two ornaments don't look like they have the same sort of symmetry. Did you notice that one of the groups is cyclic while the other is not? Go back and verify this fact for yourself. We may distinguish two groups as being structurally different if one is cyclic and the other is not, i.e., the property of being cyclic is a structural property of groups.

9. Are the symmetry group of a 6-skelion (or hexaskelion) and the symmetry group of a tristar structurally equivalent? How could you decide? Explain.

Since the structural property of being main-diagonal-symmetric is an important one for group tables, we make the following definition:

Definition: If a group G has a main-diagonal-symmetric structure table, we say that G is *commutative* or that G is a *commutative group*. (Sometimes a commutative group is called *Abelian* in honor of the Norwegian mathematician Niels Henrik Abel (1802–1829).)

10. Do you see that a group structure table is main-diagonal-symmetric if and only if it is the case that for any two elements x and y of the group we have $x \circ y = y \circ x$? Think about this and be prepared to explain it in class.

In view of what you observed in exercise 10, we can make the alternative definition:

Definition: A group G is said to be *commutative (Abelian)* if for any two elements x, y in G we have $x \circ y = y \circ x$.

Remark: Recall that commutativity is a structural property of groups, and so a commutative group cannot be structurally equivalent to a non-commutative group.

Of course, nearly all the groups with which you are familiar are commutative. However, there are many very important non-commutative groups as well. For example, none of the symmetry groups of stars with three or more points is commutative.

Section 4

Let's continue our investigation of group structure by learning about the idea of *sub-groups* and the closely related idea of *involutions*.

1. Place the structure tables you have prepared for the symmetry groups of the tristar and the triskelion side-by-side before you. Compare the upper left hand 3 by 3 block of entries in the tristar group table with the triskelion table. What do you notice?

Continuing our observations about these two structure tables, we see that the symmetry group of the tristar has a group "inside" it which is just like (structurally equivalent to) the symmetry group of the triskelion! Obviously then, we may say that the tristar has a richer symmetry than has the triskelion. A "small" group embedded in a larger one is called a *subgroup* of a larger group (which is said to be a *supergroup* of the subgroup). Of course, it would be silly to expect to find subgroups automatically clustered in the upper left hand corners of the group tables which we examine. For example, the symmetry group of the tristar has a subgroup consisting of $\{I, F_1\}$.

2. Verify that $\{I, F_1\}$ is the underlying set of a subgroup as claimed. (Hint: make a small structure table for it and show that it satisfies the axioms of the definition of group.)

The subgroup discussed in exercise 2 may be thought of as consisting of all the elements of the tristar group which do not move 1, i.e., of all motions for which $1 \leadsto 1$.

3. a. What would be the subgroup of all motions for which $2 \leadsto 2$?
   b. What would be the subgroup of all motions for which $3 \leadsto 3$?
   c. Verify that the answers you gave to a. and b. are groups.

Definition: The elements left unmoved (fixed) by a motion are said to be *fixed* or *invariant* under the action of the motion.

In exercise 3 you should have seen that deciding that something should be fixed under the motions restricts the allowable motions to a subgroup of the entire symmetry group. Most groups have many subgroups inside them. Notice that every group is trivially a subgroup of itself; furthermore, notice that the identity element of any group forms a subgroup of the group.

Definition: A group H contained within a group G and having the same binary operation as G is called a *subgroup* of G. (We denote this situation by writing $H < G$, which is read "H is a subgroup of G.")

4. a. Verify that every group is a subgroup of itself.
   b. Verify that the identity element alone forms a subgroup of the group for which it is the identity.

5. Consider the additive group of integers $(\mathbb{Z}, +)$. Show that the set of *even* integers with the operation of addition forms a subgroup of $(\mathbb{Z}, +)$. Does the set of *odd* integers with the operation of addition form a subgroup of $(\mathbb{Z}, +)$? Explain.

6. List all the subgroups of the triskelion group C_3 (denoted thus because it is a cyclic group of order 3). (Hint: there are only two distinct subgroups of C_3.)

7. List all the subgroups of the tristar group. (Hint: there are six distinct subgroups of this group.)

Remark: The property of having a family of subgroups of certain types is a structural property of groups; i.e., if a group has a subgroup with a certain structure (commutative, non-commutative, of a given order, etc.) then every group structurally equivalent to the given group must also have a subgroup with the same structure as the subgroup of the given group. Thus, two structurally equivalent groups must have equal numbers of subgroups; furthermore, the subgroups themselves can be matched up in structurally equivalent pairs.

8. Suppose G is a group with identity element e and suppose that x is an element of G such that $x \neq e$ but $x^2 = e$. Prove: $\{e, x\} < G$. (Hint: Construct a structure table for $\{e, x\}$ and verify the four axioms for a group.)

Definition: Suppose G is a group with identity element e and that x is an element of G such that $x \neq e$ but $x^2 = e$. We say that such an x is an *involution* or an *element of order 2*.

Remark: We shall see later that the study of involutions plays a vital role in determining what sorts of groups can be ornamental symmetry groups. In exercise 8, you saw that if x is an involution in a group G, then $\{e, x\} < G$. Thus, the number of elements of order 2 which it contains is a structural property of a group. If two groups contain *different* numbers of involutions, then they are not structurally equivalent. Thus, we have yet another way of distinguishing between groups. You should note that *any halfturn or flip is an involution*.

Section 5

Consider the 4-star (tetrastar) drawn below:

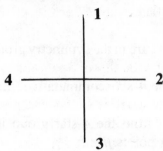

1. Using very thin paper, make a tracing of the 4-star (numbering the points as shown for convenience) and investigate what motions of the tracing will cause it to coincide with the original, i.e., find all the symmetry motions of the 4-star. List the motions in the $\begin{pmatrix} 1 & 2 & 3 & 4 \\ - & - & - & - \end{pmatrix}$ notation. For example, $\begin{pmatrix} 1 & 2 & 3 & 4 \\ 2 & 3 & 4 & 1 \end{pmatrix}$ is a symmetry motion and so is $\begin{pmatrix} 1 & 2 & 3 & 4 \\ 2 & 1 & 4 & 3 \end{pmatrix}$

    (Hint: there are 8 symmetry motions for the 4-star.)

    Did you find all eight symmetry motions for the 4-star? Obviously a 1/4 turn clockwise is allowable; call it R. Then I, R, R^2, and R^3 are allowable symmetry motions. Moreover, we have some "flips" which work also, viz., a flip around the horizontal line of the star and another flip around the vertical line of the star. Call these flips F_h and F_v, respectively. The remaining two allowable symmetry motions are also flips. Can you find them before you read on? Try to do so if you haven't already found them.

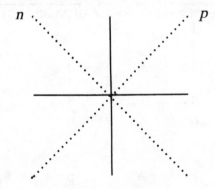

    If you look at the drawing of the 4-star just above, you will easily see that flips around the lines labelled p and n are also symmetry motions for the 4-star; call these flips F_p and F_n, respectively. Now we have all 8 symmetry motions for the 4-star.

2. List the motions I, R, R^2, R^3, F_h, F_v, F_p, and F_n using the $\begin{pmatrix} 1 & 2 & 3 & 4 \\ - & - & - & - \end{pmatrix}$ notation.

3. Do you suppose that the symmetry motions for the 4-star with the usual binary composition operation form a group? Verify your anwer by computing a structure table (chase the elements to simplify the computation) and checking to see that the four group axioms are satisfied.

4. How many elements of order 2 are in the symmetry group of the 4-star? List them.

5. Is the symmetry group of the 4-star commutative? Explain.

6. What subgroup is produced from the 4-star group if you insist that the allowable motions leave the following points *fixed*:
   a. 1 and 3?
   b. 2 and 4?

7. Using the structure table of the 4-star group which you computed in exercise 3, list as many subgroups of this group as you can find.

8. We have seen that the symmetry group of the 4-star is of order 8. Do you know of another group of this order? (Hint: think of an octoskelion.) Display a structure table for the symmetry group of an octoskelion, C_8.

9. Is the symmetry group of the 4-star structurally different from the symmetry group of the octoskelion? (Hint: think of all the structural properties such as order, commutativity, number of elements of order 2, etc., which you may use to distinguish between groups.) Explain your answer fully.

Notice the patterns in the tables below:

skelion		star	
# of legs	order of group	# of points	order of group
1	1		
2	2		
3	3	3	6
4	4	4	8
5	5	5	10
6	6	6	12
.	.	.	.
.	.	.	.
n	?	p	?

10. Fill in the missing entries in the table rows where n and p appear

11. a. For each n = 3, 4, 5, . . . the symmetry groups of an n-skelion and an n-star are not structurally equivalent. Why not? (Hint: think of the pattern you discovered in the tables.)

    b. Moreover, none of the skelion groups indicated in the table is structurally equivalent to any of the star groups indicated in the table. Why? (Hint: think about commutativity.)

Section 6

The symmetry groups of the skelia form the family of *cyclic* groups. The groups associated with the stars form the family of *dihedral* groups. A p-star has the dihedral group D_{2p} as its symmetry group for $p \geqslant 3$. (See the diagrammed ornaments below which have symmetry groups D_{2p} for $p = 1, 2$.) Thus, we are now acquainted with two infinite families of symmetry groups, viz., the family $C_1, C_2, C_3, ..., C_n, ...$ of finite cyclic groups associated with the skelia and the family $D_2, D_4, D_6, ...,$ $D_{2p}, ...$ of finite dihedral groups associated with the stars.

These two families of finite groups constitute the collection of groups known as *rosette* groups. You will have the opportunity to identify the symmetry groups of various finite, regular ornaments in the following exercises.

Remark: The *standard* notation for a dihedral group of order 2p is D_p; however, I use D_{2p} to remind you of the order of the group.

Examples of Ornaments Having Cyclic or Dihedral Symmetry Groups

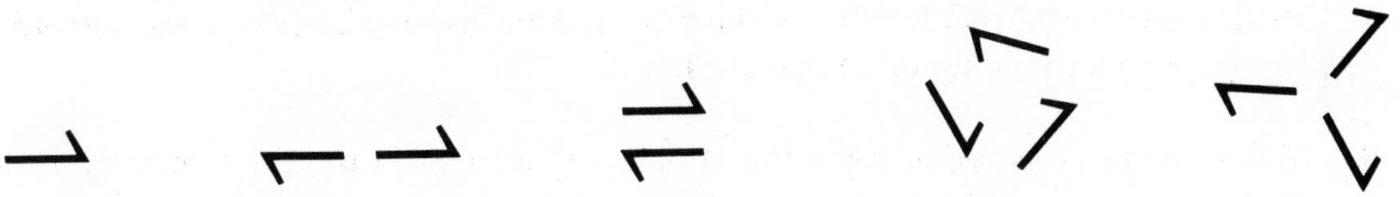

C_1 C_2 C_2 C_3 C_3

C_4 C_5 C_6

D_2 D_2 D_4

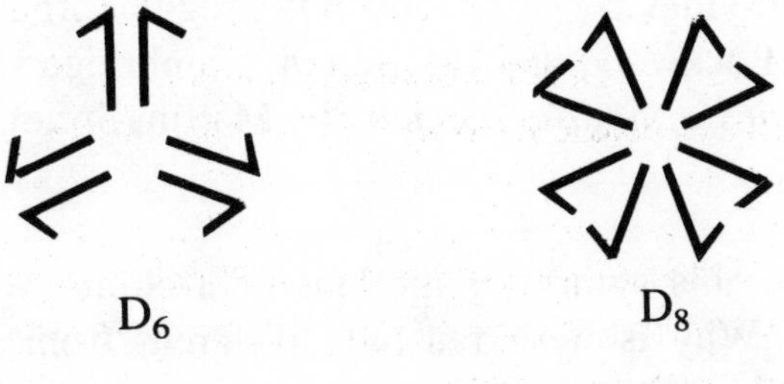

D_6 D_8

-41-

1. Identify the symmetry group of each of the following, e.g., you might say C_3, D_4, etc.

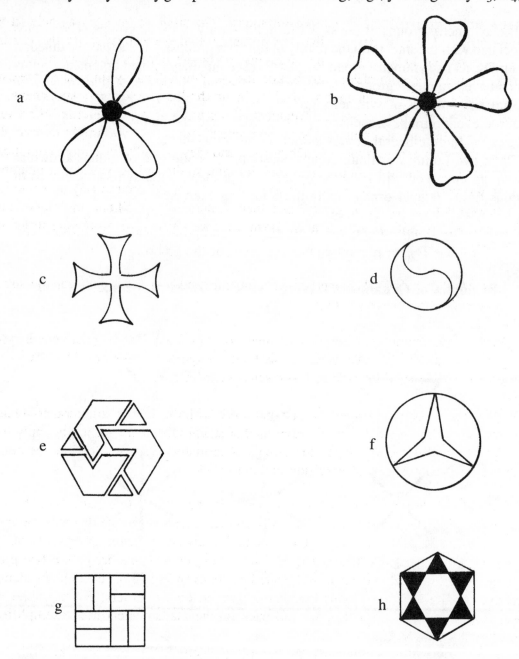

In exercise 1, did you notice that each of the finite, regular ornaments had a finite symmetry group which was either cyclic or dihedral? This was not simply an accident, nor did I cleverly choose the ornaments to make it turn out that way. It is possible (and not really very hard—but beyond the scope of this work) to prove that the rosette groups are the *only* finite symmetry groups. If you are interested in seeing *how* to prove that the rosette groups are the only symmetry groups for finite, regular ornaments, you can consult *Geometric Symmetry,* by Lockwood and Macmillan, Cambridge University Press, Cambridge, 1978; and also, *Transformation Geometry* by Martin, Springer-Verlag, New York, 1982.

2. Think about the allowable symmetry motions of a circle. What sort of symmetry group does it have? Why is it so radically different from the symmetry groups discussed above? Explain as well as you can.

Section 7

Let's study some infinite groups of symmetry. The simplest ones are associated with infinite strips of border design, like the borders found on wallpaper, in the bands of decoration on the facades of many buildings, or in the borders of many pictures and fabrics. Be alert for examples of this sort of design. You will easily find many interesting border ornaments if you sensitize yourself to be on the lookout for prize specimens. The groups associated with this sort of ornament, if we imagine it to extend *infinitely* far in a strip, are called *frieze* groups or border-ornament groups. As you might expect, there are more than two general types of such groups, and they typically have more complicated structure than the rosette groups. However, it is not so difficult as you might imagine to classify the various possible types of frieze groups. We shall need to tidy up some loose ends in our consideration of groups and their structures to facilitate the classification procedure and to clarify exactly what we mean when we say that two groups are structurally equivalent.

1. List *all* the structural properties you have learned so far which can be used to distinguish and classify groups.

2. Bring some examples of border ornaments to class. They may be your own drawings, pictures, fabrics, etc. Think about the kinds of symmetry motions which work with your examples and be prepared to discuss them in class.

We have been playing somewhat fast and loose with the idea of structural equivalence for groups. Let's see what sort of heavy mathematical machinery we might apply to the concept of structural equivalence for groups. The mathematics will endow the concept with the necessary degree of precision and clarity.

You will recall that two groups must necessarily be of the same order (i.e., have the *same number* of elements) to be structurally equivalent, even though this is by no means a condition strong enough to *force* the structural equivalence of the groups. (Look back at exercise 3.8 to see that this is so.) But how can one tell whether or not two groups have the same order? It may be tiresomely tedious or even *impossible* to count the elements directly, especially if the groups have large or even *infinite* orders! For example, what about $(\mathbb{Q}, +)$ and $(\mathbb{R}, +)$? So, we fall back on the mathematical trick exemplified in the following little story:

Suppose you were slated to preside over a large lecture class in a big auditorium with which you were not familiar. The people in the class enter, and as people will, they stand around chatting and dilly-dallying in the aisles. You wish to decide if there are enough seats for everyone present. How could you do so, being ignorant of the actual number of seats, as well as of the actual number of people, in the auditorium? Simple! You get everyone who possibly can to take a seat. Then you scan the auditorium. If some people are left unseated, there are more people than seats. If some seats are left unfilled, there are more seats than people. If no one is left unseated and no seats are left unfilled, there are exactly as many seats as people: the number of people is precisely equal to the number of seats, even though you may have no idea what that number is! There is a perfect matching of people with seats—one person to each seat and one seat to each person. In this case, the order or *cardinality* of the set of people equals the cardinality of the set of seats. It is this mathematical trick of matching which saves the day for you, even if you had the very odd case of an infinite number of people in an infinitely large auditorium!

3. It is said that the giant Polyphemus, blinded by the wily Odysseus, used the following method to keep track of his sheep. Each morning, as the sheep left his cave one-by-one, Polyphemus picked up one stone for each sheep. In the evening, as the sheep re-entered the cave one-by-one, he dropped one stone for each sheep. Thus, he was able to tell if any sheep had strayed. Explain why this procedure worked and how it is similar to the example of the lecture class above.

How do we "match" things mathematically? Recall from your study of algebra the idea of a *function* or *map* between two sets. You have already seen many examples of maps earlier in this Unit: every one of the symmetry motions we discussed was a map! Moreover, you know many more examples of maps or functions from algebra. In algebra, a function is usually given by a simple formula for matching the numbers in one set with the numbers in another set. You have practiced working with such functions, computing their values, and drawing their graphs. For example, consider these functions and their graphs:

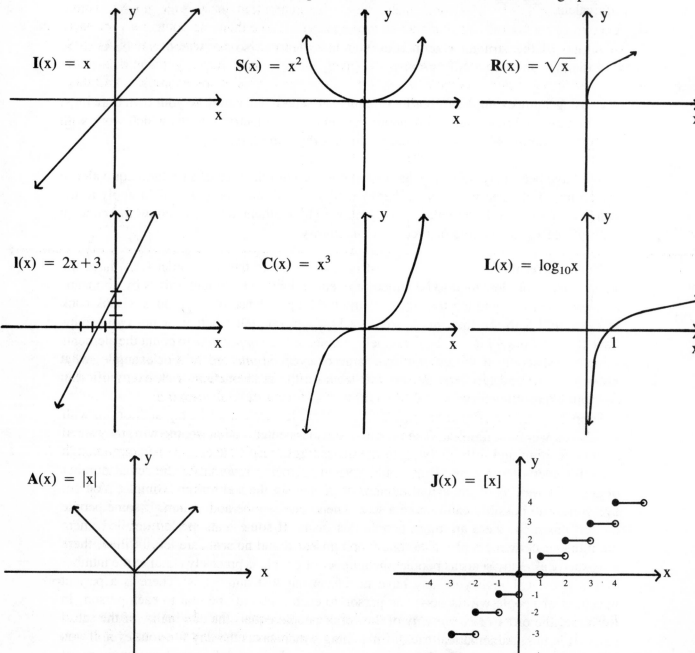

$I(x) = x$

$S(x) = x^2$

$R(x) = \sqrt{x}$

$l(x) = 2x + 3$

$C(x) = x^3$

$L(x) = \log_{10}x$

$A(x) = |x|$

$J(x) = [x]$

Of course, not all functions have such simple graphs:

$$H(x) = \frac{x-2}{x^2-1}$$

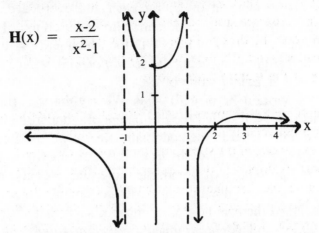

Do you recall what it is about such a graph that guarantees that it is the graph of some function of x? No vertical line may cross the graph in more than one point, i.e., for each value of x for which the function is defined there is exactly *one* corresponding value of y on the graph. So, even if you have no given formula for a graph, you can determine whether or not it is the graph of a function. Consider the following examples and make sure that you understand why they are or are not graphs of functions of x:

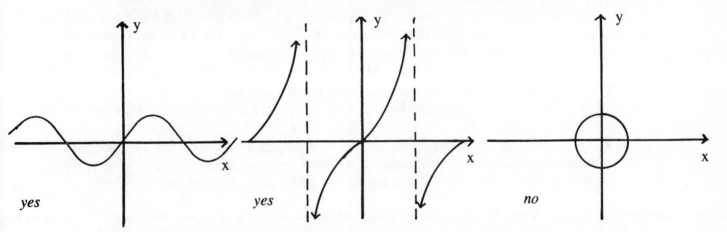

yes   *yes*   *no*

Let's make our idea of function (map, mapping) quite precise, so we'll know exactly what we mean by "matching things" mathematically. In the definition below, I use the Greek letter φ (phi—pronounced like fee) to stand for a general mapping.

Definition: A *mapping* (or *map* or *function*) φ of a set D (the *domain* of φ) to a non-empty set C (the *codomain* of φ) is an ordered triple (D, C, G) where D and C are the sets of things being "matched" and G is the "rule" for the matching. I.e., G is a set of ordered pairs (d, c) where d ∈ D and c ∈ C, satisfying the following condition: each d ∈ D appears once and only once as the first element of an ordered pair in G. Naturally, G is what you have customarily called the *graph* of the mapping. We write φ: D →C or D $\xrightarrow{\varphi}$ C to denote that φ is a mapping of D to C.

Remark: People often say, by a careless abuse of language, that the set of ordered pairs G *is* the mapping or function. It is sometimes convenient to do this if it causes no confusion.

Note that *every* element of the domain of the mapping must be "used up," i.e., $\varphi(d)$ must be defined (as an element of C) for each and every d ϵ D. However, it is *not* necessary for every element of the codomain C to be "used up." I.e., there *may be* some element(s) c ϵ C such that there is *no* d ϵ D for which $\varphi(d) = c$. The codomain of the mapping should be thought of as being the set of *potential* values of φ; it is *not* necessary for every c ϵ C to be an *actual* value of φ.

If (d, c) ϵ G, we write $d \leadsto c$ or $\varphi(d) = c$. We say that c is the *image* of d under the mapping φ; in this case, d is called the *pre-image* of c under the mapping φ. Thus, each *image* is an *actual* value of φ in the codomain, i.e., it is "used up" by φ.

For example, if $\varphi: \mathbb{R} \rightarrow \mathbb{R}$ is given by $\varphi(x) = x^2$, then $\varphi(3) = 9$, so 9 is the *image* of 3 under φ and 3 is a *pre-image* of 9 under φ (note that -3 is also a pre-image of 9 under φ). This mapping does *not* "use up" all of its codomain; e.g., -1 is *not* the image of anything under φ since there is no real number x such that $x^2 = -1$. Thus, -1 has no pre-image under φ, i.e., -1 is *not* an image (an *actual value*) under φ.

Let's illustrate the rather hard-to-understand idea of mapping with a particular example from basic algebra, say the mapping $l: \mathbb{R} \rightarrow \mathbb{R}$ given by $l(x) = 2x + 3$; the graph of this function was sketched in one of the previous examples. The function l has the set of all real numbers, $\mathbb{R}$, as its domain and also as its codomain. The graph, G, of l consists of all ordered pairs of the form (x, 2x + 3), where x may be any real number. In symbols, $G = \{(x, 2x + 3) \mid x \epsilon \mathbb{R}\}$. Notice that when the domain, D, is large (as it is in this example), one commonly specifies the graph, G, simply by using a formula such as 2x + 3 for the mapping. This is done because it is inconvenient or even impossible (as it is in the case of l) to *list* all the ordered pairs in the graph. In simple cases (such as in the examples coming up next), one may write out the entire graph; indeed, since there may be no way to give a formula for the mapping, it may be necessary to write out the entire graph in some form.

Examine the function l and its graph, and think about it very carefully to make sure you get the idea. The general definition is difficult to grasp immediately, but the underlying concept is *most important* in all of mathematics. In addition, study the examples below:

Let $D = \{0, 1, 2\}$ and $C = \{a, b, c\}$.

Suppose $G_1 = \{(0, a), (1, a), (2, a)\}$. Then (D, C, G_1) is a map of D to C.

Suppose $G_2 = \{(0, a), (1, b), (2, c)\}$. Then (D, C, G_2) is a map of D to C.

Suppose $G_3 = \{(0, a), (1, b), (2, c), (0, b)\}$. Then (D, C, G_3) is *not* a map of D to C.

Suppose $G_4 = \{(1, b), (2, c)\}$. Then (D, C, G_4) is *not* a map of D to C.

4. Verify the claims made about the four examples above; explain why each of the examples is or is not a map of D to C.

5. Let $D = \mathbb{Z}$, the set of all integers, and $C = \mathbb{Z}$ also. (There is nothing in the definition to say that $D \neq C$!).

Suppose $G_5 = \{(x, 2x) \mid x \in \mathbb{Z} \}$, i.e.,

$$G_5 = \{. \, . \, ., (-2, -4), (-1, -2), (0, 0), (1, 2), (2, 4), . \, . \, .\}.$$

Suppose $G_6 = \{(x, x/2) \mid x \in \mathbb{Z}\}$.
a. Is $(\mathbb{Z}, \mathbb{Z}, G_5)$ a map of $\mathbb{Z}$ to $\mathbb{Z}$? Explain.
b. Is $(\mathbb{Z}, \mathbb{Z}, G_6)$ a map of $\mathbb{Z}$ to $\mathbb{Z}$? Explain.

Okay. Let's assume you understand what a map or mapping or function from one set to another is. (If you don't understand, ask someone for *help!*)

Remark: Let's verify, once-and-for-all, that the composition of mappings is associative. You may recall from your study of algebra that $f \circ g$ is a function defined by $f \circ g\,(x) = f(g(x))$. Of course, the product $f \circ g$ is defined when and only when the codomain of g equals the domain of f. This is surely so for our geometric transformations since they all have the plane as both domain and codomain. Thus, we can form the product (or composite) of any two geometric transformations. If f and g are any mappings, their product $f \circ g$ has its domain equal to the domain of g and has its codomain equal to the codomain of f.

Now, is it "true" that $f \circ (g \circ h) = (f \circ g) \circ h$ for any mappings for which these products are defined? Yes! We verify the equality of the maps $f \circ (g \circ h)$ and $(f \circ g) \circ h$ by showing that these products have the same domain, the same codomain, and the same graph. The domain of each product is the domain of h. The codomain of each product is the codomain of f. Moreover, for any x in the domain of h we have:

i. $f \circ (g \circ h)\,(x) = f(g \circ h(x)) = f(g(h(x)))$
ii. $(f \circ g) \circ h(x) = f \circ g\,(h(x)) = f(g(h(x)))$.

Thus, the graph of each of the products consists of the set of ordered pairs: $\{(x, f(g(h(x)))) \mid x \text{ in the domain of } h\}$.

Hence, we have shown that $f \circ (g \circ h)$ is the same map as $(f \circ g) \circ h$, i.e.,
$f \circ (g \circ h) = (f \circ g) \circ h$!

Section 8

Let's investigate some properties of mappings and see how they may be used to match up sets so that we can decide whether or not those sets contain the same number of elements.

There are two particularly nice properties which a map may have. E.g., in the lecture class story (remember?), it was possible to have every seat filled by a person and thus to "exhaust" the codomain of the mapping of people to seats. Any map for which this happens, i.e., for which every element of the codomain is the image of some element of the domain, is called a *surjection*, or is said to be a map of the domain *onto* the codomain. In the examples above (D, C, G_2) is a surjection, but (D, C, G_1) is *not* a surjection.

1. Review Exercise 7.5 and consider the map ($\mathbb{Z},\mathbb{Z}, G_5$). Is this map a surjection? Explain.

Look back at the graphs of functions (maps) I drew for you on page 44.

Consider the map C: $\mathbb{R} \to \mathbb{R}$ given by the formula $C(x) = x^3$; is this map a surjection? I.e., is every element of the codomain $\mathbb{R}$ the image of some element of the domain under the map C? (In other words, is every real number the cube of some other real number?) Obviously, your answer should be yes. Now, what about the map S: $\mathbb{R} \to \mathbb{R}$ given by the formula $S(x) = x^2$? Is the map S a surjection? I.e., is every real number the square of some other real number? Obviously, your answer should be no. Why?

Just as there is a graphical test to determine whether a graph "represents" a function of x (remember the one using the vertical lines?), so there is a test similar to that one to test whether or not the graph of a function from $\mathbb{R}$ to $\mathbb{R}$ is a surjection. Recall that a surjection must *exhaust* the codomain; in this case, that means that every possible value of y must occur on the graph. The test to determine whether or not this happens is very simple: Any horizontal line must cross the graph *at least once*. This is the easiest way to determine whether or not a map of $\mathbb{R}$ to $\mathbb{R}$ given by a graph is a surjection. Let's give the definition of a surjection (just for the sake of completeness and precision).

Definition: A map φ: D $\to$ C is said to be a *surjection* (or is called *onto*) if for every c ϵ C there is at least one d ϵ D such that φ matches d with c, i.e., such that $\varphi(d) = c$. We write D $\overset{\varphi}{\twoheadrightarrow}$ C to denote that φ is a surjection of D onto C.

Remark: The set of all elements of C which actually appear as images of elements in the domain under the mapping φ is called the *image* of φ. (Sometimes this set is called the *range* of the mapping; we shall not use that terminology.) We denote the image of φ by Imφ. Note that Imφ is always a subset of the codomain of φ and is equal to the codomain if and only if φ is a surjection.

2. Look back at the maps I graphed on page 44. Except for R and L they are all maps of $\mathbb{R}$ to $\mathbb{R}$.
   a. What is the image of each of the eight maps?
   b. Using the graphical test for surjectivity, which of the maps is/are surjective? Explain.
   c. Why can't we regard R as being a map from $\mathbb{R}$ to $\mathbb{R}$? (Hint: consider the domain of R.) What about L?

3. Just to make sure that you've grasped the idea of a surjection give a new example of a map which is a surjection, and also a new example of a map which is not a surjection. You must specify the Domain, Codomain, and Graph of each of your

examples. (Hint: You can specify a map from $\mathbb{R}$ to $\mathbb{R}$ by drawing a graph like the ones I drew or you can use "little" sets for the domain and codomain as I did in the examples of mappings found above.)

In our lecture class story, we insisted that only one person occupy a seat (no sitting on friendly laps, etc.) i.e., two different people had to occupy two different seats. So, if we began with two distinct elements of the domain set, the mapping of people to seats had to give two distinct images in the codomain. Any mapping with this property is called an *injection* or is said to be a one-to-one map, denoted by the symbol, "1-1". For example, among the maps previously graphed, the map $l:\mathbb{R}\to\mathbb{R}$ is 1-1; this is so because if $a \neq b$, then $2a + 3 \neq 2b + 3$, i.e., if $a \neq b$, then $l(a) \neq l(b)$. However, among those same maps, the map S given by the formula $S(x) = x^2$ is *not* 1-1. This is so because we can start with two distinct pre-images, such as 2 and -2, and get the same image for both, namely 4, since $(2)^2 = (-2)^2 = 4$. Thus, for the map S, it is *not* true that if $a \neq b$, then $S(a) \neq S(b)$. Is there a graphical test for determining whether or not a map is 1-1? Yes! However, it is very similar to the graphical test for surjectivity, and so you must be careful to keep the two tests straight! The graphical test for 1-1 is this: Any horizontal line must cross the graph *at most once*.

4.   Write out the graphical tests for determining whether or not a map from $\mathbb{R}$ to $\mathbb{R}$ is onto or 1-1. Compare and contrast these tests so you will be sure not to confuse them!

5.   Consider each of the maps I graphed for you. Using the graphical test, tell whether or not each of them is a 1-1 map.

6.   Just to make sure you've grasped the idea of 1-1, give a new example of a map which is 1-1 and also a new example of a map which is not 1-1. You must specify the Domain, Codomain, and Graph of each of your examples. (Hint: see the Hint for exercise 3).

Remark: A map may be 1-1 but not onto; onto but not 1-1; both 1-1 and onto; or neither 1-1 nor onto. I.e., 1-1 and onto are independent.

7.   Produce one map of each of the four types mentioned in the remark just above. (Hint: see the Hint for exercise 3.) I.e., you are required to give an example of a mapping which is:

   a.   1-1 and onto   c.   not 1-1 but onto
   b.   1-1 but not onto   d.   neither 1-1 nor onto

Indicate the Domain, Codomain, and Graph for *each* of your four examples.

Here is the definition of an injection (just for the sake of completeness and precision).

Definition: A map $\varphi: D \to C$ is said to be an *injection* (or is called 1-1) if $a \neq b$ implies that $\varphi(a) \neq \varphi(b)$ for all elements a,b of D; in other words, $\varphi(a) = \varphi(b)$ implies $a = b$. We write $\varphi: D \rightarrowtail C$ to denote that φ is an injection of D into C.

Warning: The most common mistake made by students when they talk about injectivity consists of saying that a mapping is injective (1-1) because it matches each element in its domain with one and only one element in its codomain. This, however, simply amounts to saying that a mapping is a mapping! Think about why that is so. The confusion seems to be produced by the phrase "with one and only one." *Avoid this common error!*

8. Suppose $\varphi\colon D \twoheadrightarrow C$ is a surjection. Could C have more elements than D? Explain.

9. Suppose $\varphi\colon D \rightarrowtail C$ is an injection. Could D have more elements than C? Explain.

10. Suppose $\varphi\colon D \rightarrowtail\twoheadrightarrow C$ is both an injection and a surjection, i.e. is both 1-1 and onto. What can be said about the number of elements in D and C? Explain.

   Obviously, in the lecture class story there are just as many people as seats if and only if the matching of people with seats is both injective and surjective (i.e., both 1-1 and onto). So, we say that two sets of things have the same number of elements (even if we have no idea what that number is) provided that there is a mapping from one set to the other which is both injective and surjective—such a map is called a *bijection* between the two sets. This idea may even be used to compare the sizes of sets which are infinite!

11. Show that there are precisely as many perfect squares as there are counting numbers; do this by producing a bijection between the set of counting numbers:
$\mathbb{N} = \{1, 2, 3, 4, \ldots, n, \ldots\}$ and the set of perfect squares:
$\mathbb{S} = \{1, 4, 9, 16, \ldots, n^2, \ldots\}$.

Remark: The number of elements in each of the sets in exercise 11 is aleph-zero or aleph-null. This is probably the first infinite number you've ever encountered. It is, in fact, only the smallest of an infinite family of infinite numbers!

Section 9

We are almost ready to clarify the concept of structural equivalence of groups. To do this we must be prepared to understand something of the interplay between maps and group structures. This is a concept which is somewhat hard to understand in the abstract so let's look at a concrete example first; it should help to ease us into the more abstract and general viewpoint.

1. To do this exercise you will need the following:
   i. A structure table for the symmetry group of the triskelion (you will find one in Section 2);
   ii. A structure table for the group of integers mod 3 (you will find one in Section 2);
   iii. A structure table for the symmetry group of the tetraskelion (you made one in exercise 3.8);
   iv. A structure table for the group of integers mod 4 (you made one in exercise 2.1).

Gather all these things and then go on:

   a. Compare the structure tables for the triskelion and the integers mod 3. What do you notice? Explain.
   b. Compare the structure tables for the tetraskelion and the integers mod 4. What do you notice? Explain.

You probably said that the two groups considered in each part of exercise 1 were "just alike," i.e., structurally equivalent. This really means that there is a way of mapping (renaming) one group to the other using a map which is bijective and which transforms the structure table of the domain group into the structure table of the codomain group. Let's look in detail at $\mathbb{Z}$ mod 3 and C_3 (the triskelion group). One possible map (renaming) of $\mathbb{Z}$ mod 3 to C_3 is given by:

$$\varphi$$
$$0 \rightsquigarrow I$$
$$1 \rightsquigarrow R$$
$$2 \rightsquigarrow R^2$$

2. Answer the following questions about the map φ defined just above:
   a. Is φ injective (i.e., 1-1)? Explain.
   b. Is φ surjective (i.e., onto)? Explain.

Consider what the action of φ does to the structure tables; if we simply use φ to transform every entry in the structure table of $\mathbb{Z}$ mod 3, what is the outcome? Look below to see:

+	0	1	2
0	0	1	2
1	1	2	0
2	2	0	1

$\xrightarrow{\varphi}$

$\circ$	I	R	R^2
I	I	R	R^2
R	R	R^2	I
R^2	R^2	I	R

The outcome is the structure table for C_3, the symmetry group of the triskelion! What we really mean when we say φ preserves (or respects) the group structure is that the structure tables transform like this.

Consider the map ψ of $\mathbb{Z}$ mod 3 to C_3 given by:

$$\psi$$
$$0 \rightsquigarrow I$$
$$1 \rightsquigarrow R^2$$
$$2 \rightsquigarrow R$$

The Greek letter ψ, called psi, is read like psee (silent "p").

3.   Answer the following questions about the map ψ:
   a. Is ψ injective (i.e., 1-1)? Explain.
   b. Is ψ surjective? (i.e., onto)? Explain.

   You may object that ψ doesn't preserve the group structure—but your objection may be a wee bit hasty. Let's see what happens if we use the map ψ to transform every entry in the structure table of $\mathbb{Z}$ mod 3 as follows:

$\bigcirc$	I	R^2	R
I	I	R^2	R
R^2	R^2	R	I
R	R	I	R^2

$\rightsquigarrow \xrightarrow{\psi}$

+	0	1	2
0	0	1	2
1	1	2	0
2	2	0	1

4.   Examine the table that results from the transformation of $\mathbb{Z}$ mod 3 under the action of ψ. Is the outcome the structure table of the symmetry group of the triskelion? Explain.

   So, now you should know two distinct ways, φ and ψ, to "rename" $\mathbb{Z}$ mod 3 to get C_3. These are the only maps which can be used to show the structural equivalence of these two groups. Any other map from $\mathbb{Z}$ mod 3 to C_3 will fail to preserve the structure, or will fail to be 1-1, or will fail to be onto. Only φ and ψ have all three properties.

5.   There also just happen to be two distinct ways to rename $\mathbb{Z}$ mod 4 to get C_4 (the tetraskelion group). One of the ways is quite easy to see but the other may require some serious thought. Specify at least one map from $\mathbb{Z}$ mod 4 to C_4 which is 1-1, onto, and preserves the group structure. Verify that your map has all the desired properties just as we did in the examples for φ and ψ.

   Now, if the groups under consideration are large (even infinite) it would be tedious (even impossible) to check directly to see if a map between the groups is nice enough to preserve group structure. So, I am going to ask you to do one rather long, laborious exercise which should serve to give you a concrete example of the general method of testing a map for the preservation of group structure. Please be patient and diligent enough to do *all* the computations! It will help you to understand a difficult and abstract concept.
   Consider the map φ from $\mathbb{Z}$ mod 3 to C_3 given by:

$$\varphi(0) = I, \; \varphi(1) = R, \text{ and } \varphi(2) = R^2.$$

I am going to ask you to do several computations like the following sample:

Sample: $\varphi(2 + 2) = \varphi(1) = R$
$\varphi(2) \circ \varphi(2) = R^2 \circ R^2 = R$
So, $\varphi(2 + 2) = \varphi(2) \circ \varphi(2)$.

6. Compute each of the following:

a. $\varphi(0 + 0) =$; $\varphi(0) \circ \varphi(0) =$
b. $\varphi(0 + 1) =$; $\varphi(0) \circ \varphi(1) =$
c. $\varphi(0 + 2) =$; $\varphi(0) \circ \varphi(2) =$
d. $\varphi(1 + 0) =$; $\varphi(1) \circ \varphi(0) =$
e. $\varphi(1 + 1) =$; $\varphi(1) \circ \varphi(1) =$
f. $\varphi(1 + 2) =$; $\varphi(1) \circ \varphi(2) =$
g. $\varphi(2 + 0) =$; $\varphi(2) \circ \varphi(0) =$
h. $\varphi(2 + 1) =$; $\varphi(2) \circ \varphi(1) =$
i. $\varphi(2 + 2) = \varphi(1) = R$; $\varphi(2) \circ \varphi(2) = R^2 \circ R^2 = R.$

What do you notice about each pair of answers above? Express your answer in terms of an equation: For every x and y in $\mathbb{Z} \bmod 3$,   you found $\varphi(x + y) =$ _____ .

You should have discovered in 9.6 the basic interplay between maps and group structure expressed in your equation. Let's formalize your discovery by giving the following abstract general definition:

Definition: Let $(G, \circ)$ and $(H, \diamond)$ be groups. A map $\varphi: G \to H$ is said to *preserve* or *respect* group structure if for every x, y in G, $\varphi\,(x \circ y) = \varphi(x) \diamond \varphi(y)$. We call such a map φ a *homomorphism* of G into H.

Remark: The word homomorphism comes from homo (similar) and morphe (structure). Note that a map need *not* be either injective or surjective to be a homomorphism of groups.

1. Consider the map, χ: $\mathbb{Z}$ mod $3 \to$ C_3 where $0 \rightsquigarrow I$
$$1 \rightsquigarrow I$$
$$2 \rightsquigarrow I$$

The Greek letter χ, chi, is read like key.

a. Is χ 1-1? Explain. I.e., is χ injective?
b. Is χ onto? Explain. I.e., is χ surjective?
c. Is χ a homomorphism of $\mathbb{Z}$ mod 3 into C_3? I.e., do we have for every x, y in $\mathbb{Z}$ mod 3, $\chi(x + y) = \chi(x) \circ \chi(y)$? (Hint: It is not at all hard to answer this; think about what $\chi(x) \circ \chi(y)$ always is for this rather odd map.)

So, in 1 you have seen an example of a homomorphism of groups which "obliterates" much of the structure but still "respects" the group structure according to the definition above.

Let's examine a few examples of mappings between groups to clarify the method(s) one may use to show that such a mapping is: 1) an injection, 2) a surjection, and 3) a homomorphism of groups.

Example 1.

Let the domain be $(\mathbb{Z}, +)$, the additive group of all integers (this is the group $(G, \circ)$ in the definition of homomorphism). Let the codomain be $(3\mathbb{Z}, +)$, the additive group of all integral multiples of 3 (this is the group $(H, \diamond)$ in the definition of homomorphism). Let $\varphi: (\mathbb{Z}, +) \to (3\mathbb{Z}, +)$ be given by the rule $x \rightsquigarrow 3x$, i.e., $\varphi(x) = 3x$. I claim that this map φ is: 1) an injection, 2) a surjection, and 3) a homomorphism of groups. How can I verify my claims?

First, to verify that φ is an injection:

We must show that: if a $\neq$ b, then $\varphi(a) \neq \varphi(b)$.

Suppose a $\neq$ b. Then, 3a $\neq$ 3b, i.e. $\varphi(a) \neq \varphi(b)$.

Thus, φ is an injection since a and b could be *any* two elements of the domain.

Of course, for this mapping one could also sketch its graph and use the graphical test to show that it is injective. Think about how that would work.

Second, to verify that φ is a surjection:

We must show that the codomain is "used up" by φ, i.e., that *any* element of the codomain is an *actual* image value of φ. Suppose z is an element of the codomain. Then z is an integral multiple of 3, say $z = 3a$ where a is some integer. The pre-image of z is obviously a since $\varphi(a) = 3a = z$. Since z could be *any* element of the codomain, we see that φ is a surjection. Of course, for this mapping one could use the graphical test to show that it is a surjection. Think about how that would work.

Third, to verify that φ is a homomorphism of groups:

We must show that: for any x, y in the domain, $\varphi(x \circ y) = \varphi(x) \, \Diamond \, \varphi(y)$, i.e., in this case, $\varphi(x + y) = \varphi(x) + \varphi(y)$.

Now, $\varphi(x + y) = 3 \cdot (x + y) = 3x + 3y = \varphi(x) + \varphi(y)$.

Thus, we see that φ is a homomorphism of groups, i.e., φ respects the group **structure**.

Example 2.

Let the domain be $(\mathbb{R}, +)$, the additive group of *all* real numbers. Let the codomain be $(\mathbb{R}^+, \cdot)$, the multiplicative group of all *positive* real numbers. Let the mapping $\varphi: (\mathbb{R}, +) \to (\mathbb{R}^+, \cdot)$ be given by the rule $x \rightsquigarrow 2^x$, i.e., $\varphi(x) = 2^x$. E.g., $\varphi(3) = 2^3 = 8$. I claim that this map φ is: 1) an injection, 2) a surjection, and 3) a homomorphism of groups.

First:

We must show that: if $a \neq b$, then $\varphi(a) \neq \varphi(b)$.

Suppose that $a \neq b$. Then $2^a \neq 2^b$, i.e., $\varphi(a) \neq \varphi(b)$.

Thus, φ is an injection.

Of course, for this mapping one could sketch its graph (see below) and use the graphical test to show that it is injective. Think about how that would work.

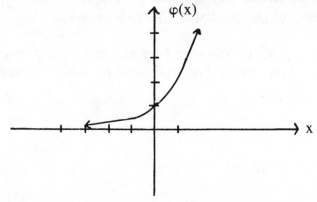

Second:

We must show that any element z of the codomain is an actual image value of φ.

Let $a = \log_2 z$. Then $\varphi(a) = 2^a = 2^{\log_2 z} = z$ by definition of logarithm. Thus, φ is a surjection.

Of course, one could also use the graphical test on the graph of φ to show that φ is a surjection. Think about how that would work.

Third:

We must show that: for any x, y in the domain, $\varphi(x \circ y) = \varphi(x) \, \Diamond \, \varphi(y)$, i.e., in this case, $\varphi(x + y) = \varphi(x) \cdot \varphi(y)$,

Now, $\varphi(x + y) = 2^{x + y} = 2^x \cdot 2^y = \varphi(x) \cdot \varphi(y)$.

Thus, we see that φ is a homomorphism of groups.

There are many mappings for which the graphical tests are inconvenient or essentially impossible to use. Thus, you should strive to understand how to use the non-graphical methods found in the examples above.

2.   Verify that the maps φ and ψ from $\mathbb{Z}$ mod 3 to C_3 given in Section 9 are 1-1, onto, homomorphisms of groups. Thus, these maps are *very* nice preservers of structure.

3.   Let $(G, \circ)$ be the group $(\mathbb{Z}, +)$ and $(H, \diamond)$ be the group $(2\mathbb{Z}, +)$, the additive group of all even integers. Suppose $\varphi: \mathbb{Z} \to 2\mathbb{Z}$ is given by $\varphi(x) = 2x$ for all x in $\mathbb{Z}$. Verify that φ is a 1-1, onto, homomorphism of groups.

4.   Let $(\mathbb{R}^+, \cdot)$ be the multiplicative group of all positive real numbers and $(\mathbb{R}, +)$ the additive group of all real numbers. Verify that the function (map) log: $\mathbb{R}^+ \to \mathbb{R}$ is a 1-1, onto, homomorphism of these groups. (Hint: Recall what you know about logarithms from your study of algebra.)

Finally, we make the idea of structural equivalence of groups precise by giving the following definition:

Definition: A group $(G, \circ)$ is *structurally equivalent* to a group $(H, \diamond)$ if there exists a 1-1, onto, homomorphism $\varphi : G \to H$. Such a map is called an *isomorphism*, and the two groups are said to be *isomorphic* to one another.

Remark: The word isomorphism comes from iso (same) and morphe (structure). Note that an isomorphism is a *very* special map indeed; it must be both injective and surjective while preserving the group structure.

5.   Look back at exercises 2, 3, 4 and see that the maps considered there were really isomorphisms of groups. Explain why this is so.

To finish up this brief section go back and review any of the ideas about mappings which you are not quite certain of and make sure you are in command of all the basics.

Let's get on to the long-delayed discussion of infinite symmetry groups of strip or frieze ornaments. It may have occurred to you during our consideration of the symmetry groups of finite, regular ornaments such as the skelia and stars that any such ornament may be thought of as being composed of several basic congruent pieces. So, if you made a rubber stamp of the basic piece, you could produce the finite, regular ornament by stamping it out in the appropriate pattern.

Frieze patterns are made up of a basic piece (called the *motif*) which is endlessly repeated in a straight line:

(a) . . . . . . _____⌐_____⌐_____⌐_____⌐_____⌐ . . . .

which could be thought of as having been printed by a roller-type rubber stamp with the motif _____⌐ . Run the roller endlessly along a straight line and you will produce the frieze ornament.

1. Under what sort of symmetry motion(s) will strip (a) above coincide with itself? Make a tracing, if necessary, and investigate. (Obviously no rotational motion except the identity will work.)

In your investigation of strip (a), you should have found that besides the identity, I, there is a basic symmetry motion which consists of a slide or *Translation,* T, of the strip by one "design unit" to the right. Of course, T can be repeated over and over, so we also have T^2, T^3, T^4, . . ., T^n, . . . as symmetry motions of this strip. Notice that, unlike the basic rotations and flips in the rosette groups, T has no positive power which collapses to the Identity motion. (We make the not-too-startling convention that $T^0 = I$.) Thus, there are infinitely many distinct symmetry motions for strip (a).

Clearly, a translation of one design unit to the left is also an allowable symmetry motion for strip (a). For fairly obvious group-theoretic reasons we'll denote this slide to the left by T^{-1}, and its repetitions by T^{-2}, T^{-3}, . . . , T^{-n}, ...

So, for symmetry motions of strip (a), we have: $\{. . ., T^{-3}, T^{-2}, T^{-1}, T^0, T^1, T^2, T^3, . . .\}$. Are there any other allowable symmetry motions for strip (a)? We mentioned the lack of rotations. Moreover, the asymmetry of the motif indicates that no flips are allowable. Thus, it appears that we have captured the entire collection of symmetry motions for the strip (a), and so we have.

Let's denote the collection of symmetry motions of strip (a) as **Z**.

2. Verify that **Z** is a group under the usual operation ○ on motions. (Hint: you'll need to observe that the usual laws of exponents which you learned in algebra hold in **Z**.)

3. Is the group (**Z**, ○) isomorphic to any very familiar group? If your answer is yes, specify the isomorphism map and verify that it *is* an isomorphism. If your answer is no, explain.

You have, no doubt, already noticed that every element in **Z** is a power of a single element, viz. T, and you will recall that groups which have such a structure are called *cyclic*. In fact, **Z** is a prototypical example of an infinite cyclic group. The canonical example of such an infinite cyclic group is the one you probably discussed in exercise 3, namely $(\mathbb{Z}, +)$.

4. Find and bring to class at least one example of a border ornament which has the same symmetry type as strip (a). A sketch will do if no portable example is available. You may wish to create your own example. Be imaginatively creative!

5. Bring in at least one example of a border ornament which has a symmetry type different from that of strip (a). Try to find as many different types of symmetry in border ornaments as you possibly can. Compare all the examples in class, and try to draw some conclusions about the number of distinct symmetry types in border ornaments. Again, be imaginatively creative!

In our discussion of strip (a), we found it to have symmetry group C_∞ which is an infinite cyclic group. Recall that a generator was T, the basic translation of the strip one design unit to the right.

Section 12

Consider the following strips. In each case determine the allowable symmetry motions for the strip and make a record of them. It will be very helpful if you think of the strip as having been printed one motif at a time, as we noted could be done with the finite, regular ornaments. Make a tracing of the motif (which in each case is the same as it was in strip (a)), and think what sort of motions "cause" the motif to "print" the strip: these are the motions to record. Remember that the basic symmetry motions we have discovered are: rotation, flip (or reflection), and translation (of one design unit in magnitude). This list may not exhaust all of the possible allowable motions for strips!

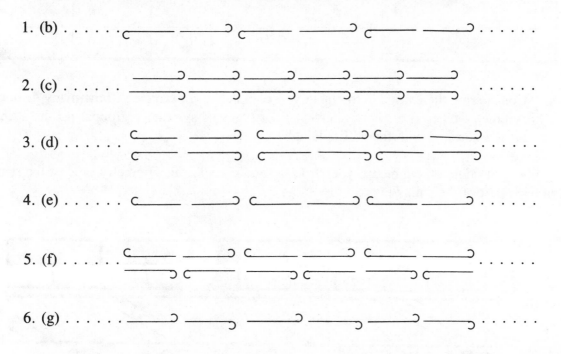

1. (b) . . . . . .

2. (c) . . . . . .

3. (d) . . . . . .

4. (e) . . . . . .

5. (f) . . . . . .

6. (g) . . . . . .

Did you find the new allowable motion for strips (f) and (g)? It is called a *glide-reflection*, and consists of sliding the strip ½ design unit to the right and turning it over top to bottom.

As you know, we may associate each type of ornament with the group of symmetry motions allowable for it. These motions are sometimes called *rigid* motions because they preserve the size and shape of the ornament.

Consider the following list of symmetry maps for strips:

T — Translate the strip one design unit to the right.

F_h — Flip the strip over by bringing the top edge to the bottom edge, and vice versa (i.e., flip the strip in a horizontal line running down its middle).

F_v — Flip the strip around a vertical line at right angles to it (i.e., reverse the left and right sides of it).

R — Rotate the strip a half turn around some point (Note: $R = F_h \circ F_v = F_v \circ F_h$).

G — Glide the strip (i.e., perform a glide-reflection on it).

7. In the table below put an X in each entry where the map is an allowable symmetry motion for a strip of the indicated type:

	(a)	(b)	(c)	(d)	(e)	(f)	(g)
T							
F_h							
F_v							
R							
G							

8. Considering the entries in the table you completed in exercise 7, how many distinct symmetry types (i.e., how many distinct types of symmetry groups) do the strips have associated with them? Explain.

Use your table of symmetry types from 7, and classify the symmetry type of the strip in each part of the following exercise.

9.

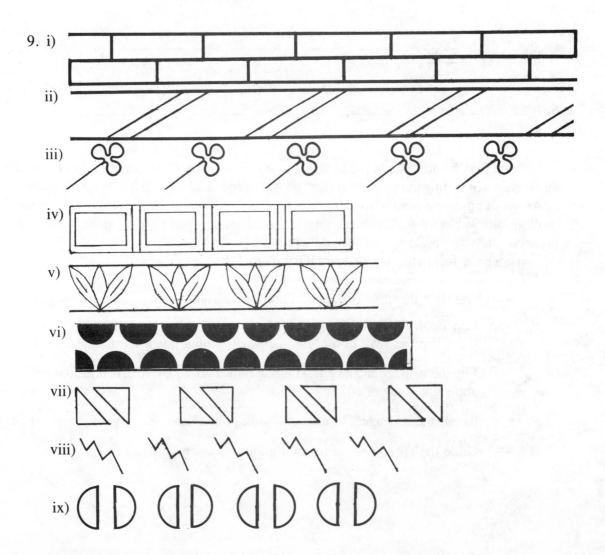

-60-

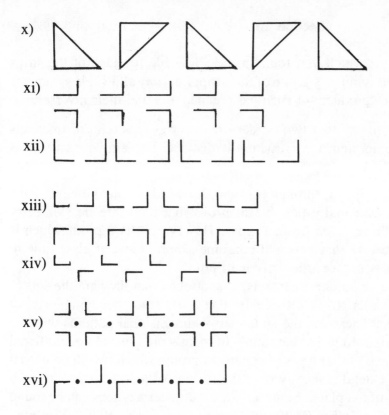

x)

xi)

xii)

xiii)

xiv)

xv)

xvi)

All the strips in exercise 9 were created by girls in my classes who read the preliminary versions of this text. Each strip was classed as being of the same type as one of the seven strips for which you created the table of types in 7. This is no accident, nor was it due to any clever choice of strip design on the part of these girls. In fact, there are *only* these *seven* distinct types of symmetry for strip ornaments!

Section 13

The basic symmetry motions which you found to be allowable for each of the strips form a set of *generators* for the symmetry group of that strip; i.e., *any* allowable symmetry motion for the strip is a finite "product" of such basic generators and their inverses.

1. Does it seem reasonable to say that two border ornament groups with distinct sets of generators are non-isomorphic, i.e., structurally distinct? Explain your answer as well as you can.

In your investigation of the strips (a) through (g), you should have found them to have distinct symmetry groups. It is actually possible to *prove* that there are no symmetry groups for strips other than these seven distinct types. However, it is a proof which is sufficiently laborious and intricate that it would consume several days of class time to give in detail (even though it is not a particularly hard proof).

In my introduction to frieze or border ornaments, I mentioned that they are the sort of patterns found in wallpaper border strips. Obviously, one could study the symmetries of wallpaper patterns themselves. These are the sorts of two-dimensional patterns that can also be found in tiled floors, painted walls, etc. Study of them would introduce additional allowable symmetry motions and further types of symmetry groups. Such two-dimensional patterns must be assumed to extend endlessly over the surface of a plane; they are very closely related to *tesselations* of the plane. Some very intriguing tesselations can be found in *The Graphic Work of M. C. Escher* (Ballantine Books, Inc., NY, 1973). You may wish to learn more about Escher and, indeed, about tesselations in general. Another very good reference for such study (and for much, much more about symmetry) is *Geometric Symmetry* (by Lockwood and Macmillan, Cambridge University Press, 1978). You can learn how to make your own patterns in Escher fashion if you refer to *Creating Escher-Type Drawings* (by E. R. Ranucci and J. L. Teeters, Creative Publications, Palo Alto, CA, 1977).

A complete study of the two-dimensional tesselating designs would reveal the surprising fact that there are only 17 distinct symmetry groups associated with such designs, i.e., there are only 17 different types of wallpaper patterns!

For a complete explanation of why there are only 7 frieze groups and only 17 wallpaper groups, refer to *Transformation Geometry* (by G. E. Martin, Springer-Verlag, NY, 1982). While this is an advanced reference, it is nevertheless fairly easy to read and understand.

You may know from other study that the Mohammedans were forbidden by their religion to represent people or animals in their art. Thus, they developed the very highest proficiency in decorating and embellishing their structures with purely geometric designs. What is absolutely amazing is that the decorations in the Alhambra (a palace built by the Muslims in Granada, Spain) include patterns corresponding to each of the 17 possible two-dimensional symmetry groups! The existence of these patterns demonstrates what a wonderful (although only intuitive) grasp the old Muslim artists had of the possibilities of design. It would be difficult to overestimate the degree of geometric insight and inventiveness required for them to have achieved their results without any knowledge of the underlying theory of symmetry. Although no one in their day had yet heard of a group, etc., they must have had an implicit understanding of the utter impossibility of finding any designs beyond the basic 17!

For some very nice examples of Muslim designs you may wish to refer to *Islamic Patterns* by K. Critchlow (Schocken Books, NY, 1976). You will find many appealing examples of wallpaper and frieze ornament in *Geometric Patterns and Borders* by D.

Wade (Van Nostrand, Reinhold, NY, 1982). Also of general interest is the comprehensive text *Symmetry in Science and Art* by Shubnikov and Koptsik (Plenum Press, NY, 1974).

The consideration of groups of symmetry may be extended into three dimensions, and even beyond. It becomes a much more complex study in three dimensions; there are 230 distinct types of symmetry for three-dimensional objects! However, the hard work involved in the study pays excellent dividends. Among them are: the determination by crystallographers that only certain specific crystal structures are possible in Nature, the determination and analysis of various molecular structures, etc.

In our brief study of groups we have barely skimmed the surface of a very extensive and extremely important branch of mathematics, the abstract theory of groups. (If you are interested in learning more about groups, you should consult *The Fascination of Groups* by F. J. Budden, Cambridge University Press, 1972. It is a very readable and informative exposition of lots of group theory.) The theory of groups arose from the work of the French mathematical genius, Evariste Galois. You may be interested to learn more about Galois. He had a brief, tumultuous, and fascinating life. He was slighted by the Establishment and perished in a senseless duel at the age of 21. One can only wonder what marvels of mathematics he might have produced if he had lived longer. You will find a readable biography of Galois in T. Rothman's article, "The Short Life of Evariste Galois," in the *Scientific American* of April 1982, pp. 136–149.

The work of Galois which gave rise to the theory of groups centered on the idea of solving equations, an idea familiar to all of you from your previous study of algebra. Indeed, one of the powerful applications of groups (an application which "revolutionized" algebra) deals with the problem of determining whether or not there is a "simple, algebraic" way of finding the solutions to an equation in terms of its coefficients.

You all memorized the formula for solving a general quadratic equation; you should recall that it says that if $ax^2 + bx + c = 0$ then $x = (-b \pm \sqrt{b^2 - 4ac})/(2a)$. Now there are similar sorts of formulae for solving general equations of the third degree, i.e., equations like $ax^3 + bx^2 + cx + d = 0$, and also for solving equations of the fourth degree, i.e., equations such as $ax^4 + bx^3 + cx^2 + dx + e = 0$. It follows from group theory that no such general formula can *ever* be found for solving equations of degree higher than four!

Obviously, group theory has wide-ranging applications. We have used it extensively in studying geometric symmetry. Physicists use groups in studying quantum theory, the theory of elementary particles, and the theory of spectra. Chemists use groups in analyzing molecular structure. Groups are found in music, and they play a large role in the study of topology (a very general geometry). Indeed, one might say that the theory of groups has significant applications in most branches of mathematics.

There are other interesting applications of group theory to topics in geometry which we will study—applications which, when discovered, completely solved three problems which had puzzled geometers for more than two thousand years! Most important for us, and the real reason we have been studying groups, is that a "modern" way of classifying various geometries identifies a geometry as the study of those properties of figures which are preserved under a group of allowable transformations (maps).

The transformations we have studied—rotation, reflection (or flip), translation, and glide reflection—are *almost* all the transformations needed for the study of Euclidean geometry. In fact, reflection in a line is a generator of all these motions.

2. See if you can figure out how to express the basic geometric transformations as products of reflections. Explain your answer carefully.

3. Are both the size and shape of figures preserved under the geometric transformations we have studied so far? Explain.

4. We mentioned in Unit I that the basic relationship in Euclidean geometry is similarity. What sort of transformation do you think a similarity map would be? (Hint: look back at the definition of similarity and consider how it differs from congruence.)

We will have all the transformations needed to characterize the Euclidean geometries once we add similarity maps to our inventory of allowable transformations. We'll see how that works a bit later.

Since you now know a lot about groups and their properties, it will be easy for us to finish this Unit by giving the long-promised proof of the Latin Square Property for group structure tables. Recall that this property says that every element of a group must appear once and only once in any row or column of the structure table for the group, i.e., there are no repetitions of any element in a row or column.

Theorem: There are no repetitions of any element in a row (or column) of a group structure table.

Proof: (We shall use the method of proof by contradiction.)

Suppose there were a repetition of the element y in the row of products with x as the left factor; i.e., suppose $x \circ z = x \circ w$ for two distinct elements z and w of the group. Then, $x^{-1} \circ (x \circ z) = x^{-1} \circ (x \circ w)$. So, by the axiom of associativity for groups $(x^{-1} \circ x) \circ z = (x^{-1} \circ x) \circ w$. Thus, $e \circ z = e \circ w$ and so $z = w$. But z and w were supposed to be distinct elements heading two separate columns of the table. Thus, we have arrived at a contradiction. Hence, our supposition that there was a repetition in the row of x products must have been false, i.e., there must be no such repetition.

Q.E.D.

5. Following the model proof above, write a proof that there can be no repetition of an element in any column of the group structure table. Why must each element of the group appear *at least* once in any row or column of the table?

6. As the last exercise in this Unit, prove that isomorphism of groups is an equivalence relation on the collection of all groups. (See Unit I, section 1 for the idea of equivalence.)

Unit II: Review Topics

1. Symmetry—definition and examples; uses of symmetry in science, etc.

2. Motions—idea, notation, products (composites).

3. Group structure table—idea, notation, Latin Square Property.

4. **Modular (clock) arithmetic.**

5. Group—idea, definition, examples.

6. Order of a group.

7. Cyclic and dihedral groups and the associated finite, regular ornaments; rosette groups.

8. Structural equivalence for groups; methods for determining whether or not groups are structurally equivalent.

9. Commutativity; main diagonal symmetry of group structure tables.

10. Subgroups; involutions (elements of order two).

11. Elements left fixed (invariant) under a motion.

12. Mapping—idea, definition, domain, codomain, graph, image, pre-image, injection (1-1), surjection (onto), examples, graphical tests.

13. Homomorphism, isomorphism of groups—definitions, examples, formal definition of structural equivalence of groups.

14. Frieze patterns and their symmetry motions; types of symmetry groups.

15. Identification, using table, of symmetry type of frieze ornament.

16. Generators of a group.

17. The four basic congruence motions—reflection, rotation, translation, glide reflection; similarity motion.

18. Uses of groups in mathematics, science, etc.

Unit III

Geometry via Transformations

The universe is transformation. . .
– Marcus Aurelius Antoninus –

By the end of Unit II, we had discovered all the motions necessary for "doing" the Euclidean geometry of congruence. The concluding remarks of that Unit indicated that we had to add one more type of motion, viz., similarity motion, to complete the collection of motions needed to "do" the Euclidean geometry of similarity. Once we have that, we can "do" both of the Euclidean geometries.

In exercise 13.4 of Unit II, most of you probably answered by saying that a similarity transformation would change the size but not the shape of the figure being transformed. That's *almost* entirely correct! Actually, a similarity transformation *may* (but need not necessarily) change size. Recall that congruent objects are necessarily similar; so, even if the transformation doesn't change size, it is a similarity so long as it doesn't change shape. Thus, you already know many similarity motions, viz., the congruence transformations.

Every congruence map is a similarity map.

There's really only one basic new motion we must introduce to have *all* similarity motions at our disposal. But, before we can do that, we need to make sense of the notion of *size* by carefully defining the *distance between two points*. Let's do that now.

Suppose we are working in a plane where coordinate axes have been introduced, as you are accustomed to from your study of algebra. Such a plane is said to have been *coordinatized.* You will recall that each point in such a coordinatized plane has *two coordinates,* an x-coordinate and a y-coordinate, which when taken *together* and *in order* uniquely specify the point by giving its "address" with respect to the coordinate axes.

In terms of maps, the coordinates are determined by a one-to-one, onto map between $\mathbb{R} \times \mathbb{R} = \mathbb{R}^2$ (which is the set of *all ordered pairs* of real numbers) and the set of points in the plane. In fact, we often think of an ordered pair such as (1, 3) as *being* the point it is associated with under the coordinate mapping. Such a way of thinking not only does no harm but is immensely convenient and useful. Hence, we will almost always (unless confusion could result) identify a point of a coordinatized plane with its coordinate "address."

The standard formula for the Euclidean distance between two points (a, b) and (c, d) in $\mathbb{R}^2$ is given in the following definition:

Definition: The *Euclidean distance*, denoted by D(A, B) or AB, between two points A = (a, b) and B = (c, d) in $\mathbb{R}^2$ is given by the formula:
$$D(A, B) = AB = \sqrt{(a - c)^2 + (b - d)^2}.$$

Note: The distance between two points A and B is more usually denoted by AB, but we shall write it as D(A, B) whenever we need to do so for the sake of clarity.

Remark: Remember that $\sqrt{(a-c)^2 + (b-d)^2}$ denotes the *non-negative* square root of $(a-c)^2 + (b-d)^2$; so, we see that $D(A, B) \geq 0$ for all A, B in $\mathbb{R}^2$. Beware of saying $\sqrt{(a-c)^2 + (b-d)^2} = (a-c) + (b-d)$! For example, if A = (0, 0) and B = (8, 6), we have D(A, B) = AB = $\sqrt{64 + 36}$ = $\sqrt{100}$ = 10, *not* D(A, B) = AB = $\sqrt{64 + 36}$ = 8 + 6!

Remark: The definition of Euclidean distance in $\mathbb{R}^2$ is motivated by using perhaps the best known result of classical Euclidean geometry, the Pythagorean Theorem (which we shall prove later). You may recall that the theorem asserts that $c^2 = a^2 + b^2$, where a and b are the lengths of the legs of a right triangle and c is the length of the hypotenuse (the side of the triangle opposite the right angle). Consider the sketch below:

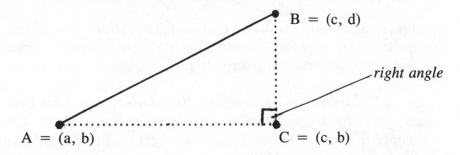

Given the two points A = (a, b) and B = (c, d), we want to compute AB, the distance between A and B. Draw a "line" starting at A and extending parallel to the x-axis. Then drop a "line" down from B parallel to the y-axis. These two lines meet at a point C and form a *right angle* there. Thus, $\triangle ABC$ is a right triangle, and the Pythagorean theorem tells us that $(AB)^2 = (AC)^2 + (BC)^2$. So, we see that AB = $\sqrt{(AC)^2 + (BC)^2}$. But what are the coordinates of C? You should easily see from the way in which C was constructed that C = (c, b). Think about why this is so. Now we can see that $AC^2 = (c-a)^2 = (a-c)^2$, and $BC^2 = (d-b)^2 = (b-d)^2$. Thus, we get the rule:
$$AB = \sqrt{(a-c)^2 + (b-d)^2}.$$

Notice that what I have just said is *not a proof* of the definition of Euclidean distance in $\mathbb{R}^2$! One does not need to prove definitions; they are simply stated and then worked with. (We'll learn more about this later when we extend our ideas of logic and proof in geometry.) What we have done in this remark is provide a plausible explanation for our making the particular definition we did for Euclidean distance in $\mathbb{R}^2$.

1. Using the formula, compute the Euclidean distance between the given pair of points in each of the following:

> a. (3, 0) and (7, 0)   b. (-2, 3) and (-2, 8)
> c. (2, 5) and (-1, -3)   d. (-3, 0) and (0, 2)

(*Remark:* leave your answers in simplest radical form where needed. E.g., A = (5, 2), B = (-1, 3) gives AB = $\sqrt{(5-(-1))^2 + (2-3)^2}$ = $\sqrt{36 + 1}$ = $\sqrt{37}$.)

Interestingly, there are many ways to define other (non-Euclidean) distances in $\mathbb{R}^2$, but the distance function D is the one which fits naturally with our intuition of what

Euclidean distance ought to be! Just for fun, however, let's examine a few of the others.

Notice that a *distance (metric)*, d, is simply any mapping such that d: $\mathbb{R}^2 \times \mathbb{R}^2 \to \mathbb{R}$ and such that d satisfies the following four axioms:

D0:	If $d(A,B) = 0$, then $A = B$	for all A,B in $\mathbb{R}^2$
D1:	If $A = B$, then $d(A,B) = 0$	for all A,B in $\mathbb{R}^2$
D2:	$d(A,B) = d(B,A)$	for all A,B in $\mathbb{R}^2$
D3:	$d(A,B) + d(B,C) \geqslant d(A,C)$	for all A,B,C in $\mathbb{R}^2$

2. Verify that the Euclidean distance map, D, satisfies D0, D1, and D2. (Hint: Let $A = (a, b)$ and $B = (c, d)$; then use the definition of D.)

3. Prove, using only the distance *axioms* given above, that $d(A, B) \geqslant 0$ for all A, B in $\mathbb{R}^2$. (Hint: Replace C by A in D3. Can this statement be manipulated, using D1 and D2, to give the desired result?)

Axiom D3, which you used in solving exercise 3, is a most important property of distance or metric mappings. You may recognize it as the so-called *triangle inequality* (mentioned in Unit I, Section 1) which says that the sum of the lengths of any two sides of a triangle is greater than the length of the third side. It is difficult to verify D3 for Euclidean distance (and for most distances), so we won't try to do so here.

Section 2

I mentioned the possibility of defining non-Euclidean distance maps on the plane. If we were to adopt one or another of these distances, we would get a non-Euclidean geometry—one with many seemingly strange properties. Let's consider a few of the non-Euclidean distance maps. Note that we reserve the symbol D for the standard Euclidean distance map on $\mathbb{R}^2$. Let $A = (a, b)$ and $B = (c, d)$. Then we can give the formulas for three different non-Euclidean distances as follows:

i.	$d_1(A, B) = |a-c| + |b-d|$	for all A, B in $\mathbb{R}^2$
ii.	$d_2(A, B) = $ the maximum of $|a-c|$ and $|b-d|$	for all A, B in $\mathbb{R}^2$
iii.	$d_3(A, B) = D(A, B)/[1 + D(A,B)]$	for all A, B in $\mathbb{R}^2$

1. Try to verify at least D0, D1, and D2 for each of the three distances defined above. While it is hard to verify D3, some of you may wish to try to do so for extra credit.

Example:

Consider the following computations of the non-Euclidean distances between the pairs of points given: $A = (1, 3)$, $B = (4, 7)$; $C = (0, 0)$, $E = (4, 8)$.

d_1	d_2	d_3
1. $AB = |1-4| + |3-7|$ $= |-3| + |-4|$ $= 3 + 4 = 7$	1. $AB = $ the maximum of $|1-4|$ and $|3-7|$ $= $ the max. of 3 and 4 $= 4$	1. $AB = 5/(1+5)$ $= 5/6$
2. $CE = |0-4| + |0-8|$ $= 4 + 8 = 12$	2. $CE = $ the max. of 4 and 8 $= 8$	2. $CE = \sqrt{80}/(1+\sqrt{80})$ $= 4\sqrt{5}/(1 + 4\sqrt{5})$ $\approx .899$

2. Compute each of the indicated distances between the points $A = (2, 3)$ and $B = (-1, 4)$. Show your work.
    a. $D(A, B) =$
    b. $d_1(A, B) =$
    c. $d_2(A, B) =$
    d. $d_3(A, B) =$

    (Hint: your answers should be $\sqrt{10} \approx 3.16$, 4, 3, $\dfrac{\sqrt{10}}{(1+\sqrt{10})} \approx .76$.)

Let's look at some of the strange results you can get using non-Euclidean distances.

Definition: A *circle* with *center* O and *radius r* is the set of all points (in a plane) which are at a distance of r from O.

Let's consider the circle with radius 1 (called the unit circle) and center $O = (0, 0)$ in each of the planes with distances D, d_1, d_2, and d_3 to see how "odd" some of the results seem; ponder these four examples carefully since the results may seem bizarre.

A. Using D, the usual Euclidean distance, we wish to derive an equation having as its graph the unit circle centered at the origin. An arbitrary point (x, y) is on this circle if and only if $D((0, 0), (x, y)) = 1$, i.e., $\sqrt{(0 - x)^2 + (0 - y)^2} = 1$. If we square both sides of the equation to get rid of the radical, we get the equation $x^2 + y^2 = 1$.

So, the unit circle desired consists of all the points of $\mathbb{R}^2$ such that $x^2 + y^2 = 1$. The graph of this equation is the pleasingly familiar circle shown below:

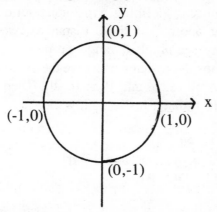

B. Using d_1, we wish to derive an equation having as its graph the unit circle centered at the origin. An arbitrary point (x, y) is on the circle if and only if $d_1((0, 0), (x, y)) = 1$, i.e., $|x| + |y| = 1$. So, the desired unit circle consists of all the points of $\mathbb{R}^2$ such that $|x| + |y| = 1$. The graph of this equation is the startlingly unfamiliar circle shown below:

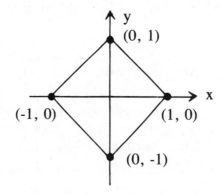

C. Using d_2, we wish to derive an equation having as its graph the unit circle centered at the origin. An arbitrary point (x, y) is on this circle if and only if $d_2((0, 0), (x, y)) = 1$, i.e., the maximum of $|x|$ and $|y|$ is 1. So, the unit circle consists of all the points of $\mathbb{R}^2$ such that the maximum of $|x|$ and $|y|$ is 1. The graph of this equation is the rather odd circle shown below:

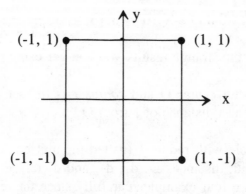

D. Using d_3, we wish to derive an equation having as its graph the unit circle centered at the origin. An arbitrary point (x, y) is on this circle if and only if $d_3((0, 0), (x, y)) = 1$, i.e.:

$$\frac{\sqrt{x^2 + y^2}}{(1 + \sqrt{x^2 + y^2})} = 1$$

So, the unit circle consists of all the points of $\mathbb{R}^2$ such that
$$\sqrt{x^2 + y^2} = 1 + \sqrt{x^2 + y^2}.$$
But there are no such points! Hence, the graph here is an *empty* one! Now that's really very odd indeed. You see, using the distance d_3, every point in the plane is *less than* 1 unit away from the origin!

You should know that metrics are important in areas other than geometry. An interesting, easy to understand example of a non-geometric metric comes to us from the field of computer science: the Hamming distance. The Hamming distance between two strings of symbols of the same finite length is defined to be the number of positions in which the two strings differ from one another.

E.g., the Hamming distance between 01101 and 00101 is 1 because the two strings differ in only one position (the second); the Hamming distance between 01010 and 10101 is 5 since these two strings differ in all five positions.

Remark: Technically speaking, there are actually an infinite number of Hamming distances—one for strings of length 1, one for strings of length 2, etc. Moreover, the strings of symbols are usually restricted to being strings of zeros and ones since the arithmetic of computing is often done using such strings (which, as you may know, represent *binary* numbers).

3.   Do you think that the Hamming distances are metrics? Explain. If you do think that they are metrics, can you verify that they are?

Note: Any of you who are interested may wish to read the remarks on "taxicab geometry" in the Mathematical Games section of *Scientific American,* November, 1980. You may wish to present a brief talk on taxicab geometry to your class for extra credit. Another useful reference is *Taxicab Geometry* by E.F. Krause (Addison-Wesley, 1975).

While the results we obtained from our investigation of non-Euclidean distances may seem quite strange, the best ideas which physicists have concerning the geometry of our universe indicate that it is non-Euclidean of a very special type not yet mentioned. In fact, the data seem to indicate that the space in which we live has a slight "curvature" (now thought to be positive). Those of you who are interested in such ideas as curved space, non-Euclidean geometry, etc., may wish to investigate one or more of the following:

Abbott, E.A. *Flatland*. (Reprint) New York: Dover Publications, Inc., 1952. This wonderfully entertaining little book is *still* available for less than $2.00! I recommend it most highly.

Gamow, G. "The Evolutionary Universe," *Scientific American,* Sept., 1956. A readable account of Einstein's development of the geometry of relativity from the ideas of Riemannian geometry.

Gardner, M. *Relativity for The Million*. New York: Macmillan, 1962. An excellent elementary book on relativity. Very readable.

Gray, J. *Ideas of Space* (Euclidean, Non-Euclidean and Relativistic). Oxford: Oxford University Press, 1979. A fascinating and historically oriented perspective on the development of various theories of space—requires only high school mathematics background.

Kaufmann, W.J. *Relativity and Cosmology*. New York: Harper and Row, 1973. Gives wide-ranging coverage of such topics as black holes, white holes, worm holes, quasars, etc., from the viewpoint of the astronomer-author.

Penrose, R. "The Geometry of the Universe." In *Mathematics Today,* ed. L. Steen. New York: Springer-Verlag, 1978. An excellent, rather technical account of some of the most recent mathematical ideas concerning the structure of the universe. This book and its sequel, *Mathematics Tomorrow*, are wonderful reference resources for students and teachers of mathematics.

Rucker, R.v.B. *Geometry, Relativity and the Fourth Dimension*. New York: Dover Publications, Inc., 1977. Another wonderful, inexpensive paperback from Dover. Very readable but a bit technical in places.

Several of the references cited above are excellent sources for extra-credit projects.

Review the triangle inequality (axiom D3 for distances). Suppose A = (a, b), B = (c, d), and C = (e, f) are three points of $\mathbb{R}^2$. If these three points are the vertices of a triangle, $\triangle ABC$, as in

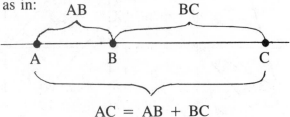

then we have AB + BC > AC. When is AB + BC = AC? Precisely when A, B, and C are all on a line with B between A and C as in:

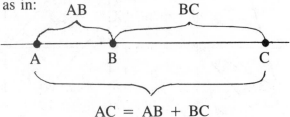

$$AC = AB + BC$$

Since this idea is of some importance to us, we make the following two definitions:

Definition: We say a set of points is *collinear* if there is some line which contains them all.

Definition: We say *B is between A and C,* denoted by A-B-C or C-B-A, if AB + BC = AC for three distinct points A, B, C.

Remark: AB + BC = AC if and only if A, B, and C are *collinear* with B between A and C. In Euclidean geometry, if we are given three collinear points, we assume that one and only one of them is between the other two. Moreover, since the names of the points are entirely arbitrary, we shall use the equation AB + BC = AC as the condition which characterizes the collinearity of three points.

1.   Does the assumption that for any three collinear points one and only one of them is between the other two seem silly to you? Well, silly or not, it is an axiom which Euclid overlooked; he said nothing about the order of points in his axioms. Can you give an example where this axiom of betweenness fails to hold? (Hint: think of what might happen if your lines were interpreted as being great circles on a sphere (i.e., circles with the same center as the sphere). Sketch a picture of this model, draw a line (i.e., a great circle) on the surface of the sphere, choose three points on the line and see if you think it makes any sense at all to say that one of them is between the other two.) Explain your answer as well as you can.

You may recall from algebra that one form for an equation of a line is y = mx + b, where m is the *slope* of the line and b is the *y-intercept* of the line. The slope of the line containing A = (r, s) and B = (t, u) is

$$\frac{u-s}{t-r} = \frac{s-u}{r-t} = \frac{rise}{run} = \frac{\Delta y}{\Delta x}$$

The Greek letter Δ, delta, denotes a change in something; so Δy is the change in y, while Δx is the change in x as you move from one point to another on the line. The slope is a measure of the steepness of the line (i.e., of the rate of change of y with respect to x). Consider the examples graphed below to remind yourself of some of the important ideas concerning slope.

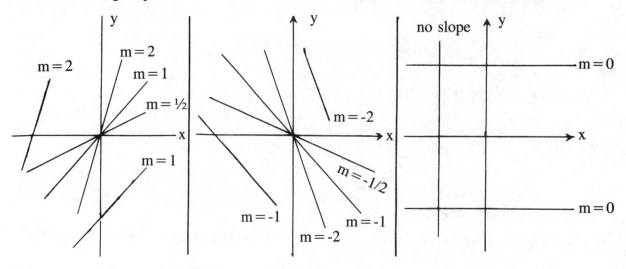

Warning: Vertical lines *have no slope!* Note that "having no slope" does *not* mean having slope = 0. Vertical lines have no slope; horizontal lines have slope 0.

2. Compute the slope, if any, of the line containing the two points given in each part of the following; write an equation in the form of y = mx + b for each line and sketch the graph of each line. For example, if A = (5, -3) and B = (2, -6), we see that m = 1. To find an equation of the line, we use m = 1 and plug in, say x = 5 and y = -3 to solve for b; we get -3 = 1 · 5 + b. So, b = -8. Thus, the equation is y = x – 8. The graph is:

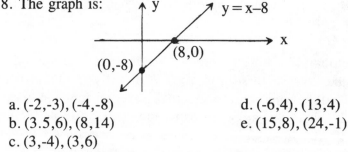

    a. (-2,-3), (-4,-8)   d. (-6,4), (13,4)
    b. (3.5,6), (8,14)   e. (15,8), (24,-1)
    c. (3,-4), (3,6)

3. Use the definition of betweenness to show B is between A and C for A = (2, 6), B = (4, 10), and C = (6, 14). Are these three points collinear? Sketch a graph to illustrate what is going on here.

The idea of coordinatizing a plane may have occurred first to the great French philosopher-biologist-physicist-mathematician Rene Descartes (1596–1650). In any case, in his honor, such coordinates are usually called Cartesian coordinates. Although Descartes is usually credited with being the founder of "analytic geometry" (i.e., geometry done by using coordinates), Pierre de Fermat (1601–1665), a French attorney and member of the Toulouse district assembly who did mathematics as a "hobby," should also be credited as being at least a co-founder of analytic geometry. Fermat's contributions to the development of analytic geometry are often overlooked because he himself never published any of his mathematical work (although it was published by his son in 1679, about 14 years after Fermat's death).

The idea of a coordinatized plane, simple as it now seems, was a very long time in arising and, once thought of, added enormously to the power of the mathematician in analyzing curves and functions and in building up the mathematical theory of functions. We shall be doing analytic geometry (i.e., geometry in a coordinatized plane) for quite a while now.

Section 4

The concept of distance is the key to the idea of size. With this concept now well-in-hand, we can define the basic similarity motion in the plane, $\mathbb{R}^2$.

Definition: A map $S: \mathbb{R}^2 \rightarrow \mathbb{R}^2$ is called a *similarity* transformation if for any two points A, B of $\mathbb{R}^2$ we have $D(S(A), S(B)) = k \cdot D(A, B)$, where k is some *positive* real number called the *scale factor* of the similarity S.

N.B. A similarity map with scale factor $k = 1$ is called an *isometry* (iso = same, metrein = to measure).

Remark: In other words, the definition says that a similarity map "moves" any two points to two other points which are k times as far apart as the original two points were. An isometry is so named since it "moves" any two points to two other points which are *exactly* as far apart as the original two, i.e., an *isometry preserves distance*. Therefore, an isometry preserves both size and shape, i.e., it is a congruence map. We shall see that the only isometries (congruence maps) of the plane are products of a finite number (at most 3) of reflections.

E.g., the map $(x, y) \overset{S_k}{\rightsquigarrow} (kx, ky)$ is a basic similarity transformation of the plane. Notice that the origin(0, 0) is fixed under S_k, but no other point is fixed under S_k if $k \neq 1$.

1. Verify that (0,0) is the *only* point fixed by S_k if $k \neq 1$. (Hint: recall that (x,y) is fixed by S_k means that $S_k((x,y)) = (x,y)$.)

Let's verify that S_k is a similarity transformation of the plane. Let A = (a,b) and B = (c, d). If we denote the images of A and B under S_k by A' and B', respectively, we know $A' = (ka,kb)$ and $B' = (kc,kd)$, where k is a fixed positive real number. We must now prove that $k \cdot AB = A'B'$ (i.e., $k \cdot D(A,B) = D(S_k(A), S_k(B))$). But that's easy to do; do it now.

2. Verify that $k \cdot AB = A'B'$ in the example just above. (Hint: use the definition of Euclidean distance and remember that k is positive.)

Similarity maps are both injective and surjective. Since it's much easier to verify the injectivity of similarities, let's do that first.

3. Supply the missing reasons in the following verification that any similarity map S with scale factor k is injective. Recall that we must show that: if $A \neq B$, then $S(A) \neq S(B)$. (Why?) Suppose $A \neq B$. Then $D(A, B) \neq 0$. (Why?) Now, it follows that:
   $D(S(A), S(B)) = k \cdot D(A,B) \neq 0$. (Why?) Since $D(S(A), S(B)) \neq 0$, we have $S(A) \neq S(B)$. (Why?) Thus, S is injective. (Why?)

4. Explain why the basic transformations S_k with $k > 0$ are injective.

5. Are congruence transformations injective? Explain.

Later on in the text, we shall see that *any* similarity transformation is also surjective. But for now, supply the missing reasons in the following verification that any S_k is surjective.

6. Recall that $S_k: \mathbb{R}^2 \to \mathbb{R}^2$. To show that S_k is surjective, we must verify that every (x,y) in $\mathbb{R}^2$, the codomain of S_k, is *actually the image* under S_k *of some point* (a,b) in $\mathbb{R}^2$, the domain of S_k. I claim that $(a,b) = (x/k, y/k)$ works as a pre-image of (x,y) under S_k. You verify that my claim is correct. Thus, S_k is surjective.

Q.E.D.

Let's look now at a trio of exercises which will draw our attention to some other interesting properties of the basic similarity transformations S_k.

7. Use graph paper and put the origin of your coordinate system well down toward the left-hand corner to give yourself plenty of room. Draw a graph of triangle ABC with corners (vertices) at A = (1,2), B = (5,1), and C = (4,3). We are going to transform $\triangle$ABC by applying S_2 to the coordinate plane which contains it. Recall that: $S_2(x,y) = (2x,2y)$.

  i. Fill in the blanks:

$$S_2$$

$$(1,2) \longrightarrow (\quad , \quad)$$
$$(5,1) \longrightarrow (\quad , \quad)$$
$$(4,3) \longrightarrow (\quad , \quad)$$

  ii. Let A', B', C' denote the images of A, B, C under S_2, as found in part i. Draw a graph (in red) of $\triangle$A'B'C' on the same graph paper as before. Examine the two triangles. Describe what has happened to $\triangle$ABC under the transformation S_2.

  iii. Test what you said about the triangles in part ii. by using a ruler to measure the following distances on your graphs:

AB =	A'B' =
BC =	B'C' =
AC =	A'C' =

  iv. What do you notice about the corresponding distances? E.g.,how are AB and A'B' related?

  v. Consider the ratios $(A'B')/(AB), (B'C')/BC$, and $(A'C')/AC$; what do you find?

  vi. Use a protractor to measure each of the angles of the two triangles. (Hint: extend the sides of the triangles to help yourself measure the angles.) Record your results.

$m\angle A =$	degrees	$m\angle A' =$	degrees
$m\angle B =$	degrees	$m\angle B' =$	degrees
$m\angle C =$	degrees	$m\angle C' =$	degrees

vii. What do you notice about the measures of the corresponding angles?

viii. Describe exactly what the transformation S_2 does to $\triangle ABC$ in transforming it to $\triangle A'B'C'$.

8. If we *began* with the triangle $A'B'C'$, what transformation would we have to apply to it to end up with the triangle ABC as the image?

9. Considering the previous exercises,
   a. What do you notice about S_k when $k > 1$?
   b. What do you notice about S_k when $k < 1$?
   c. What do you think the map S_1 is? Explain.

The basic similarity transformation S_k is called:

   i. a *k-stretch* if $k > 1$;
   ii. a *k-shrink* if $k < 1$;
   iii. the *identity* if $k = 1$.

Mathematicians generally lump together all the S_k's under the name *dilations*.

Remark: It can be shown that *any* similarity map is a composite (i.e., a mapping product) of a finite number of maps which are either reflections or dilations.

Thus, having introduced the S_k mappings, now we have seen all the "building blocks" needed to construct every allowable transformation for *both* the Euclidean geometry of similarity *and* the Euclidean geometry of congruence.

Section 5

Recall that injectivity and surjectivity are important properties of mappings. Let's examine similarity transformations to see that they are surjective as well as being injective. (Remember that we already proved that *any* similarity is injective; review exercise 4.3.)

1. Fill in the details of the following proof that the composite (product) of any two surjective mappings is a surjective mapping. Suppose that f: S↠T and g: T↠U are surjective mappings. We wish to show that g ○ f: S↠U is also a surjective mapping. To show that g ○ f is surjective, we must show that every u in U is actually the image of some s in S under the mapping g ○ f, i.e., that there is some s in S such that g(f(s)) = u. (why?) Let u be an element of U. Then, there is some t in T such that g(t) = u. (why?) Moreover, there is some s in S such that f(s) = t. (why?) Thus, g ○ f(s) = g(f(s)) = g(t) = u. So g ○ f is surjective. (why?)

    Q.E.D.

2. Recall the map (flip), F: $\mathbb{R}^2 \rightarrow \mathbb{R}^2$ given by reflection in a line. Is F a surjection? Explain as well as you can. (Hint: You should try to give a plausible explanation of why *every* point in the plane is actually the image under F of some point in the plane. Draw a picture to illustrate your plausible explanation.)

3. In exercise 1 we proved that the composite of two surjections is a surjection. Thus, the composite of any finite number of surjections is a surjection. Why? Explain as well as you can.

4. Explain now why *any* similarity map S: $\mathbb{R}^2 \rightarrow \mathbb{R}^2$ is a surjection. (Hint: keep exercises 4.6, 2 and 3 in mind and look back at the concluding remark of Section 4.)

Thus, we have shown that any similarity map is a *bijection,* i.e., is *both* an *injection and a surjection*.

Let's examine some very important properties of similarity transformations. In particular, let's show that similarities preserve lines (i.e., that the image of a line under a similarity is a line). Any mapping which preserves lines is called a *collineation*.

Theorem SPL (Similarities Preserve Lines)

Suppose A, B, C are collinear points and S is a similarity map with scale factor k. Then the points S(A), S(B), and S(C) are collinear.

Proof: Recall that we agreed to use the distance condition AB + BC = AC to characterize collinearity of A, B, C. Since A, B, C are given as collinear points, we have AB + BC = AC. By definition of a similarity transformation, we have the following:

$$D(S(A), S(B)) = k \cdot AB$$
$$D(S(B), S(C)) = k \cdot BC$$
$$D(S(A), S(C)) = k \cdot AC$$

-79-

Since AB + BC = AC, multiplication by k gives k · AB + k · BC = k · BC, i.e.:
D(S(A), S(B)) + D(S(B), S(C)) = D(S(A), S(C)). Thus, the points S(A), S(B), and S(C) are collinear by definition of collinearity. Since S maps collinear points to collinear points, S preserves lines; i.e., if l is a line, its image under S, S(l) is also a line.

Q.E.D.

5. Explain why any congruence map preserves lines.

6. Recall that a circle with center O and radius r is the set of all points X in a plane such that D(O,X) = r. Examine the proof of Theorem SPL very carefully and then try to prove that any similarity map preserves circles.
   (Hint: the basic idea is to prove that a similarity map S with scale factor k transforms a circle with center O and radius r into a circle with center S(O) and radius k · r.)

If we assume, in keeping with Euclid, that one and only one line contains any two given points, we can determine exactly what the basic dilations S_k do to lines by examining the equations of lines and the equations of the images of the lines under S_k.

Suppose A = (2, 3) and B = (5, 8). What is an equation of the unique line, l, containing (passing through) the points A and B?

7. Verify that the slope of the unique line, l, passing through A and B as given above is 5/3; then verify that an equation of the line is y = (5/3) x − 1/3.

Let's find an equation for the unique line which passes through S_k(A) and S_k(B) by using the fact that S_k(A) = (2k, 3k) and S_k(B) = (5k, 8k). We can find the slope of S_k(l) by using

$$m = \frac{\Delta y}{\Delta x} = \frac{8k - 3k}{5k - 2k} = \frac{5k}{3k} = \frac{5}{3}$$

(Note that the slope of l and the slope of S_k(l) are the same.) Thus, we find an equation of S_k(l) to be y = (5/3)x − k/3.

Recall that vertical lines have *no* slope and are represented by equations of the form x = a, where a is some constant. E.g., an equation for the unique vertical line, l, through (2, 3) is x = 2. What is an equation for S_k(l)? Since l is completely determined by any two of its points, let's use (2, 3) and (2, 4) to help us determine an equation for S_k(l). The S_k-images of these points are (2k, 3k) and (2k, 4k), respectively. Thus, the unique vertical line that contains these images has the equation x = 2k.

In general, we could show that each dilation S_k acts on lines as follows:

Equation of l	S_k	*Equation of S_k(l)*
y = mx + b	⟶	y = mx + kb
x = a	⟶	x = ka

8. For each of the following pairs of points, state an equation for the unique line l which passes through them; also state an equation for the image of l under each of the dilations S_3 and $S_{0.5}$:

a. (-2, 3) and (3, 6)

b. (5, 2) and (5, -4)

For both a. and b., graph the original line l and both its images on the same graph; label the lines clearly as l, $S_3(l)$, and $S_{0.5}(l)$.

You may recall from your study of algebra that two lines in the same plane (called *coplanar* lines) are parallel if and only if they have the same slope, or they are both vertical (and so have *no* slope).

9. Look back at the claim about the action of S_k on lines. Do you think that each dilation S_k preserves parallelism? I.e., do you think that if l is parallel to m, then $S_k(l)$ is parallel to $S_k(m)$? Explain your conjecture as well as you can before you read on.

Obviously, you should have conjectured in exercise 9 that each dilation S_k preserves parallelism of lines. We can easily prove this preservation of parallelism. In fact, we can prove that *any* similarity map S preserves parallelism. In order to do so, we need a rigorous geometric definition of parallelism.

Definition: Two coplanar lines l and m are said to be *parallel*, denoted by $l \parallel m$, if they have no points in common.

Remark: If we regard lines as being sets of points, we may say $l \parallel m$ if and only if $l \cap m = \emptyset$.

Theorem SPP (Similarities Preserve Parallelism)

Suppose $l \parallel m$ and let S: $\mathbb{R}^2 \rightarrow \mathbb{R}^2$ be a similarity map with scale factor k. Then $S(l) \parallel S(m)$

Proof: We shall use the technique of proof by contradiction. Suppose that $S(l)$ and $S(m)$ are *not* parallel. Then there is some point, say X, common to $S(l)$ and $S(m)$. Since $X \in S(l)$, X is the image of some point $A \in l$, i.e. $X = S(A)$; similarly, $X = S(B)$ for some point $B \in m$. Now, $A \neq B$ since $A \in l$ and $B \in m$, and $l \parallel m$ (so lines l and m have no point in common). But $A \neq B$ and $S(A) = S(B)$ is a direct contradiction to the injectivity of S. Thus, by the principle of proof by contradiction we have proved $S(l) \parallel S(m)$.

Q.E.D.

10. Do congruence transformations preserve parallelism? Explain.

Section 6

Consider the dilations S_2 and S_3. We can compose (multiply) these mappings and figure out the result. Be very alert to the meaning and use of the notation here; it's usually troublesome at first.

$$
\begin{aligned}
S_2 \circ S_3 (x, y) &= S_2(S_3(x, y)) \\
&= S_2(3x, 3y) \\
&= (6x, 6y) \\
&= S_6(x, y)
\end{aligned}
$$

Thus, we see that $S_2 \circ S_3 = S_6$. Similarly, $S_3 \circ S_2 = S_6$. So, $S_2 \circ S_3 = S_3 \circ S_2$.

1. Consider now the composite $S_2 \circ S_{1/2}$. Direct computation shows $S_2 \circ S_{1/2}(x, y) = (x, y)$. Verify this. Also examine $S_{1/2} \circ S_2(x, y)$. What do you notice? Describe the effect of the mapping $S_2 \circ S_{1/2}$ on $\mathbb{R}^2$.

   Now, having had some specific experience with composites of dilations, let's step bravely out to the general stage.

2. i. Write the formula for $S_k \circ S_j : \mathbb{R}^2 \to \mathbb{R}^2$; find it by directly computing $S_k \circ S_j(x, y) = (\quad , \quad)$.

   Is the composite $S_k \circ S_j$ a dilation? If so, what dilation is it?

   ii. What mapping is S_1?

   iii. Compute $S_k \circ S_{1/k}(x, y) = (\quad , \quad)$ and $S_{1/k} \circ S_k(x, y) = (\quad , \quad)$. What do you notice?

   iv. Does all this remind you of anything?

   v. Would you care to make a conjecture about the collection of all dilations S_k and the operation of composition? Can you prove your conjecture? Try to do so.

Let's consider translations of the plane, $\mathbb{R}^2$, and develop a general formula which will describe the action of a translation on $\mathbb{R}^2$. Recall that in studying frieze (strip) ornaments, we discovered an allowable symmetry motion, called T. This T was a slide or translation of the ornament one design-unit to the right. Of course, T^{-1} was a similar slide to the left. Now, when we consider translations of the entire plane, $\mathbb{R}^2$, we have the freedom to do more than simply slide things to the right or left because the plane is two-dimensional while the strip ornaments were, essentially, only one-dimensional. E.g., consider the figure below; there, flag #2 is the image of flag #1 under a translation which moves the plane 3 units to the right and 3 units up.

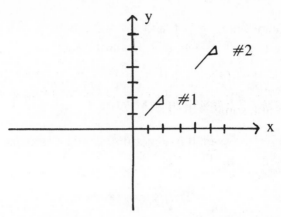

3. Using graph paper, plot the points A = (1, -1), B = (3, -1), C = (1, 1), and D = (-1, -3). Connect these points with pieces of straight lines in the following order: A to B to C to D to A. The resulting figure, ABCD, is an example of a *quadrilateral*, i.e., a *four-sided* figure. Now, let the map f: $\mathbb{R}^2 \to \mathbb{R}^2$ be defined by the formula:

$$f(x, y) = (x + 3, y + 2).$$

a. Sketch, in green, the image of ABCD under the mapping f. (Hint: plot the points f(A), f(B), f(C), and f(D) and then connect them with *line segments,* as you did in the original quadrilateral. Note that we are assuming that f is a collineation.)

b. We might describe the action of f on the plane by saying that f moves the points of the plane ____ units to the right and ____ units up.

c. What type of congruence transformation is the mapping f?

d. Suppose that g: $\mathbb{R}^2 \to \mathbb{R}^2$ moves the points of the plane 3 units to the right and 2 units down. Write a formula for g, i.e., fill in the blanks:
g(x, y) = (,   ).

e. Sketch, in blue, on the same graph as before, the image of ABCD under the mapping g.

f. What type of congruence transformation is g?

g. Suppose that h: $\mathbb{R}^2 \to \mathbb{R}^2$ moves the points of the plane 3 units to the left and 2 units up; write a formula for h, i.e., fill in the blanks: h(x, y) = (,   ).

h. Sketch, using red, on the same graph, the image of ABCD under h.

i. What type of congruence transformation is h?

In exercise 3, part d, you should have said g(x, y) = (x + 3, y − 2). Recall that f(x, y) = (x + 3, y + 2). Thus, the formula for g $\circ$ f(x, y) can be computed as:
g $\circ$ f(x, y) = g(f(x, y)) = g(x + 3, y + 2) = (x + 3 + 3, y + 2 − 2) = (x + 6, y).

4. Using the mappings from exercise 3, compute formulas for the following composites:

      a.   f $\circ$ g(x, y) = (,   )
      b.   g $\circ$ h(x, y) = (,   )
      c.   h $\circ$ g(x, y) = (,   )

What do you notice about g ○ f and f ○ g? About g ○ h and h ○ g? What type of transformations are g ○ f, f ○ g, g ○ h, and h ○ g?

5.   Based on what you saw and did in exercises 3 and 4, state your conjecture for the formula of a *general* translation $T(x, y) = ($, $)$.

In exercise 5, you guessed the general formula for a translation $T: \mathbb{R}^2 \to \mathbb{R}^2$. You probably guessed something like this:

$$T(x, y) = (x + a, y + b).$$

In any case, that's the correct idea. Let's denote such a translation by $T_{(a, b)}$ so that $T_{(a, b)}(x, y) = (x + a, y + b)$ for all $(x, y) \in \mathbb{R}^2$.

6.   Using this new notation, we can express the map f of exercise 3 by saying that $f = T_{(3, 2)}$. Refer to exercise 3 and write the representation of each of the following mappings:

        a. g $= T_{(}$, $)$ c. g ○ f $= T_{(}$, $)$
        b. h $= T_{(}$, $)$ d. f ○ g $= T_{(}$, $)$

In exercise 6, you should have written $g = T_{(3, -2)}$. Since $f = T_{(3, 2)}$, we get that $g \circ f = T_{(3, -2)} \circ T_{(3, 2)} = T_{(6, 0)}$. Similarly, we can see that $T_{(2, 4)} \circ T_{(-5, 6)} = T_{(-3, 10)}$. The notation here is a bit complex and somewhat difficult to understand so think about it carefully. If you don't understand it, ask someone for help.

7. Consider $T_{(a, b)} \circ T_{(c, d)}$.
    a. Write a formula for this composite by filling in the blanks:
       $T_{(a, b)} \circ T_{(c, d)}(x, y) = ($, $)$;

    b. Is $T_{(a, b)} \circ T_{(c, d)}$ a map of the form $T_{(}$, $)$? Explain.

    c. What mapping is $T_{(0, 0)}$?

    d. Compute $T_{(a, b)} \circ T_{(-a, -b)}(x, y)$.   What do you notice? Compute $T_{(-a, -b)} \circ T_{(a, b)}(x, y)$. What do you notice?

    e. Does all this remind you of anything? Would you like to make a conjecture about the collection of all maps $T_{(a, b)}$ with the operation ○?

    f. Can you prove your conjecture? Try to do so.

In exercise 7, you should have seen that the collection $\{T_{(a, b)} | (a, b) \in \mathbb{R}^2\}$ with the operation ○ forms a group. In fact, it is a commutative group which is new to us. It is isomorphic to the infinite additive group $(\mathbb{R} \oplus \mathbb{R}, \oplus)$ with the underlying set $\mathbb{R}^2$ and the operation $\oplus$ defined by $(x, y) \oplus (u, v) = (x + u, y + v)$.

8.   Verify that $(\mathbb{R} \oplus \mathbb{R}, \oplus)$ is indeed an infinite commutative group. (Hint: you may

assume that $(\mathbb{R}, +)$ is an infinite commutative group; then use the definitions of infinite, commutative, and group to finish the exercise.)

Section 7

A bit later, we'll find the general formula for a reflection in a mirror line. Meanwhile, we can examine special cases of reflections which have very easy formulas; let's look at them now.

1.   Suppose F_h is the reflection in the x-axis. I claim that $F_h(3, 2) = (3, -2)$, $F_h(4,-2) = (4, 2)$, $F_h(-3, 0) = (-3, 0)$. Think about my claim and why it is correct; look at a graph to assist you in your thinking. Fill in the blanks to express
$F_h(x, y) = ($, $)$.

2.   Suppose F_v is the reflection in the y-axis. I claim that
$F_v(3, 2) = (-3, 2)$, $F_v(4, -2) = (-4, -2)$, $F_v(0, -3) = (0, -3)$. Think about my claim and why it is correct; look at a graph to assist you in your thinking. Fill in the blanks to express
$F_v(x, y) = ($, $)$.

3.   Suppose F_p is the reflection in the line y = x. I claim that $F_p(3, 4) = (4, 3)$, $F_p(-2,-1) = (-1, -2)$, $F_p(2,2) = (2, 2)$. Think about my claim and why it is correct; look at a graph to assist you in your thinking. Fill in the blanks to express
$F_p(x, y) = ($, $)$.

4.   Suppose F_n is the reflection in the line y = -x. I claim that $F_n(3, 4) = (-4, -3)$, $F_n(-2,-1) = (1, 2)$, $F_n(2, -2) = (2, -2)$. Think about my claim and why it is correct; look at a graph to assist you in your thinking. Fill in the blanks to express
$F_n(x, y) = ($, $)$.

Make sure that your formulas for the four reflections F_h, F_v, F_p, and F_n are correct before you go on.

Let's examine the effect of these maps on certain figures in the coordinate plane.

5.   Using graph paper with the origin near the center of the page, sketch the triangle, $\triangle ABC$, with vertices A = (1, 1), B = (4, 6), and C = (9, 2). Label the vertices with both letter and coordinates. Now, using the formulas you found in exercises 1 and 2, sketch all the following figures on the same graph:

a. In green, $F_v(\triangle ABC)$; label the vertices A′, B′, C′ with both letter and coordinates.

b. In blue, $F_h(\triangle ABC)$; label the vertices A″, B″, C″ with both letter and coordinates.

c. In red, $F_h \circ F_v(\triangle ABC)$; label the vertices A*, B*, C* with both letter and coordinates.

d.   Consider the result of part c. Do you think $F_h \circ F_v$ is a reflection? Explain. (Hint: recall the products of flips in the dihedral groups.) Complete the
formula: $F_h \circ F_v(x, y) = ($, $)$.

e.   In black, $F_v \circ F_h (\triangle ABC)$. What do you notice about this image? What do you notice about $F_h \circ F_v$ and $F_v \circ F_h$? What type of congruence transformations are $F_h \circ F_v$ and $F_v \circ F_h$?

6. Do all graphs for this exercise on a new set of axes with the origin near the center of the sheet of graph paper. Sketch the graph of the triangle, $\triangle ABC$, with vertices $A = (6, 2)$, $B = (10, 7)$, and $C = (14, 4)$. Draw the graphs of the mirror lines $y = x$ and $y = -x$. Now, using the formulas you found in exercises 3 and 4 for F_p and F_n, repeat the five steps of exercise 5; in each step replace F_v by F_p and F_h by F_n.

Let's give a more general examination to reflection in a line.

7. Suppose l is a line in the plane and A is a point in the plane. E.g.,

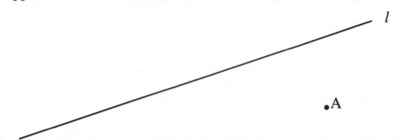

Explain how you would find A', the image of A under reflection in the mirror line l. (Hint: Use *any* convenient drawing tools to help find A'.) Draw the line segment $\overline{AA'}$; let M be the point where $\overline{AA'}$ crosses l. Measure $\overline{AM}$ and $\overline{MA'}$ with your ruler; what do you notice? Use your protractor to measure the angles formed by l and $\overline{AA'}$; what do you notice? What if the point A were on the mirror line l?

Remark: Based on your findings from exercise 7, we see that A' is the image of A under reflection in the mirror line l if and only if l is the *perpendicular bisector* of the line segment $\overline{AA'}$, i.e., l forms 90 degree angles with $\overline{AA'}$ and passes through the midpoint of $\overline{AA'}$.

Let's consider a coordinatized plane and examine the general formula for reflection in a mirror line, l.

First, suppose that the mirror line l is vertical; then l has an equation of the form $x = a$. Let's make our equation more specific: $x = 2$.

8. For each of the points A_1, A_2, and A_3 in the graph below, find the coordinates of the image under reflection in the mirror defined by the formula $x = 2$. Sketch the complete graph, including the images, and label all the points with their coordinates. $A_1 = (5, 3)$, $A_2 = (2, -3)$, and $A_3 = (1, -2)$.

In general, if the mirror line l is a *vertical* line with equation $x = a$, we have:

$$(u, v) \xrightarrow{\quad F_l \quad} (2a - u, v)$$

Note that if A is on l, A $= (a, v)$ and so $F_l(A) = (a, v) =$ A.

Now, suppose the mirror is *not vertical*; it has an equation of the form $y = mx + b$. Let F_l denote the reflection in l. A tiresomely long but perfectly straightforward computation gives the result:

$$(u, v) \xrightarrow{\quad F_l \quad} \left(\frac{u(1 - m^2) + 2m(v - b)}{1 + m^2}, \quad \frac{v(m^2 - 1) + 2(mu + b)}{1 + m^2} \right).$$

9. Check the formula for F_l above by letting l be the line:
    a. $y = x$ ($m = 1$, $b = 0$). Is F_l the same as F_p?
    b. $y = -x$ ($m = -1$, $b = 0$). Is F_l the same as F_n?
    c. $y = 0$ ($m = 0$, $b = 0$). Is F_l the same as F_h?
    d. (Extra Credit) If A $= (u, v)$ is on $y = mx + b$, i.e., if $v = mu + b$, show that $F_l(A) =$ A. (Hint: Use the fact that $v = mu + b$ to simplify the expression for $F_l(u, v)$.)

10. Using the formulas for reflection discussed above, find the reflected image of the point A $= (2, 3)$ in each of the following lines:

a. $y = x$	e. $y = -2x + 1$
b. $y = -x$	f. $x = 3$
c. $y = 0$	g. $x = 0$
d. $y = x + 3$	h. $x = -2$

11. Look back at your solution to exercises 5 and 6. If we begin at A and go around $\triangle$ABC in a clockwise direction, we encounter the vertices of the triangle in the order A, B, C.
    a. If we begin at A$'$ and go around $\triangle$A$'$B$'$C$'$ in a counter-clockwise direction, we encounter the vertices of the triangle in the order __, __, __.
    b. If we begin at A$''$ and go around $\triangle$A$''$B$''$C$''$ in a counter-clockwise direction, we encounter the vertices of the triangle in the order __, __, __.
    c. If we begin at A* and go around $\triangle$A*B*C* in a clockwise direction, we encounter the vertices of the triangle in the order __, __, __.
    d. What, if anything, do you notice in your answers to parts a., b., c., as compared with each other and with the order of the original vertices of $\triangle$ABC?

12. Sketch the reflection image in the mirror line of the "right hand" shown below; the image is a _____ hand.

In exercises 11 and 12, you should have noticed a reversal of the orientation of both △ABC and the hand. Reflection in a mirror line transformed the clockwise orientation of △ABC to the counter-clockwise orientation of △A′B′C′ and the right hand to a left hand. One says that figures such as △ABC and △A′B′C′ have *opposite orientation*. Thus, we may say that reflection in a mirror line is an *orientation-reversing transformation*.

13. State whether each of the following transformations is orientation-preserving or orientation-reversing:

        a. Translation   c. Glide-reflection
        b. Rotation   d. Dilation

14. Does the composite of two reflections preserve or reverse orientation? What if we continue to compose more flips, one at a time? Discuss the effect of such product mappings on orientation.

Remark: The idea of orientation is important in chemistry, biology, and physics. If you are interested, you may wish to try to find out more about enantiomorphic crystals and compounds, or particles with right-handed spin as opposed to left-handed spin.

15. The basic congruence transformations are:

Translation
Rotation
} orientation preserving

Reflection
Glide-reflection
} orientation reversing

What if we compose (multiply) these basic maps? Make a conjecture as to how the composition's effect on orientation depends on the number of orientation preserving or reversing transformations contained as factors in the product. (Hint: think of even versus odd.)

Section 8

Alas for us, the general formula for a rotation around a given point is not easy to express. In fact, it requires the use of trigonometry. Thus, although it is true, we shall not try to *prove* that the collection of all rotations around a given point forms a group with the binary operation given by the usual composition of mappings.

1. Let P be a point of $\mathbb{R}^2$. Try to give a plausible explanation of why the rotations around P form a group. Draw diagrams to illustrate your discussion. (A bit of "handwaving" is OK here.)

It is, however, quite easy to find the formula for H_P, the *halfturn* around the point P. Halfturns are particularly important and interesting because they and the reflections (flips) are the only isometries which are involutions. Moreover, halfturns will be most useful to us in our study of parallels. Let's lay the intuitive foundation for that study.

You have already seen halfturns on several occasions, e.g., in your study of symmetry groups. In section 7 you probably noticed that $H_0 = F_h \circ F_v = F_v \circ F_h = F_p \circ F_n = F_n \circ F_p$ is a halfturn around the origin. What is it about the reflections F_h, F_v, and F_p, F_n which makes them commute and their products equal to halfturns? The mirror lines of each of these pairs of flips are *perpendicular*, i.e., they form 90° angles.

There is a very easy way to characterize the halfturn, H_P around a point P in terms of any point X, its image $H_P(X)$, and P. Let's see how this might work:

2. Make a sketch in which you mark a point P as the *center* of the halfturn H_P. Sketch in at least 3 other points A, B, and C (not all collinear with P). Let $H_P(A) = A'$, $H_P(B) = B'$, and $H_P(C) = C'$. Sketch in as best you can (on the basis of your intuition about H_P) A', B', and C'. Use a ruler and protractor to make the most accurate sketch you possibly can.

Now, measure the following distances:

$$\begin{array}{llll}
\text{i.} & AP = \underline{\quad}, & A'P = \underline{\quad}, & AA' = \underline{\quad}. \\
\text{ii.} & BP = \underline{\quad}, & B'P = \underline{\quad}, & BB' = \underline{\quad}. \\
\text{iii.} & CP = \underline{\quad}, & C'P = \underline{\quad}, & CC' = \underline{\quad}.
\end{array}$$

What do you notice about the distances in each of the three cases above? Based on your observations, make a strong conjecture about the relationship of X, P, and X' for any point X (where $X' = H_P(X)$, of course). What is $H_P(P)$? Does $H_P(X) = X$ if $X \neq P$?

Your conjectures in the previous exercise should have led you to the following:

Definition: For any point P, the *halfturn around P* — denoted by H_P — is a mapping $H_P: \mathbb{R}^2 \to \mathbb{R}^2$ such that for any point X and its image $X' = H_P(X)$, P is the midpoint of the closed segment $\overline{XX'}$, i.e., X-P-X' and XP = PX'. The *center* of H_P is P.

Now that we have, one hopes, grasped the idea of a halfturn around a central point P, let's set out to find the formula for H_p.

You may recall from algebra (or some other previous study) how to find the coordinate(s) of the midpoint of a closed line segment, provided that you already know the coordinates of the endpoints of the segment.

3. Consider the closed segments on the real line:

> i) [-2, 2] iii) [-10, -6] v) [-3, 9]
> ii) [4, 8] iv) [2, 7] vi) [-8, -1]

Make a sketch of each segment (draw a different number line for each). What is the coordinate of the midpoint of each of the segments? Explain. (Hint: Your answers should be, respectively: 0, 6, -8, 4.5, 3, -4.5.) You may check that in each case, the midpoint is simply the *average* **of the endpoints. E.g., in iv), the average of 2 and 7 is 4.5, and 4.5 is the midpoint of [2, 7] since the lengths of both [2, 4.5] and [4.5, 7] are equal to 2.5. Check that the same sort of thing is true in another case.**

4. Suppose 3 is the midpoint of the closed interval [-2, x]. Find x. (Hint: $3 = (-2 + x)/2$. Why? Solve for x.) Suppose -1 is the midpoint of [x, 2]. Find x.

Your work in exercise 4 should lead you to understand that if we know the coordinates of the midpoint and one endpoint of a closed interval (segment) on the real line, we can find the coordinate of the other endpoint. Now, let's generalize these ideas to the plane, $\mathbb{R}^2$.

You recall that each point in the plane has two coordinates, e.g., (2, 3). The simple idea of averaging the coordinates of the endpoints of a closed segment to find the coordinates of the midpoint of that segment extends naturally to the plane.

5. Suppose A = (2, 3) and B = (4, 7). Show that M = (3, 5) is the midpoint of $\overline{AB}$ by using the Euclidean distance formula to compute AM, MB, and AB. Then show that:

> i) AM + MB = AB (i.e., A-M-B),
> ii) AM = MB

It is easy but tedious to verify the following:

Theorem: Let A = (u, v) and B = (x, y). Then the point M = $((u + x)/2, (v + y)/2)$ is the midpoint of $\overline{AB}$, i.e., A-M-B and AM = MB.

6. (Extra Credit) Use the Euclidean distance formula to verify the result of the theorem just above.

7. Find the midpoint M of the closed segment $\overline{AB}$ in each of the following:
> i) A = (-3, 6) and B = (2, 3)
> ii) A = (5, -4) and B = (7, 8)

Just as on the real line, if we know the coordinates of the midpoint and one endpoint of a closed segment in the plane, it is easy to find the coordinates of the other endpoint. E.g., suppose A = (1, 3) and M = (2, 5) is the midpoint of $\overline{AB}$.

What are the coordinates of B? Let B = (x, y). Then, since the coordinates of M are found by averaging those of A and B, we can say: $(x + 1)/2 = 2$ and $(y + 3)/2 = 5$. Solving for (x, y) gives B = (3, 7).

8. Given the coordinates of one endpoint A and the midpoint M of $\overline{AB}$, find the coordinates of the other endpoint B in each of the following:

i) A = (-3, 4), M = (4, -2)
ii) A = (-5, -6), M = (8, 12)
iii) A = (s, t), M = (u, v), B = (x, y) — solve for x and y in terms of s, t, u, and v.

With the ideas we have developed, we can give the formula for the halfturn H_P around the point P:

Suppose the center of the halfturn is P = (u, v). Let X = (s, t). What are the coordinates of X′ = $H_P(X)$ = (x, y)? (Hint: Did you solve exercise 8? If so, you already know the answer.) Since P is the midpoint of $\overline{XX}$ ′, we can solve (s + x)/2 = u and (t + y)/2 = v to get:

$$x = 2u - s$$
$$y = 2v - t$$

$$(s, t) \xrightarrow{\quad H_P \quad} (2u - s, 2v - t) \text{ , if } P = (u,v)$$

Examples:

i)   P = (0, 0), X = (2, 3) $H_P(X) = (-2, -3)$ and $H_P(H_P(X)) = (2, 3)$
ii) P = (1, 1), X = (2, 3) $H_P(X) = (0, -1)$ and $H_P(H_P(X)) = (2, 3)$
iii) P = (-2, -3), X = (0, 0) $H_P(X) = (-4, -6)$ and $H_P(H_P(X)) = (0, 0)$

(Sketch a diagram to help yourself see how H_P works.) Thus, we have:

Theorem: If P = (u, v) and X = (s, t), then $H_P(X) = (2u - s, 2v - t)$.

9.   Using the formula for H_P, verify that H_P is an involution by showing that $H_P(H_P(X)) = X$ for any point X; i.e., H_P^2 = Identity.

Using the formula for H_P and the Euclidean distance formula, it is tedious but straightforward to prove:

Theorem: For any point P, H_P is an isometry of the plane.

Since H_P is an isometry, it is automatically a similarity — thus,

Theorem: For any point P, H_P is bijective (i.e., both injective and surjective), a collineation (i.e., preserves lines), preserves parallelism, etc.

Remark: The "etc." in the theorem above is meant to indicate that H_P has any property which follows from its being an isometry (and thus a similarity) of the plane.

10.   (Extra Credit) Verify that, for any point P, H_P is an isometry. (Hint: You will want to use coordinates and the Euclidean distance formula to show that for any two points X and Y, D(X, Y) = D($H_P(X)$, $H_P(Y)$)).

11. Let P = (u, v) and Q = (w, z). Show that $H_P \circ H_Q$ is a *translation*, and identify what translation it is. (Hint: $H_P \circ H_Q(s, t) = H_P(H_Q(s, t))$.)

   Thus, the set of all halfturns is *not* closed under the operation of composition of mappings.

Section 9

Since the four basic types of congruence transformations preserve both size and shape, so will *any* possible composite of finitely many such maps. Moreover, since any of the four basic congruence transformations may be represented as a composite of reflections, the reflections form a set of generators for the group of allowable transformations for Euclidean congruence geometry, the so-called group of isometries.

Definition: An *isometry* is a mapping of the plane to itself which preserves distance; i.e., a mapping f of the plane to itself is an isometry iff for every pair of points, A, B we have d(A, B) = d(f(A), f(B)).

Remark: Thus, an isometry (i.e., a congruence map) is simply a similarity mapping with scale factor 1. Any isometry is a finite product of reflections.

Caution: Do not confuse isometry with isomorphism.

1. Contrast an isometry mapping with an isomorphism mapping.

Definition: We say two figures are *congruent* if there is an isometry which maps one onto the other.

Remark: Be sure to learn the definition of congruence just above; it is the rigorous formulation of the intuitive idea of having the same size and shape.

Congruent figures fall naturally into two separate classes: the directly congruent, and the oppositely congruent.

Definition: Two figures are said to be *directly congruent (oppositely congruent)* if the isometry which maps one onto the other is orientation preserving (orientation reversing).

2. Give a specific example of i) a direct isometry and ii) an opposite isometry. (Hint: look back at exercise 7.15.) Illustrate your examples by sketching a rough "graph" as part of the discussion.

The following two crucial theorems contain the key to why the congruence transformations are basic to the (plane) Euclidean geometry of congruence:

Congruence Theorem I: Any two directly congruent figures in the plane can be made to coincide by means of translations and rotations.

Congruence Theorem II: Any two oppositely congruent figures in the plane can be made to coincide by means of reflections and glide-reflections.

Thus, the congruence transformations suffice to do all we want in studying (plane) Euclidean congruence geometry.

Definition: *Euclidean congruence geometry* is the science which studies figural properties which are not altered by reflections.

Remark: Since translations, rotations, reflections, and glide-reflections can be represented as composites of reflections, Euclidean congruence geometry is really the science which studies figural properties preserved by translation, rotation, reflection, or glide-reflection.

Just as we distinguished between direct and opposite congruence, so we may distinguish between direct and opposite similarity.

3. Give a specific example of i) a direct similarity and ii) an opposite similarity. (Hint: Think of dilation and then of a dilation composed with a reflection.) Illustrate your examples by sketching a rough "graph" as part of the discussion.

The basic generators for the group of similarities are the reflections and the dilations. Thus, we can make the following definition:

Definition: A *similarity* is a product of finitely many reflections and dilations.

Remark: It can be shown that our previous definition of similarity agrees perfectly with this new characterization.

Definition: We say two figures are *similar* if there is a similarity which maps one onto the other.

The following two crucial theorems contain the key to why similarities are basic to (plane) Euclidean similarity geometry:

Similarity Theorem I: Any two directly similar figures in the plane can be made to coincide by means of translations, rotations, and dilations.

Similarity Theorem II: Any two oppositely similar figures in the plane can be made to coincide by means of reflections, glide-reflections, and dilations.

Thus, the similarity transformations suffice for us to do all we want in studying (plane) Euclidean similarity geometry.

Definition: Euclidean similarity geometry is the science which studies figural properties which are not altered by reflections and dilations.

Remark: Now we know precisely what Euclidean geometry is all about!

You might be interested to know that this transformational approach to geometry via groups was first suggested in a famous speech given by the German mathematician Felix Klein in 1872 on the occasion of his being admitted to the faculty of the University of Erlangen. According to the so-called Erlanger Programm, every sort of geometry is simply the study of the properties of figures left invariant (unaltered) by a certain group of allowable transformations. There are new geometries which cannot be characterized in the way proposed by Klein; his idea, however, remains important and productive.

4) Try to think of some of the properties of figures which would be studied in:
    a. Euclidean congruence geometry;

b. Euclidean similarity geometry.

List them. (Hint: List properties which are preserved by the appropriate types of mappings.)

In Unit IV, we shall study Euclidean geometry axiomatically and use transformations wherever we can to develop the ideas contained in the relevant parts of Euclid's *Elements*. Thus, we shall be able to appreciate something of the beauty and order of Euclid's exposition of geometry as viewed from a modern perspective.

Unit III: Review Topics

1. Euclidean distance between two points of a coordinate plane.
2. Definition, including the four distance axioms, of a general distance (metric).
3. Non-Euclidean distances; examples.
4. Collinearity and betweenness of points.
5. Slope and y-intercept of a line.
6. Definition of a similarity transformation; scale factor; examples.
7. Stretch, shrink, dilation.
8. Similarity maps are bijective (injective and surjective).
9. Theorem SPL (Similarities Preserve Lines).
10. Action of S_k on a line.
11. Definition of parallel lines.
12. Theorem SPP (Similarities Preserve Parallelism).
13. Composites of similarities, in particular, all S_k's.
14. Definition of and formula for translation.
15. Idea of rotation transformation, especially a halfturn around a central point, midpoint formula, formula for the halfturn with center (u, v); properties of halfturns: similarity, isometry, involution, bijection, etc.
16. Reflection in a line; examples such as F_h, F_v, F_p, F_n and their formulas.
17. Orientation; effect of various transformations on orientation.
18. Definition of isometry (congruence map).
19. Definition of congruence (direct and opposite) of figures.
20. Definitions of Euclidean congruence and similarity geometries.
21. Klein's Erlanger Programm.

Unit IV
A Transformational Approach to Neutral Geometry

"Would you tell me please, which way I ought to go from here?" "That depends a good deal on where you want to get to," said the Cat.

– Lewis Carroll –

Well, where *do* we want to get to now? We want to cover as much as we can of neutral geometry, i.e., that part of elementary Euclidean geometry which does not refer to or make use of parallel lines in any essential way. Since we want to use the techniques of axiomatization to make our approach locally rigorous, we shall begin with a brief reminder about the axiomatic way.

"Logic can be patient for it is eternal.

– O. Heaviside –

"Contrariwise," continued Tweedledee, "if it was so, it might be; and if it were so, it would be; but as it isn't, it ain't. That's logic."

– Lewis Carroll –

Probably the most important thing for you to get out of this course is a reasonably accurate idea of what mathematics, and in particular geometry, is all about. I believe that the essence of mathematical activity is to be found in problem solving and the subtle inter*play* between the creative insights born of a carefully cultivated intuition and the rigorously objective procedures for proving (testing) these subjective insights for correctness. I stress the *play*ful aspect of mathematics because I am convinced that the elemental pleasure to be derived from *doing* mathematics is very like the joyous satisfaction we get from taking an active part in a challenging, fascinating game. Moreover, success in playing mathematics provides an important way for each of us to affirm the power of "the mind's I," the ego. I hope that you may be gratified, as I am, by the intellectual beauty of mathematics. It is primarily for the sake of this beauty that the mathematician pursues the muse of mathematics. Without some sense of the intellectual passion for beauty which drives mathematicians, you will surely fail to grasp the essence of mathematics and become lost in a seemingly random and meaningless hodgepodge of tricks and techniques—perhaps memorized, but surely never really understood.

Because your intuition can be so helpful in geometry, a careful study of some of the major ideas of geometry may be an ideal vehicle for introducing you to the essence of mathematics.

Let's examine briefly the context in which axiomatization is appropriate and also renew and extend our understanding of axiomatics. Once a reasonably large collection of interesting ideas has been amassed, e.g., ancient geometry prior to the Greeks, one proves (tests) them using the techniques of the axiomatic method. This procedure serves a double purpose: 1) it enables us to winnow out the correct ideas and discard the erroneous ones, and 2) it helps us to tease out the deductive or logical structure which relates the ideas to one another. Notice that one brings the axiomatic method into play only *after* one has a well-established body of knowledge, such as ancient geometry.

1. Write a short essay (about one page long) on the axiomatic method. What is it? How does it work? Re-read the relevant parts of Unit I and flesh out your discussion by consulting, say, the Encyclopedia Brittanica about such items as: the formal axiomatic method, undefined terms, axioms, logic, theorems and proof, etc. Be prepared to discuss your essay in class.

We mentioned in Unit I that a useful system of axioms must be *consistent*.

2. What does it mean to say that a system of axioms is *consistent*? How does one show that a system of axioms is (at least *relatively*) consistent? (Hint: What is a *model* of a system of axioms?)

There is another major property of an axiom system which, while not absolutely necessary, is often desirable: *independence*. Let's consider independence in some detail, since it will be quite important for us in Unit V.

Definition: The axioms of a system are said to be *independent* if none of the axioms can be proved as a theorem which depends upon (can be deduced from) the other axioms of the system.

Remark: When the axioms of a system are independent, we often say (by a harmless abuse of language) that the system itself is independent.

How does one prove that a given system of axioms is independent? The procedure is as follows: first, select any specific axiom of the system. Then, produce a consistent model (interpretation) where the selected axiom fails to hold while all the other axioms of the system are satisfied. If this procedure can be carried out for *any* specific axiom of the system, then the system is independent. The proof of independence follows by *reductio ad absurdum*. If one of the axioms were dependent on the others, then the model in which that specific axiom failed while all the others were satisfied would be inconsistent; it would be possible to derive the specified axiom from the others—thus, in the model, the axiom would be simultaneously both valid and invalid. Since the model is assumed to be consistent, the situation described above would be impossible. Thus, if the procedure can be carried out, the system is independent.

Recall the definition of a group (Unit II, Section 2). We can prove that the axiom of commutativity (Axiom C: for all x, y in G, $x \circ y = y \circ x$) is independent of the other axioms for a group. To do so, we must produce a model in which all the other axioms hold (i.e., the model must be a group) while Axiom C fails (i.e., the group must be non-commutative).

3. Complete the proof that Axiom C is independent of the other group axioms by giving a model as described above.

If we were to add Axiom C to our axiom system for groups, we would be restricting ourselves to the study of commutative groups. Suppose that we wished for some reason to restrict our study to the theory of finite groups. We might include the following:

Axiom F: All groups are finite.

4. a. Prove that Axiom F is independent of the set of axioms contained in the definition of group.
   b. Prove that Axiom F is independent of the set of axioms consisting of Axiom C and the other axioms contained in the definition of group.

As I said, the idea of the independence of the axioms in a system will be very important to your understanding and appreciation of Unit V; so make sure you have a good grasp of this idea.

It is often convenient, however, to study axiom systems which are *not* independent: it may be difficult to produce or to understand clearly an independent system of axioms for the body of knowledge we wish to study. Moreover, we may be able to proceed more rapidly and naturally in our study if we permit ourselves to assume as axioms certain things which *could* be proved as theorems. Remember, however, that even though we do not insist that our axiom systems be independent, we absolutely must demand that they be consistent.

In the thinking you have done up to now about the axiomatic method and how it works, you may have wondered how—in view of the fact that axiomatization begins with *undefined* terms and *assumed axioms* about these terms—you could get a "feel" for the method and its working. The easiest way to do so is simply to plunge in and *learn by doing*. This is really the only way to learn mathematics: *do* it!

"Why," said the Dodo, "the best way to explain it is to do it."

– Lewis Carroll –

Getting a "feel" for what something is by seeing how it is used is known as getting an *operational definition*. I intend for you to get an operational definition of logic and the axiomatic method, coupled with a reasonably accurate appreciation of how this method acts as a watchful guardian which can prevent your intuition from leading you into error. So, let's plunge right on into a logical, axiomatic development of neutral geometry.

Section 2

As we begin our logical development of geometry, it is appropriate for us to discuss briefly what level of *rigor* will be expected of us.

1. Look up "rigor" in an unabridged dictionary and copy down the parts of the definition which seem applicable to mathematics.

The degree of rigor which is suitable in the study of mathematics depends upon the level of maturity and accomplishment of the target audience. At our level of study and in view of our overall purpose (getting a good grasp of the *spirit* of mathematics), it would be wildly inappropriate for us to get bogged down splitting logical hairs. So, lest our zeal for rigor lead to mental *rigor mortis* instead of to the glorious *rigor vitae* of living mathematics, our motto will be the quote from Moore given above. Thus, while we strive to make our study and exposition clear and complete, we shall not hesitate to suppress logical subtleties which may threaten to obscure the main point.

2. Comment briefly on the following quote attributed to Albert Einstein: "There is no rigorous definition of rigor." What do you suppose that Einstein was trying to tell us in this somewhat paradoxical statement? Do you agree with him? Explain as well as you can.

Now let's begin our axiomatization of geometry:

Undefined Terms:
1. Point
2. Line
3. Plane

We shall regard the plane as being a set of points; figures such as lines, triangles, etc. are special subsets of the plane. If m is a line and P is a point of m, we write (using set-theoretic notation) that $P \in m$ (read P is an element of m) to mean that P is on m, or m passes through P, or m contains P, etc.

I expect you to get an operational definition of the undefined terms by studying the properties implied by the axioms governing them. Use your intuition to help you understand and visualize (by drawing relevant diagrams) what is going on here. The Greeks felt that they were abstracting the ultimate nature of physical reality from their intuitive perceptions of real objects and the relationships between them. Thus, we may choose to represent a point by a small dot since the original idea of a point was surely an abstraction from a dot, or a grain of sand, or a dust mote, etc. We may also choose to represent (part of) a line by drawing a mark along the edge of a straight ruler, and we may choose to think of a plane as being a flat surface extending without limit in all directions. Of course, this is *very* intuitive and other choices of interpretation are possible since the basic terms are, after all, *undefined*. It is the possibility of other reasonable interpretations, other models, which helps to make the axiomatic method so powerfully general. We need not fret over the "true" nature of the objects we are discussing; we can devote ourselves strictly to the study of their properties and their relationships as drawn from the axioms.

Recall that we have already defined a set of points to be *collinear* if there is some line which contains them all.

3. What would it mean, then, to say that a set of points is *noncollinear*?

We shall begin our list of axioms for geometry by assuming that there is *something* for us to talk about, i.e., we assume:

Axiom 0: There exists a plane containing at least three noncollinear points.

4. *An ongoing exercise:* Make up and keep for your reference three separate and complete lists:
  i) list *all* the axioms as they occur;
  ii) list *all* the definitions as they occur;
  iii) list *all* the theorems as they occur!

Euclid seems to have understood neither the necessity for the explicit assumption of an *existence axiom* (such as *Axiom 0*), nor the necessity for leaving some terms undefined. He began his *Elements* by giving 23 "definitions":
  1. A point is that which has no part,
  2. A line is breadthless length,
  4. A straight line is a line which lies evenly with the points on itself,
  7. A plane surface is a surface which lies evenly with the straight lines on itself.

These "definitions" may have been useful, intuitive guides to Euclid's readers, but we understand now (as Euclid seemingly did not) that we *must* leave certain terms undefined. (If you are interested in a reference which shows our present understanding of the content of Euclid's *Elements,* consult: Heath, T.L., *The Thirteen Books of Euclid's Elements.* New York: Dover Pub., 1956.)

As I mentioned, Euclid did not understand the need for existence axioms. This is surprising, for Aristotle had already made clear that just because something has been defined, it does *not* follow automatically that such a thing exists; e.g., one can define a unicorn, but that doesn't ensure that a unicorn actually exists.

We can't fault Euclid too much for overlooking some of the logical fine points of axiomatization. We must keep in mind that mathematicians were, in his time, just getting started with the axiomatic method. No one could reasonably demand or expect absolute perfection at the *initial* stages of the axiomatization of as complex a science as geometry.

There is a moral to this long digression. Euclid was, undoubtedly, very familiar with the obvious, intuitive properties of the geometric objects. He failed to see the necessity for 1) not saying some things about them (e.g., for not trying to define *all* the terms) and, 2) saying other things about them (e.g., for asserting the existence and uniqueness of some of them). Despite the logical shortcomings of his axiomatization in the *Elements* (Euclid unconsciously made use of properties he had not explicitly stated), his great genius kept him from falling into serious geometric error; but you must be ever on your guard against trusting too much to your geometric intuition. The crucial idea of the axiomatic method is to show how everything can be deduced from a "few" assumptions that have been *explicitly* stated. You must not appeal to *hidden* assumptions of any sort, lest you be led into disaster.

5) Represent two distinct points, A and B, by making two dots on a sheet of paper (which itself represents part of the "plane").
   a. Is it reasonable to say that one could draw (say, by using a ruler) a "straight line" passing through these two points?
   b. Is it reasonable to say that one could draw *more* than one "straight line" pasing through these same two points?

Your work in exercise 5 should have convinced you that it is reasonable to assume the following:

Axiom 1:   For any two distinct points A and B, there is one and only one line, denoted by $\overleftrightarrow{AB}$, which contains A and B.

Remark: Axiom 1 does *not* say that a line must contain at least 2 points! In fact, we have as yet no idea how many points might be on a line, although surely we want lines to be thickly packed with infinitely many points—and we shall see later that they are. However, we need to add more axioms to force this to be the case.

We are now in a position to prove two theorems.

Theorem 1:   Two distinct lines have at most one point in common.

Proof: We shall use the method of proof by contradiction (*reductio ad absurdum*, RAA) with which you are already familiar. Suppose that the two distinct lines, l and m, have at least two points in common; let's say P and Q are two points on both l and m. By Axiom 1, there is a *unique* line containing P and Q. Thus, $l = m$. But this is a direct contradiction to the distinctness of l and m. Therefore, by RAA the two lines l and m have at most one point in common.

Q.E.D.

Theorem 2:   There exist at least three distinct lines.

6. Try to prove Theorem 2. (Hint: Axiom 0 guarantees the existence of at least three non-collinear points, say P, Q, and R. Consider $\overleftrightarrow{PQ}$, $\overleftrightarrow{QR}$, and $\overleftrightarrow{PR}$. Use RAA to show that these three lines must be distinct.)

Section 3

If you think intuitively (draw a picture), you should easily see that it is reasonable to assume:

Axiom 2: Each line splits the plane into two non-empty, disjoint sets of points (excluding the line itself) called halfplanes of the line.

Remark: While the intuitive appeal of Axiom 2 is obvious, what does it really mean? Axiom 2 means that for any line m there exist two non-empty, disjoint sets $\mathbf{H}_1$ and $\mathbf{H}_2$, the halfplanes of m, such that the whole plane is the union of m, $\mathbf{H}_1$ and $\mathbf{H}_2$; moreover, no two of the sets m, $\mathbf{H}_1$ and $\mathbf{H}_2$ have a point in common.

1. a) Draw a picture to illustrate for yourself the idea contained in Axiom 2.
    b) Using Axiom 2, prove that there are at least 4 distinct points.
       (Hint: The halfplanes of any line are nonempty.)

You have already seen a definition of *betweenness* in terms of distance (X is between A and B if AX + XB = AB). Now, however, let's give a different (but equivalent) definition of betweenness which uses the idea stated in Axiom 2.

Definition: Let $X \in \overleftrightarrow{AB}$. Then we say X is *between A and B,* denoted by *A-X-B* or *B-X-A,* if there is some line l containing X such that A is in one half-plane of l while B is in the other half-plane of l.

2. Draw a picture to illustrate the idea contained in this "new" definition of betweenness.

In his *Elements*, Euclid did not deal with entire lines as much as with parts of lines called segments. The following definition should serve to clarify the idea of a segment.

Definition: Let l be a line, and let A and B be points of l. (Note: it is *not* necessary that A ≠ B!)
    a) The *open segment* of l determined by A and B, denoted by $\overset{\circ\!-\!\circ}{AB}$ (or]A,B[) consists of all the points $X \in l$ such that A-X-B, i.e., the open segment consists of all the points of l *between* A and B, but does *not* include the *endpoints* A and B; if A = B, then: $\overset{\circ\!-\!\circ}{AB} = \emptyset$.

    b) The *closed segment* of l determined by A and B, denoted by $\overline{AB}$ (or [A,B]), consists of the open segment $\overset{\circ\!-\!\circ}{AB}$ with the endpoints A and B included. If A = B, then $\overline{AB} = \{A\} = \{B\}$.

Remark: One ordinarily writes A instead of $\{A\}$ in geometry; I shall do so whenever I think no confusion will result.

E.g., on the real number line $\mathbb{R}$, the open segment]-3,5[consists of all x such that $-3 < x < 5$ while the closed segment [-3,5] consists of all x such that $-3 \leqslant x \leqslant 5$; these segments are drawn below:

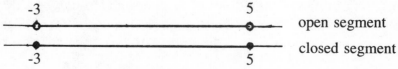

-104-

3. In each of the following, use inequalities as in the example above to describe the open and closed segments of the real line determined by the given points and sketch the graph of each segment; label the graphs as done in the example above.

a) 0 and 3

b) -2 and 6

While it is intuitively clear (draw a picture!) what we mean by saying that two points A and B are on opposite sides of a line l, we make this idea precise by assuming:

Axiom 3: Two distinct points A and B are in different half-planes of a line l if and only if $l \cap \overset{\circ}{\overline{AB}} \neq \emptyset$.

4. Draw a picture to illustrate the idea contained in Axiom 3.

We can use Axiom 3 to prove an important theorem about triangles, but first we must define a triangle.

Definition: Given 3 noncollinear points, A, B, and C, the *triangle* determined by them, $\triangle ABC$, consists of the three closed segments $\overline{AB}$, $\overline{BC}$, and $\overline{AC}$ which are called the *sides* of $\triangle ABC$. The points A, B, and C are called the *vertices* of $\triangle ABC$.

5. Sketch a picture to illustrate the idea in the definition of a triangle.

Remark: By a standard abuse of language, we refer to $\triangle ABC$ as *containing* angles $\angle ABC$, $\angle ACB$, and $\angle CAB$. It should be clear from your sketch what this means. If not, ask for an explanation. We say, for example, that $\angle CAB$ is *included* between $\overline{CA}$ and $\overline{AB}$.

Remark: Each of A, B, C is a *vertex* of $\triangle ABC$. Note that the singular form of vertices is vertex and *not* "vertice."

Pasch's Theorem (PT): If a line, m, intersects one side of $\triangle ABC$ but does not pass through any vertex of $\triangle ABC$, then m intersects exactly one other side of $\triangle ABC$.

Diagram:

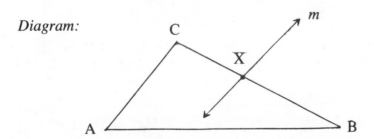

Proof: Look at the diagram above to help you understand the idea of the proof. Suppose m intersects side $\overline{BC}$ of $\triangle ABC$, as shown, at the point X. Then B and C are in different halfplanes of m. Since m does not pass through a vertex of $\triangle ABC$, we know $A \notin m$. Thus, A is in one or the other of the different halfplanes of m. Suppose A is in the same halfplane of m as is the point C (as shown). Then

A and B are in different halfplanes of m and so $\overset{\circ}{\overline{AB}}\overset{\circ}{} \cap m \neq \varnothing$. Thus, m intersects side $\overline{AB}$ of $\triangle ABC$. We see that m does not intersect side $\overline{AC}$, for if it did, A and C would be in different halfplanes of m—contrary to our supposition that A and C are in the same halfplane of m. The proof if A and B are in the same halfplane of m (not shown) is similar to that already given. Thus, m intersects exactly one other side of the triangle.

Q.E.D.

We shall see how Pasch's theorem will help us prove several important theorems. For example, it will help us discover 1) that the lines of our geometry are densely packed with points and, 2) how much information is needed to determine an isometry of the plane. It turns out that each line contains infinitely many points. (There *are* geometries—so called "finite" geometries—in which there are a finite number of points and lines; you may want to refer to either of the following references for more information on finite geometries. They are both very readable and cover much of interest:

> Lockwood, J.R. and Runion, G.E., *Deductive Systems: Finite and Non-Euclidean Geometries*. Reston, VA: National Council of Teachers of Mathematics, 1978.

> Beck, A., Bleicher, M., and Crowe, D., *Excursions Into Mathematics*. New York: Worth Pub., 1969.)

Moreover, it turns out that we need to know what an isometry does to only *three non-collinear points* to determine what it does to *all* points!

As a first small step in our effort to show that there are infinitely many points on any line, we can prove:

Theorem: There are at least three points on any line.

Remark: Proving this theorem may seem silly to you—or at least unnecessary. Your intuition leads you to think of a line as an endless "string" of points. Remember, however, that a line is undefined and that your intuition is not always infallible.

Diagram:

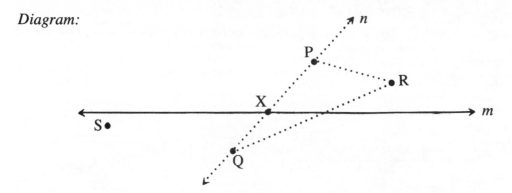

Proof: Let m be a line. By Axiom 2, each of the halfplanes of m is non-empty. Suppose the point P lies in one halfplane of m while the point Q lies in the other halfplane of m. Then, by definition, $\overset{\circ}{\overline{PQ}}\overset{\circ}{} \cap m \neq \varnothing$. Let $X = \overset{\circ}{\overline{PQ}}\overset{\circ}{} \cap m$. So far, then, we have at least one point, X, on m. Now, again by Axiom 2, each of the halfplanes of $n = \overleftrightarrow{PQ}$ is non-empty. Suppose R is in one halfplane of n while S is in the other. If R is on m, we have yet another point on m. If R is not on m, consider $\triangle$PRQ. Since m does not contain a vertex of $\triangle$PRQ, Pasch's theorem assures us that, since m intersects $\overline{PQ}$, m intersects exactly one other side of $\triangle$PRQ. Thus, there is a second point on m. By exactly the same sort of argument using S in place of R, we get yet a third point on m. Thus, m contains at least three points. Since m could have been any line, we are done.

Q.E.D.

You may recall that if we have three distinct collinear points, it is reasonable to say that one and only one of them is between the other two. We ensure that our geometry has this property by assuming:

Axiom 4:   For any three distinct collinear points A, B, and C, exactly one of the following holds:

i) A-B-C

ii) B-A-C

iii) B-C-A

Remark: Axiom 4 ensures that the points of the lines in neutral geometry are "ordered" in a way which corresponds to our intuition. Contrast this situation with that of the points on the great circles (lines) of the geometry on a sphere. In spherical geometry, it is impossible to define betweenness in an easy, intuitive way so that for any three collinear points one and only one of them is between the other two.

6.   Draw a picture to illustrate the idea contained in Axiom 4.

In our previous, more-or-less intuitive study of geometry (Unit III, Sections 1, 2, 3) we assumed that a distance or metric could be defined on the plane. Recall that a metric (distance) is a map, d, defined on pairs of points in the plane and satisfying certain basic, intuitive conditions abstracted from our experiences with "distance" in the real world (see Axiom 5 below for the conditions). In order to enable us to use the very powerful idea of distance, we assume the following metric axiom:

Axiom 5:   There is a metric, d, defined on the plane and satisfying the following conditions for any points A, B, C:

D0: If $d(A, B) = 0$, then $A = B$

D1: If $A = B$, then $d(A, B) = 0$

D2: $d(A, B) = d(B, A)$

D3: $d(A, B) + d(B, C) \geq d(A, C)$

D4: For any three distinct points A, B, C we have:

$d(A, B) + d(B, C) = d(A, C)$ if and only if A-B-C.

Remark: It is customary to denote the distance between A and B by AB instead of d(A, B) whenever no confusion can result from doing so. Remember that AB is a *non-negative number* which represents the distance between A and B; thus, we can perform arithmetic operations such as addition, subtraction, etc. with distances.

7. Review the material on metrics in Unit III, Sections 1, 2 and 3. Refresh your memory on the ideas.

Section 4

Let's examine the axioms which guarantee the existence and the desired properties of the basic motion of Euclidean congruence geometry: reflection in a mirror line. We assume:

Axiom 6:   For each line m, there exists a distance-preserving map F_m which maps the points of each halfplane of m onto the points of the other halfplane of m.

Remark: Recall that to say the map F_m is distance-preserving means that for any two points A, B, we have $d(A, B) = d(F_m(A), F_m(B))$. Of course, the mapping F_m assumed to exist in Axiom 6 is precisely the transformation we have called the reflection of the plane in the mirror line m. Axiom 6 assures us that any reflection preserves both distance and halfplanes.

    In Unit III we proved that distance-preserving maps (then viewed as similarities with scale factor 1) have some very nice properties. In particular, because of the conditions assumed in Axioms 5 and 6, we could easily repeat (but won't) the steps needed to prove the following:

Theorem: Any reflection is bijective (i.e., both injective and surjective) and preserves collinearity, betweenness, and segments.

You will recall that a reflection is a special kind of isometry, i.e., a distance-preserving mapping: a map f such that $d(A, B) = d(f(A), f(B))$ for all A, B. It is possible to prove from the general definition of isometry that any isometry is a finite product of reflections (do you recall that we said this same thing earlier, when we claimed that the reflections generated the group of isometries?). I shall not give the proof, but I will give an indication of where the proof could be given when we get there. In the meantime, however, we shall take as a definition:

Definition: An *isometry* is a finite product of reflections.

Remark: An isometry is a bijective map (i.e., is both injective and surjective) which preserves distance, betweenness, collinearity, halfplanes, etc.

Do you remember that isometries were the key to giving a formal definition of congruence? Let's clarify by defining:

Definition: A *figure*, **F**, is simply any set of points.

Definition: We say two figures, **F** and **F'**, are *congruent*—denoted by $\mathbf{F} \cong \mathbf{F'}$—if there is an isometry f such that $f(\mathbf{F}) = \mathbf{F'}$.

Remark: If f is an isometry, i.e., a finite product (composition) of reflections, we can write $f = F_1 \circ F_2 \circ F_3 \circ F_4 \circ \ldots \circ F_n$ where each F_i is a reflection. Then $f^{-1} = F_n \circ \ldots \circ F_4 \circ F_3 \circ F_2 \circ F_1$. You can check to see that $f \circ f^{-1} = f^{-1} \circ f = $ Identity and so see that f^{-1} is really the inverse of f. (Hint: You will want to use the fact that each reflection is its own inverse.)

1. Complete the check that f^{-1} is as described above. Thus, if f is an isometry such that $f(\mathbf{F}) = \mathbf{F}'$, then f^{-1} is an isometry such that $f^{-1}(\mathbf{F}') = \mathbf{F}$. Explain.

2. Verify that the relation of congruence on the collection of all figures is an equivalence relation, i.e., show it to be reflexive, symmetric, and transitive. Thus, you have proved:

Theorem: Congruence is an equivalence relation on the collection of all figures.

To give you a bit of easy practice working with reflections, consider the following:

Theorem: Let F_p be a reflection in some line p. If lines m and n intersect at point X, then lines $F_p(m)$ and $F_p(n)$ intersect at $F_p(X)$.

3. Prove the theorem above, i.e., prove that *reflections preserve points of intersection of lines*.

4. Recall what you know intuitively about reflections to answer the following questions. Let m be any line.
   a. What is $F_m(F_m(A))$ for any point A? (Hint: If $F_m(A) = A'$, then what is $F_m(A')$? Draw a picture if needed.)
   b. What is $F_m(A)$ if $A \in m$? Can $F_m(A) = A$ if $A \notin m$? Explain.

We formalize your results from exercise 4 by assuming two more axioms:

Axiom 7: For each line m, $F_m \circ F_m = I$, the identity map.

Remark: Axiom 7 says that each reflection is its own inverse, i.e., is an involution.

Axiom 8: For all points $X \in m$, $F_m(X) = X$.

Remark: Axiom 8 guarantees that *the set of points left fixed by F_m is exactly the line m*.

For more practice with reflections, consider the following: recall that [X,Y] means the same as $\overline{XY}$.

Theorem: $[A,F_m(A)] \cap m \neq \varnothing$, for any point A and any line m.

This theorem should seem most reasonable to you if you draw a diagram to illustrate what it means.

5. Draw such a diagram. (Hint: there are two cases to consider: a) $A \in m$, and b) $A \notin m$. Sketch a diagram for each case.)

6. Fill in the missing steps to complete the proof of the theorem.
   Proof: Either $A \notin m$ or $A \in m$, so there are two cases:
   Case 1: If $A \in m$, then $F_m(A) = A$ (why?). Thus, we have $[A,F_m(A)] = A$. (why?)
   So, $[A,F_m(A)] \cap m = A$, and the theorem works (why?).

Case 2: If A $\notin m$, then A and $F_m(A)$ lie in different halfplanes of the line m. (why?) Thus, $[A,F_m(A)] \cap m \neq \varnothing$, and the theorem works (why?).

In either case, the desired result follows. Since *one* of the two cases *must* be so, the theorem is proved.

Q.E.D.

Section 5

To extend our list of axioms for neutral geometry requires us to state several preliminary definitions. Let l be a line and $P \in l$. P determines two *rays* (each of which might be thought of as a "halfline"). The sketch that follows the formal definition should clarify the idea.

Definition: Let l be a line and $P \in l$. Each of the two opposite *rays* determined by P on l consists of the *endpoint* P added to the intersection of l with one of the halfplanes determined by any line m $(m \neq l)$ passing through P.

Remark: The sketch below should clarify the meaning of the term *"ray."*.

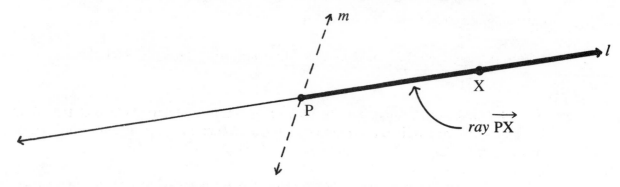

The ray having endpoint P and containing X is denoted by $\overrightarrow{PX}$.
The ray $\overrightarrow{PX}$ consists of $\overline{PX}$ and every point Z such that P-X-Z.

Definition: The union of two rays with a common endpoint P, say $\overrightarrow{PX}$ and $\overrightarrow{PY}$, is the *angle* with *vertex* P and *sides* $\overrightarrow{PX}$ and $\overrightarrow{PY}$. If the sides of $\angle XPY$ are neither the same nor opposite rays, the *interior* of $\angle XPY$ is the intersection of the halfplane of $\overleftrightarrow{PX}$ containing Y with the halfplane of $\overleftrightarrow{PY}$ containing X. If $\overrightarrow{PX} = \overrightarrow{PY}$, the *interior* of $\angle XPY$ is the empty set. If $\overrightarrow{PX}$ and $\overrightarrow{PY}$ are opposite rays, the *interior* of $\angle XPY$ is a suitably chosen halfplane of $\overleftrightarrow{XY}$.

Remark: In the notation for an angle, the name of the vertex point *must* be mentioned second.

1. Sketch a picture to illustrate the ideas in the definition of an angle.
    Prove that at least 3 angles must exist.

You have probably had some experience measuring angles with a protractor. In any case, I am assuming you know how to do so. (If you don't, ask someone who does to explain it to you.) As you know, the typical protractor measure of an angle is a number between 0 and 180 which you can read from a graduated scale on the edge of the protractor. We shall introduce the powerful idea of measuring angles by assuming the following angle measurement axiom (The Greek letter μ (read: moo or mew) denotes the measure mapping):

Axiom 9: There is a map, μ, having as domain the collection of all angles and as codomain the closed interval [0,180] such that:

M0: $\mu\angle XPY = 0$ if and only if $\overrightarrow{PX} = \overrightarrow{PY}$

M1: $\mu\angle XPY = 180$ if and only if $\overrightarrow{PX}$ and $\overrightarrow{PY}$ are opposite rays

M2: If Z is any point in the interior of $\angle XPY$, then
$$\mu\angle XPZ + \mu\angle ZPY = \mu\angle XPY.$$

M3: If $\angle 1 \cong \angle 2$, then $\mu(\angle 1) = \mu(\angle 2)$

Remark: The measure of any angle must be a real number between 0 and 180 inclusive. Since angle measures are numbers, it makes sense to perform arithmetic operations such as addition, subtraction, etc. upon them. The units of measure are called *degrees.*

2. Sketch a diagram to illustrate each part of the angle measurement axiom.

Continuing our definitions, we come to:

Definition: An *angle bisector* of $\angle XPY$ is a line *m* passing through P such that
$$F_m(\overrightarrow{PX}) = \overrightarrow{PY}.$$

3. **Sketch a diagram to illustrate the idea of an angle bisector. Note that the angle bisector splits the original angle into two angles. What do you conjecture about these two angles? Explain.**

Remark: We don't have enough axioms to prove the existence of angle bisectors, so we assume:

Axiom 10: For any angle, there exists a *unique* angle bisector.

Remark: On the basis of axiom 10 we know that for any angle there is one and only one line which, as you have guessed, splits the angle into two congruent angles, i.e., bisects the angle.

Definition: Let A and B be two distinct points. A *perpendicular bisector* of $\overline{AB}$ is a line *m* such that $F_m(A) = B$. The point $M = m \cap \overline{AB}$ is called a *midpoint* of $\overline{AB}$.

4. Sketch a picture to illustrate the idea in the definition of the perpendicular bisector of a segment; note that a perpendicular bisector splits the original segment into two segments. **What do you conjecture about these two segments? Explain.**

Remark: We don't have enough axioms to prove the existence of perpendicular bisectors, so we assume:

Axiom 11: For any two distinct points A and B, there exists a unique perpendicular bisector of $\overline{AB}$.

Remark: We could have *proved* the uniqueness of the angle bisector and perpendicular bisector assumed in Axioms 10 and 11, respectively, but we *assumed* the uniqueness in order to speed up the development of neutral geometry. We shall justify the names perpendicular bisector and angle bisector:

It follows from axiom 11 that every segment $\overline{AB}$ has a midpoint, M, since the points A and B are in different halfplanes of the perpendicular bisector, m, of $\overline{AB}$. Moreover, it follows that every segment $\overline{AB}$ has only one midpoint, M, since the midpoint of $\overline{AB}$ is by definition the unique point of intersection of $\overline{AB}$ with its unique perpendicular bisector, m. Thus, we have:

Theorem: Every segment has one and only one midpoint.

5. Prove that each line contains infinitely many points by showing that any closed segment contains infinitely many points. (Hint: Think about how you might produce an endless sequence of midpoints of smaller and smaller parts of the original segment.)

Definition: A line m is *perpendicular* to a line n, denoted by $m \perp n$, if $m \neq n$ and $F_n(m) = m$.

6. Sketch a picture to illustrate the idea in the definition of perpendicular lines.

Remark: By giving a fussy, not particularly informative proof (which I shall therefore omit), one can show that the relation of perpendicularity on the collection of lines is symmetric, i.e., one could prove:

Theorem: If $m \perp n$, then $n \perp m$.

The theorem just above should seem intuitively obvious to you from the illustration you drew of perpendicular lines.

We can now justify the name for the perpendicular bisector, m, of a segment $\overline{AB}$; i.e., we can show that $m \perp \overleftrightarrow{AB}$ and $\overline{AM} \cong \overline{MB}$ where M is the midpoint of $\overline{AB}$. Thus, m is perpendicular to $\overleftrightarrow{AB}$ and bisects $\overline{AB}$, i.e., it cuts $\overline{AB}$ into two congruent halves.

Your illustration of perpendicular bisection should have looked something like this:

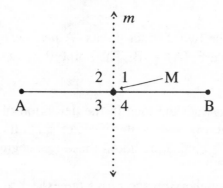

Since, by definition, $F_m(A) = B$, we have $F_m(B) = F_m(F_m(A)) = A$, by Axiom 7. Hence, F_m simply interchanges A and B. Since F_m preserves betweenness and collinearity, $F_m(\overleftrightarrow{AB}) = \overleftrightarrow{AB}$, i.e., $\overleftrightarrow{AB} \perp m$ (so $m \perp \overleftrightarrow{AB}$, by symmetry). Moreover, since $F_m(M) = M$, we see that $F_m(\overline{MB}) = \overline{MA}$, i.e., $\overline{AM} \cong \overline{MA} \cong \overline{MB}$, so M divides AB into two congruent halves. It is this situation which leads us to call M the *midpoint* of $\overline{AB}$, and also to say that m *bisects* $\overline{AB}$. Thus, it makes sense to call m the perpendicular bisector of $\overline{AB}$.

7. Explain why, in the illustration of perpendicular bisection (see above),
$\angle 1 \cong \angle 2 \cong \angle 3 \cong \angle 4$.

Definition: The four congruent angles formed by perpendicular lines are said to be *right* angles.

8.   Verify that the unique bisector of an angle splits it into two congruent parts (if you haven't already done so) and thus justify the name, "angle *bisector*."

Section 6

Let's begin this section by giving an easy example to show that our ideas of distance and congruence are related as we would wish them to be:

Theorem: $\overline{AB} \cong \overline{CD}$ if and only if $AB = CD$.

Proof: Part 1. Suppose $\overline{AB} \cong \overline{CD}$. Then there is an isometry f such that f($\overline{AB}$) = $\overline{CD}$. (why?) Thus, $AB = CD$. (why?)

Part 2. Suppose $AB = CD$. Consider the diagram below to help yourself follow the steps of the proof.

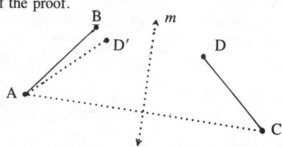

Let m be the perpendicular bisector of $\overline{AC}$. Then $F_m(C) = A$. (why?) If $D' = F_m(D)$ is not on $\overrightarrow{AB}$ (as shown), then reflect $\overrightarrow{AD'}$ in the angle bisector of $\angle BAD'$ to move the image of D onto $\overrightarrow{AB}$ in such a way that A is still the image of C. Thus, we have an isometry f such that f(C) = A and f(D) $\in \overrightarrow{AB}$. Of course, we want f(D) = B. (why?) How can we show that f(D) = B? We use RAA. Suppose f(D) = X $\neq$ B. Since X $\in \overrightarrow{AB}$, we must have either A-X-B or A-B-X. (why?)

Case 1. A-X-B. In this case $AX + XB = AB$ (why?) Since $AB = CD$ (why?), we have $AX + XB = CD$. (why?) Now, f($\overline{CD}$) = $\overline{AX}$, so $CD = AX$. (why?) Thus, $AX + XB = AX$. (why?) Hence, $XB = 0$ (why?) and so X = B. (why?) But this directly contradicts our assumption that X $\neq$ B. Thus, by RAA, X = B, i.e., f(D) = B, in this case.

Case 2. A-B-X. The proof in this case is entirely similar to that in case 1 so we shall not bother to do it.

Since f(D) = B in either case (and since one of the cases *must* be so), we have that f(D) = B. Thus, $\overline{CD} \cong \overline{AB}$. (why?)

$\hspace{10cm}$ Q.E.D.

1. Answer the questions in the proof above.

A proof analogous to the one above could be given to show that our ideas of angle measure and congruence are related as we would wish them to be:

Theorem: $\angle ABC \cong \angle XYZ$ if and only if $\mu\angle ABC = \mu\angle XYZ$.

2. (Extra Credit) Give a proof of the theorem just above. (Hint: model your proof ideas on those of the preceding proof.) Draw a diagram to illustrate the steps of your proof and label everything clearly.

Remark: The theorem just above assures us that isometries preserve angle measure as well as distance (length).

Recall that your illustration of perpendicular lines looked like this:

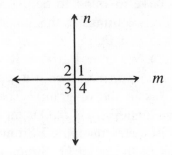

You should have proved $\angle 1 \cong \angle 2 \cong \angle 3 \cong \angle 4$ (Since $F_n(\angle 1) = \angle 2$, etc.). Now, since congruent angles have the same measure, we have $\mu\angle 1 = \mu\angle 2$. By the angle-measure axiom, we have $\mu\angle 1 + \mu\angle 2 = 180$.

Thus, $2 \cdot \mu\angle 1 = 180$, i.e., $\mu\angle 1 = 90$. So, any right angle has angle measure 90. Thus, since any two angles with the same angle measure are congruent, we have the following:

> *Theorem:* Every right angle has angle measure 90.
> *Corollary:* All right angles are congruent.

In diagrams we indicate that an angle is a right angle or that certain lines, rays, segments, etc., are perpendicular by drawing the special symbol illustrated here:

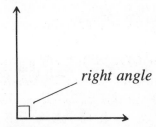

right angle

We will often need the following two theorems to help us prove that two figures are congruent. The Ruler Theorem can be used to guarantee that a given segment maps onto a desired image; the Protractor Theorem works similarly for an angle and its image. Read through the statement of each theorem *very* carefully so you will understand clearly what it means.

Ruler Theorem: Given a segment $\overline{RS}$ and a ray $\overrightarrow{PX}$, there is one and only one point Q on $\overrightarrow{PX}$ such that $\overline{PQ} \cong \overline{RS}$, i.e. PQ = RS.

Diagram:

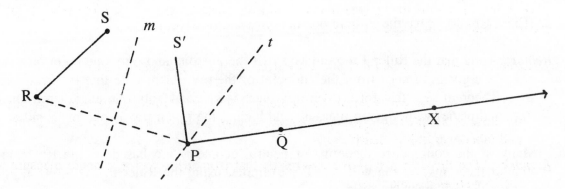

-117-

Proof: Keep the diagram above in mind to help yourself understand the idea of the proof. We want to do *two* things in this proof. First, we show the *existence* of a point Q on $\overrightarrow{PX}$ such that $\overline{PQ} \cong \overline{RS}$. Let m be the perpendicular bisector of $\overline{RP}$. Consider $F_m(\overline{RS})$. We know $F_m(R) = R' = P$ by definition of perpendicular bisector. If $F_m(S) = S'$ is on $\overrightarrow{PX}$, then it is a point Q such that $\overline{PQ} \cong \overline{RS}$. What if S' is not on $\overrightarrow{PX}$ (as in the diagram)? Then, let t be the angle bisector of $\angle XPS'$. So, $F_t(P) = P$, and $F_t(S') = Q$ is on $\overrightarrow{PX}$ by definition of angle bisector. Thus, $F_t \circ F_m$ is an isometry mapping $\overline{RS}$ onto $\overline{PQ}$, i.e. $\overline{PQ} \cong \overline{RS}$. Second, we show the *uniqueness* of the point Q. Suppose Z is any point of $\overrightarrow{PX}$ such that $PZ = RS = PQ$. We shall see that Z *must* be the point Q found in the first part of the proof. If $Z = Q$, we are done. So, suppose $Z \neq Q$. Since $Z \in \overrightarrow{PX}$, we have exactly one of the following:

$$\text{i) P-Z-Q}$$
$$\text{ii) P-Q-Z}$$

If P-Z-Q, then $PZ + ZQ = PQ$, i.e.,(since $PZ = PQ$) $PQ + ZQ = PQ$. Thus, $ZQ = 0$ and so $Z = Q$. This contradicts the assumption that $Z \neq Q$. Therefore, by RAA, $Z = Q$.

If P-Q-Z, a similar argument will show that $Z = Q$. Thus, in any case, $Z = Q$, i.e., there is one and only one point Q on $\overrightarrow{PX}$ such that $RS = PQ$, i.e., such that $\overline{RS} \cong \overline{PQ}$.

$$\text{Q.E.D.}$$

Now, let's state a similar theorem for angles:

Protractor Theorem: Given a ray $\overrightarrow{PX}$ and an angle, $\angle ABC$, in each halfplane of $\overleftrightarrow{PX}$ there is one and only one ray $\overrightarrow{PQ}$ such that $\angle ABC \cong \angle QPX$, i.e.,
$$\mu\angle ABC = \mu\angle QPX.$$

Diagram:

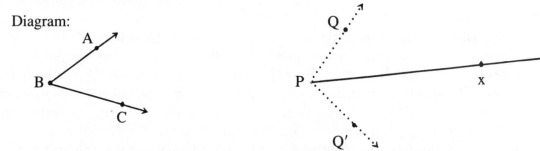

The proof of the Protractor Theorem is very similar to that of the Ruler Theorem so I leave it to you, the interested reader, to write it up if you desire.

3. (Extra Credit) Prove the Protractor Theorem.

Remark: Note that the Ruler Theorem says that there is one and only one point on a ray at a given distance from the endpoint of the ray. Also, note that the Protractor Theorem says that for a given ray there is one and only one angle (in a given halfplane) with a given measure and having the given ray as one of its sides.

Many of the congruence theorems of neutral geometry are based on the Ruler and Protractor theorems, as you will see. For example, using the Ruler theorem (etc.), you can prove the following theorem:

Theorem: P is the midpoint of $\overline{AB}$ if and only if A-P-B and $\overline{AP} \cong \overline{PB}$.

4.   Prove the theorem just above. Explain why P is the midpoint of $\overline{AB}$ if and only if A-P-B and AP = PB = ½AB. Add this to your ongoing list of theorems.

   We shall need certain theorems concerning the existence and uniqueness of perpendiculars; so let's investigate them now.

5.   Given a line *m* and a point P, does it seem reasonable that there is a line *n* such that P ∈ *n* and *n* ⊥ *m*? Explain and illustrate your answer. (Hint: You should distinguish the situation in which P ∉ *m* from the situation in which P ∈ *m*.)

   In your explanation of the exercise just above, you should have convinced yourself of the reasonableness of the following:

Theorem: Given a line *m* and a point P, there is one and only one line *n* containing P and perpendicular to *m*.

   Proof: We distinguish two cases:

   Case 1: P ∉ *m*.

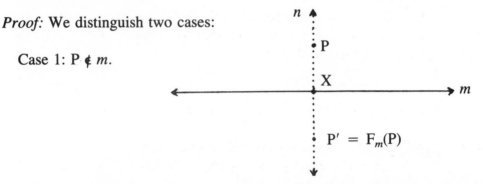

Let $P' = F_m(P)$. Then P ≠ P', since P and P' lie in different halfplanes of *m*. By Axiom 1, there is a line $n = \overleftrightarrow{PP'}$ containing P. Since P and P' are in different halfplanes of *m*, *n* intersects *m* at a point, X.
Because F_m simply interchanges P and P', we see that $F_m(n) = n$, i.e., *n* ⊥ *m*. How do we know there is only one such line *n*? Suppose **n** is any line which contains P and is perpendicular to *m*. Then, by definition of perpendicularity, we have $F_m(\mathbf{n}) = \mathbf{n}$. Thus, since P ∈ **n**, we see that $F_m(P) = P'$ ∈ **n**, i.e., both P and P' are on **n**. By the uniqueness assertion of Axiom 1, we can say that $n = \mathbf{n} = \overleftrightarrow{PP'}$. Hence, in this case, there is one and only one line *n* containing P and perpendicular to *m*.
Case 2: P ∈ *m*. This case is somewhat harder to prove, so let's "sketch" the *idea* of the proof first. We identify a closed segment of *m* having P as its midpoint. It will follow that the perpendicular bisector of this segment is a line containing P and perpendicular to *m*. Then, we finish by showing that there is *only one* line with this desired property. The actual proof follows:

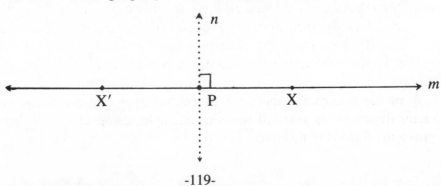

We can choose a point X on m and different from P since every line contains at least 3 points. By the Ruler Theorem, there is a unique point X' on the ray of m opposite to $\overrightarrow{PX}$ such that $\overline{PX} \cong \overline{PX'}$. By Axiom 10, there is a unique perpendicular bisector, n, of $\overline{XX'}$ which passes through the midpoint P. Of course, we know that $n \perp m$. Now, suppose **n** is any line containing P and perpendicular to m. Then, **n** is a perpendicular bisector of $\overline{XX'}$ and, by the uniqueness of perpendicular bisectors, we have $n =$ **n**. Thus, there is one and only one line containing P and perpendicular to m in this case. Since the desired result follows in either case (and since one of the cases *must* be so), the theorem is proved.

Q.E.D.

Section 7

Having laid the necessary foundations, let's establish two crucial related results: one is a basic tool for proving triangles congruent, the other is a key step in identifying all possible types of isometry maps.

1. Using a ruler and protractor, sketch a triangle, $\triangle ABC$, with AB = 2 inches, $\mu\angle A$ = 30, and AC = 3 inches. Once your triangle is constructed, compare it with those of some of your classmates (or draw a few more such triangles yourself) and report what you think about all such triangles.

Remark: Since an angle consists of two *rays* with a common endpoint, a triangle contains no angles! Nevertheless, it is a common abuse of language (which we shall follow) to say that $\triangle ABC$ contains $\angle A$, $\angle B$, and $\angle C$. Each angle of $\triangle ABC$ is said to be *included* between the sides of the triangle whose intersection is the vertex of the angle; moreover, each side of $\triangle ABC$ is said to be *included* between the angles whose vertices are the endpoints of the side. For example, $\angle B$ is included between $\overline{AB}$ and $\overline{BC}$, while $\overline{AC}$ is included between $\angle A$ and $\angle C$.

Your results in the triangle construction exercise above should make the following theorem seem quite reasonable:

Theorem (SAS): If two triangles have two pairs of congruent sides and if the angles included between these sides are congruent, then the two triangles are congruent.

SAS Illustration:

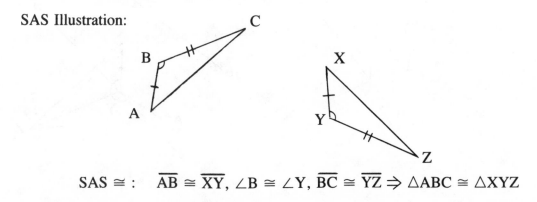

$$ \text{SAS} \cong : \quad \overline{AB} \cong \overline{XY}, \ \angle B \cong \angle Y, \ \overline{BC} \cong \overline{YZ} \Rightarrow \triangle ABC \cong \triangle XYZ $$

Note that congruent parts of the figure are marked with the same symbol. It will be helpful for you to use symbols and also to draw with markers so that the congruent parts of your diagrams are the same color.

SAS asserts that $\triangle ABC \cong \triangle XYZ$, i.e., there is an isometry f such that $f(\triangle ABC) = \triangle XYZ$; and so we have:

$$
\begin{array}{ccc}
\angle A \cong \angle X & & \overline{AB} \cong \overline{XY} \\
\angle B \cong \angle Y & \textbf{\textit{AND}} & \overline{AC} \cong \overline{YZ} \\
\angle C \cong \angle Z & & \overline{BC} \cong \overline{YZ}
\end{array}
$$

since, by definition, corresponding parts of congruent figures are congruent.

Remark: We shall be using the phrase "corresponding parts of congruent figures are congruent" so often that it will be convenient to abbreviate it by "*cpcfc*."

Proof of SAS: (Keep referring to the sequence of diagrams to help yourself understand the steps of the proof.)

We are given that $\overline{AB} \cong \overline{XY}$, $\angle B \cong \angle Y$, and $\overline{BC} \cong \overline{YZ}$ (as in the illustration). We must prove that $\triangle ABC \cong \triangle XYZ$, i.e., we must show that there is an isometry f such that f($\triangle ABC$) = $\triangle XYZ$. This isometry f is the composite of (at most) the three reflections described below:

Let *m* be the perpendicular bisector of $\overline{BY}$, and let $F_m(\triangle ABC) = \triangle A'B'C'$. Then $F_m(B) = B' = Y$, (why?), so $F_m(\triangle ABC) = \triangle A'YC'$ (see diagrams 1 and 2).

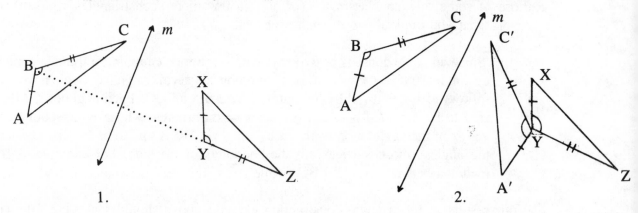

1.   2.

Now, let *n* be the angle bisector of $\angle C'YZ$. Then, $F_n(\triangle A'YC') = \triangle A*YZ$. (why?) (See diagrams 3 and 4.) (Why is $F_n(C') = Z$?)

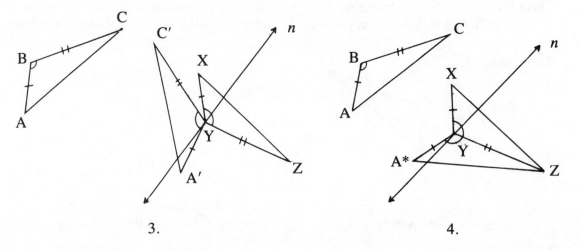

3.   4.

Let $p = \overleftrightarrow{YZ}$. Then, $F_p(\triangle A*YZ) = \triangle XYZ$. (why?) (See diagrams 5 and 6.)

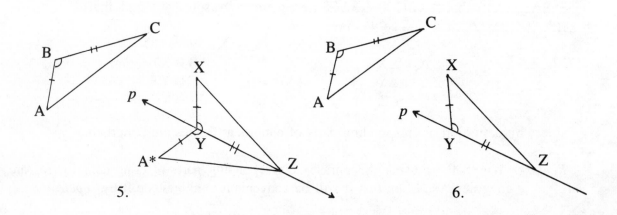

5.   6.

Thus, $F_p \circ F_n \circ F_m$ is an isometry f mapping $\triangle ABC$ onto $\triangle XYZ$. Therefore, $\triangle ABC \cong \triangle XYZ$.

Q.E.D.

2. Carefully and thoughtfully read through the proof of SAS; answer the questions in it. The diagram below, a "combination" of all the diagrams in the proof, may be helpful to you. (Hint: the last "why?" requires some very careful explanation. For example, use the Protractor theorem to explain why F_p must map $\angle A*YZ$ onto $\angle XYZ$, and use the Ruler theorem to explain why F_p must map A* onto X. Then, explain further why the desired result follows.)

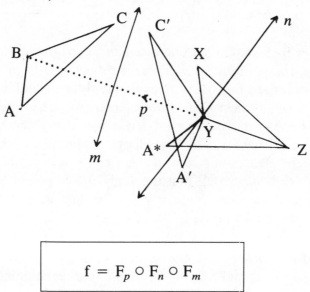

$$f = F_p \circ F_n \circ F_m$$

Since you will soon be asked to write many proofs on your own, let me point out certain essentials:

1. Use a diagram or diagrams to help you and the reader follow the steps of your proof. The givens (hypotheses, data) should be included in the diagram(s) by use of appropriate symbols or colors.

2. After you have puzzled out the whole proof on scratch paper, write a complete, coherent and correct exposition of why and how the desired conclusion is implied by the hypotheses. Remember that there must be no *unremovable* shadow of doubt about the validity of your proof—in particular, you *must* not appeal to hidden assumptions. You must also avoid "handwaving," i.e., waving your hand at the diagram and claiming that something *must* (?!) be so because of the picture. From a given diagram you *may* assume that the general arrangement of the figure is accurately drawn, e.g., that points which *seem* collinear *are* collinear, that points are "ordered" as shown, that points which *seem* to be in the same halfplane of some line *are* in the same halfplane of that line, etc.. However, you must *never assume* anything not explicitly given about *lengths* or *angle measures*!

3. If you have any doubts about proof form or techniques, refer to the examples in the text or ask for guidance and advice.

3. Given: $\overline{AD} \cong \overline{BC}$, M is midpoint of $\overline{AB}$, $\angle A \cong \angle B$.
   Prove: $\overline{MD} \cong \overline{MC}$.

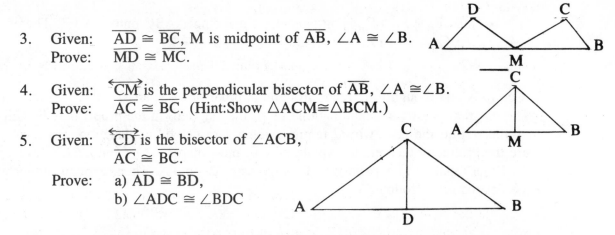

4. Given: $\overleftrightarrow{CM}$ is the perpendicular bisector of $\overline{AB}$, $\angle A \cong \angle B$.
   Prove: $\overline{AC} \cong \overline{BC}$. (Hint:Show $\triangle ACM \cong \triangle BCM$.)

5. Given: $\overleftrightarrow{CD}$ is the bisector of $\angle ACB$,
   $\overline{AC} \cong \overline{BC}$.

   Prove: a) $\overline{AD} \cong \overline{BD}$,
   b) $\angle ADC \cong \angle BDC$

The proof of SAS shows that one of a pair of congruent triangles can be mapped onto the other by a composite of *at most three* reflections. If we knew that any isometry is completely determined by what it does to any three noncollinear points (and so by what it does to any triangle), then—since any isometry maps a triangle onto a triangle congruent to the original one—we would know that *any* isometry can be represented as a product of at most three reflections. This knowledge would be the key to identifying every type of isometry of the plane. Let's consider how one would go about making such a complete identification. You may recall that the study of the points left *fixed* by an isometry is crucial to the identification procedure. So, we turn our attention briefly to fixed points and prove a few lemmas ("small," helpful theorems used to prove a major result).

Lemma 1: If an isometry f fixes two distinct points A and B, i.e., if
f(A) = A and f(B) = B, then f fixes each point of the entire line $\overleftrightarrow{AB}$.

Proof: Suppose f is an isometry which fixes two distinct points A and B, i.e.,
f(A) = A and f (B) = B.Then, since f is a collineation (i.e., a preserver of lines), and since there is a unique line passing through any two distinct points, we have that f($\overleftrightarrow{AB}$) = $\overleftrightarrow{AB}$. Thus, the line $\overleftrightarrow{AB}$ is fixed by f. However, we must show that f fixes *each point* of $\overleftrightarrow{AB}$. So let X be any point of $\overleftrightarrow{AB}$. If X = A or X = B, we are done. So, suppose that X is different from both A and B. Then exactly one of the following holds:

   i) X-A-B
   ii) A-X-B
   iii) A-B-X

Suppose X-A-B. Then, since f preserves betweenness, f(X)-A-B. Since f preserves distances, d(f(X), A) = d(X, A). Thus, by the Ruler Theorem, f(X) = X.
The proof in the other two cases is entirely analogous to that just given, and so we shall skip giving it in detail.
Thus, since X could have been any point of $\overleftrightarrow{AB}$, we see that f fixes each point of the entire line AB.

Q.E.D.

Remark: One could show that the f described in the lemma must be either the identity map or the reflection in the line $\overleftrightarrow{AB}$.

6. Complete the other two cases of the proof of Lemma 1.

Lemma 2:   If f is an isometry which fixes three noncollinear points, A, B, and C, then f is the identity map.

Remark: The idea of this proof is to use Lemma 1 and Pasch's theorem to prove that f must fix every point of the plane, i.e., f is the identity map.

Proof: Suppose f is an isometry which fixes each of the noncollinear points A, B, and C. Then f must fix each point of the lines $\overleftrightarrow{AB}$, $\overleftrightarrow{BC}$, and $\overleftrightarrow{AC}$. (why?) Thus, f must fix each point of the triangle $\triangle ABC$. (why?) Now, let X be any point; we want to show that f(X) = X. If X is a point on any of the three lines $\overleftrightarrow{AB}$, $\overleftrightarrow{BC}$, or $\overleftrightarrow{AC}$, then we already know that it is fixed by f. (why?) So, suppose X is not on any of those three lines. Let M be the midpoint of $\overline{AB}$. Then the line $\overleftrightarrow{XM}$ must intersect $\triangle ABC$ in two distinct points: M and exactly one other point of $\triangle ABC$. Indeed, if $\overleftrightarrow{XM}$ contains a vertex of $\triangle ABC$, it must be C (why?); if $\overleftrightarrow{XM}$ contains no vertex of $\triangle ABC$, it must intersect $\triangle ABC$ in exactly one other point (why?). In any case, $\overleftrightarrow{XM}$ must contain two distinct points of $\triangle ABC$, say M and S. Now, f(M) = M and f(S) = S (why?). Thus, f fixes each point of the line $\overleftrightarrow{MS}$. In particular then, f must fix X, i.e., f(X) = X (why?). Thus, f fixes every point of the plane, i.e., f is the identity map.

Q.E.D.

7. Answer the questions in the proof above.

Lemma 3:   Suppose f and g are isometries such that f(A) = g(A), f(B) = g(B), and f(C) = g(C) for three noncollinear points A, B, and C. Then, f = g, i.e., f(X) = g(X) for any point X.

Remark: This lemma assures us that if two isometries agree on three noncollinear points, then they agree *everywhere*. Thus, any isometry is completely determined by what it does to any three noncollinear points.

Proof: Suppose f and g are isometries such that:

$$f(A) = g(A)$$
$$f(B) = g(B)$$
$$f(C) = g(C)$$

for three noncollinear points A, B, and C. Then we have that:

$$g^{-1} \circ f(A) = g^{-1} \circ g(A) = A$$
$$g^{-1} \circ f(B) = g^{-1} \circ g(B) = B$$
$$g^{-1} \circ f(C) = g^{-1} \circ g(C) = C \qquad \text{(why?)}$$

Thus, the isometry $g^{-1} \circ f$ fixes three noncollinear points. Therefore, $g^{-1} \circ f = I$, the identity map (why?). Thus, $g \circ g^{-1} \circ f = g \circ I$, i.e., f = g (why?).

Q.E.D.

8. Answer the questions in the proof above.

The Three Reflection Theorem (TRT):
Any isometry can be represented as a product of at most three reflections.

Proof: Let f be an isometry. Let △ABC be any triangle. Suppose that f(△ABC) = △RST. We saw in the proof of SAS that we could map △ABC onto △RST by using a product, say g, of at most three reflections. By Lemma 3, f = g; therefore, f can be represented as a product of at most three reflections.

Q.E.D.

For any two congruent figures, **F** and **F'**, each containing at least three non-collinear points—say A, B, and C in **F** and A', B', and C' in **F'**—there is one and only one isometry f which maps **F** onto **F'** in such a way that f(A) = A', f(B) = B', and f(C) = C'.

9. Explain why the above claim about the uniqueness of the isometry f is correct.

10. (Super Special Exercise) Since you know that any isometry is the product of at most three reflections, you may discover all possible types of isometry by investigating what sorts of maps are produced by composing two or three reflections. Think carefully about this and see if you can reason out why there are *only* the four distinct types of isometry which we studied in Unit III:
   1. Reflection,
   2. Rotation,
   3. Translation, and
   4. Glide Reflection

11. Prove the following theorem:

   Theorem: $F_m = F_n$ if and only if $m = n$.
   (Hint: Half of the proof is trivial, viz., if $m = n$, then $F_m = F_n$. To do the other half, try to show that F_n fixes each point of m and therefore $m = n$.)

Section 8

1. Using a ruler and protractor, draw a triangle with one side two inches long, having an angle of 50° at one end and an angle of 70° at the other end. (E.g., $_2$ ⟋⟍ 70 / 50 ⟍)

Compare your triangle with those of some of your classmates. What do you conjecture about all such triangles?

Your work in exercise 1 should have convinced you of the reasonableness of the following theorem:

Theorem (ASA):   If two triangles contain two pairs of congruent angles and the corresponding included sides are congruent, then the triangles are congruent.

Illustration of ASA:

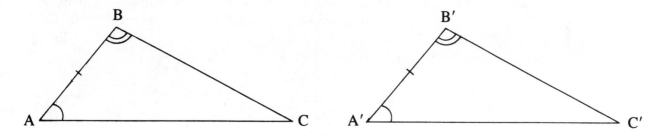

Given: $\overline{AB} \cong \overline{A'B'}$, $\angle A \cong \angle A'$, and $\angle B \cong \angle B'$.
Prove: $\triangle ABC \cong \triangle A'B'C'$.

Proof: By the given, there exists an isometry f such that f(A) = A' and f(B) = B'. Without loss of generality, we may assume that f(C) and C' are in the same halfplane of $\overleftrightarrow{A'B'}$. (If not, we could replace f by f followed by reflection in the line $\overleftrightarrow{A'B'}$ to get an isometry with the desired properties.) Now f($\overrightarrow{BC}$) = $\overrightarrow{B'C'}$ and f($\overrightarrow{AC}$) = $\overrightarrow{A'C'}$ (why?).
Moreover, f(C) = C' (why?). Thus, $\triangle ABC \cong \triangle A'B'C'$.

Q.E.D.

2. Fill in the missing reasons in the proof of ASA.

The next result we shall consider is a most important theorem about isosceles triangles.

Definition: A triangle with two congruent sides is said to be *isosceles*, (isos (same) + skelos (leg)). The angle included between the congruent sides is called the *vertex* angle; the other two angles are called the *base* angles. The side which is not necessarily congruent to the other two is called the *base* of the triangle.

3. Illustrate the idea of an isosceles triangle.

4.   (Extra Credit) *Prove* that there exists at least one isosceles triangle in neutral geometry.

5. Using a ruler and compass, draw several isosceles triangles. Using a protractor, measure the base angles of each. Make a conjecture about the base angles of any isosceles triangle. Examine each of your triangles, paying special attention to their symmetry. What is the relationship between the line which is the bisector of the vertex angle and the line which is the perpendicular bisector of the base of each of these triangles?

Based on the results of exercise 5, we can state and prove the Isosceles Triangle Theorem (ITT):

Theorem (ITT): In an isosceles triangle, the base angles are congruent and the angle bisector of the vertex angle is the same line as the perpendicular bisector of the base.

Illustration for ITT

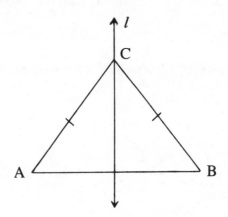

Proof: By the given we know that $\overline{AC} \cong \overline{BC}$. Let l be the angle bisector of angle C. Then $F_l(A) = B$ and $F_l(B) = A$ (why?). Thus, $\angle A \cong \angle B$, and l is the perpendicular bisector of $\overline{AB}$ (why?).

Q.E.D.

6. Fill in the missing reasons in the proof of ITT.

Because of the somewhat complex conclusion of the ITT, we can state various partial "converses:"

7. Prove each of the following three theorems (add each to your list of theorems):

Theorem: If two angles of a triangle are congruent, then the triangle is isosceles since the sides opposite the congruent angles are congruent.

Diagram:

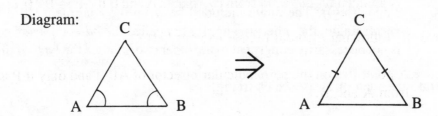

(Hint: Use ASA or reflection in the perpendicular bisector of $\overline{AB}$ to show
         $\triangle ABC \cong \triangle BAC$, and explain why this gives the desired result.)

Theorem: If the perpendicular bisector of a side of a triangle passes through the vertex
            of the opposite angle, then the triangle is isosceles.

Diagram:

Theorem: If the angle bisector of an angle of a triangle is perpendicular to the side
            opposite, then the triangle is isosceles.

Diagram:

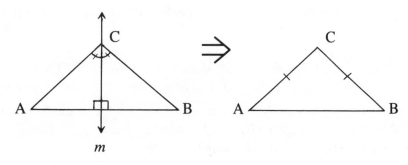

Definition: i) A triangle is called *equilateral* if all three of its sides are congruent to one
             another;
             ii) A triangle is called *equiangular* if all three of its angles are congruent to
             one another.

8.   Prove the following theorem (add it to your list):

Theorem: $\triangle ABC$ is equilateral if and only if it is equiangular.

Definition: A point P is *equidistant* from two points A and B if AP = BP (i.e., $\overline{AP} \cong \overline{BP}$).

9.   Prove the following theorem (add it to your list):

Theorem: A point P is on the perpendicular bisector of $\overline{AB}$ if and only if P is equidistant
            from A and B.

Remark: The theorem just above says that the perpendicular bisector of a closed segment
           consists precisely of the points which are equidistant from the endpoints of
           the closed segment.

Let's develop the third of the Big Three congruence theorems for triangles.

10. Draw two triangles, each having side lengths of 2, 3, and 4 inches. Compare your triangles with those drawn by at least one of your classmates. What do you notice about these triangles?

Your results in exercise 10 should lead you to believe the following theorem:

Theorem (SSS): If two triangles contain three pairs of congruent sides, then the triangles are congruent.

llustration for SSS:

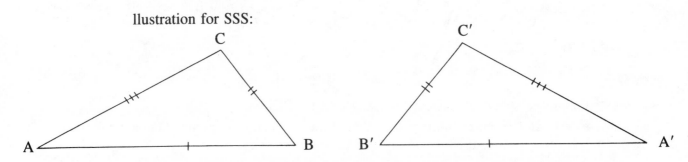

Proof: By the given, we know that there exists an isometry f such that f(A) = A' and f(B) = B' (why?). Without loss of generality we may assume that f(C) is in the same halfplane of $\overleftrightarrow{A'B'}$ as the point C'. (If it was not, we could replace f by f followed by reflection in the line $\overleftrightarrow{A'B'}$ to get an isometry with the desired properties.) If f(C) = C', we are done (why?). What if f(C) = **C** ≠ C'? Consider the diagram below to help you visualize what is "really" going on here.

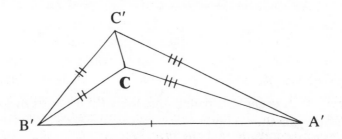

We have that △C'A'**C** and △C'B'**C** are isosceles triangles (why?). By ITT, the perpendicular bisector of the common base [C',**C**] of these two isosceles triangles is the angle bisector of both ∠A' and ∠B'. Hence, this bisector (call it *m*) passes through both A' and B'. Now, $F_m(\mathbf{C}) = C'$, $F_m(A') = A'$, and $F_m(B') = B'$ (why?).
Thus, $F_m \circ f(\triangle ABC) = \triangle A'B'C'$, and so $\triangle ABC \cong \triangle A'B'C'$.

Q.E.D.

Remark: Of course, in the proof above it is impossible that f(C) ≠ C'; thus it is difficult to visualize the case where **C** ≠ C'.

11. Fill in the missing reasons in the proof of SSS

12. Given: $\overline{AC} \cong \overline{BC}$
$\overline{AD} \cong \overline{BE}$
Prove: ∠2 ≅ ∠3

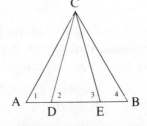

13. Using the same figure and given as in 12,
    Prove: △ACE ≅ △BCD (Hint: ASA.)

14. Given: $\overline{BC} \cong \overline{DC}$
    $\overline{BE} \cong \overline{DE}$
    Prove: $\overline{AB} \cong \overline{AD}$

    (Hint: First, show △BEC ≅ △DEC; then, show ∠1 ≅∠2. Finally,
    show △ABE ≅ △ADE.)

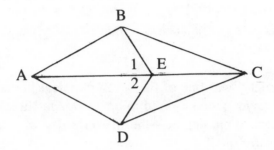

15. Given: $\overleftrightarrow{AC}$ is the bisector of ∠BAD and ∠BCD.
    Prove: ∠B ≅ ∠D.

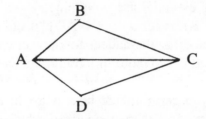

Let's digress for a moment into an historical sidelight. The result that the base angles of an isosceles triangle are congruent is Proposition 5 of Euclid's *Elements*, Book I. During the Middle Ages, this theorem became famed as the *Pons Asinorum* (Bridge of Asses). If you couldn't grasp it and its proof, you were an "ass" and probably doomed never to understand geometry! Such a fate was a major calamity; *all* learned men *had* to know geometry! (Recall that legend has it that Plato had inscribed above the entrance to his Academy the motto, "Let no one ignorant of geometry enter here.") A liberal arts education in the days of the Medieval Universities began with the study of the three basics: *logic, grammar,* and *rhetoric*.

16. Look up grammar and rhetoric in an unabridged dictionary and copy down the definitions. Recall your notes on the definition of logic.

These three basic liberal arts made up the *trivium* (3-ways), from which we get the word, "trivial."

17. Look up trivial and copy the definition.

Upon completion of the trivium, one could undertake study of the *quadrivium*. This was a four-fold branching of mathematics, supposedly handed down from the great Pythagoras. Pythagoras is credited with coining the word *mathematics*, which means "knowledge" or "learning."

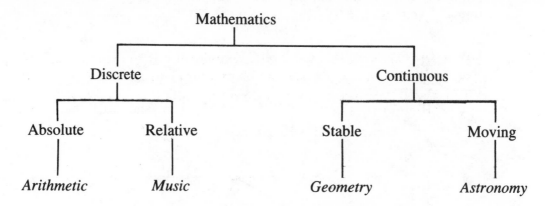

So, you see, geometry was one of the seven classical liberal arts absolutely necessary for the education of anyone who aspired to be a *magister* (a learned man, a master); even today, we have an academic degree—the master's degree—which roughly corresponds to the status of *magister*.

18.   List the seven liberal arts of antiquity.

The method—making essential use of symmetry—which we used in our proof of ITT was called by Pappus of Alexandria (c. 300 AD) "proof by the principle of least astonishment." An amusing part of mathematical folklore concerning ITT is worth telling you. Once upon a time, a band of computer programmers had prepared a computer to "create" proofs of geometric theorems. When they fed in the ITT, the computer created a proof based on SAS (see if you can think of how it might have gone; hint: the angle is the vertex angle and the pairs of sides are the legs of the isosceles triangle). The computerists were amazed. They, it seems, knew only Euclid's proof of ITT. They rushed off in great joy to report to the mathematicians about the brilliance of their program. Imagine their chagrin when they were informed that Pappus had known their "new" proof almost 1700 years before! Mathematicians need never worry about being replaced by machines.

Section 9

Now let's study some specially related angles; we'll be learning various things which will be of great use as you create proofs of your own.

When we examine geometric figures, we often find angles like this:

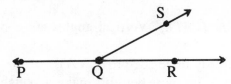

The figure shows that $\angle SQR$ and $\angle SQP$ have:

    1. The same vertex, Q.
    2. A side, $\overrightarrow{QS}$, in common.
    3. Disjoint (nonoverlapping) interiors, and
    4. Their other sides, $\overrightarrow{QP}$ and $\overrightarrow{QR}$, opposite rays.

Definition: A pair of angles satisfying the first three conditions above is said to be a pair of *adjacent* angles; a pair of angles satisfying all four of the conditions above is called a *linear pair*.

1.   Suppose $\angle SQR$ and $\angle SQP$ are a linear pair. What can you say about $\mu\angle SQR + \mu\angle SQP$? Explain.

Definition: Two angles, $\angle A$ and $\angle B$, are said to be *supplementary* (each is called a *supplement* of the other) if $\mu\angle A + \mu\angle B = 180$.

E.g., any two right angles are supplementary. In general, your intuitive notion of supplementary angles should be that they are angles which could be "pasted together" to yield a linear pair.

Your work in exercise 1 leads to the following:

Linear Pair Theorem (LPT):   The angles of a linear pair are supplementary.

2.   What can you say about two angles which are both congruent and supplementary? Explain. State your result as a theorem (and add it to your list).

3.   a) Suppose $\angle C$ and $\angle D$ are supplementary and $\angle C$ and $\angle E$ are also supplementary. What, if anything, can you conclude about $\angle D$ and $\angle E$? Try to *prove* your conclusion.

      b) Suppose $\angle C$ and $\angle D$ are supplementary, $\angle C \cong \angle C'$, and $\angle C'$ and $\angle E$ are supplementary. What, if anything, can you conclude about $\angle D$ and $\angle E$? Try to *prove* your conclusion.

      Your work in exercise 3 should have convinced you of the reasonableness of the following theorem:

Theorem (SCAC):   Supplements of congruent angles are congruent.

4.   Prove SCAC.

Definition: Two angles with vertex P, say ∠XPY and ∠UPV are called *vertical angles* if the four rays which form them make up two distinct pairs of opposite rays.

5. Illustrate the idea of vertical angles. Using a protractor, measure each angle in both of your pairs of vertical angles. What do you find? Can you make and prove a conjecture about such angles?

Vertical Angle Theorem (VAT): Vertical angles are congruent.

6. If you haven't already done so, prove VAT.
   (Hint: SCAC should be most helpful; make a sketch!)

7. Given: $\overline{TA} \cong \overline{EL}$
   ∠L ≅ ∠A
   ∠T ≅ ∠E
   Prove: ∠1 ≅ ∠2

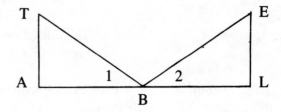

8. Given: $\overline{SA} \cong \overline{AF}$
   $\overline{SO} \cong \overline{OF}$
   Prove: ∠S ≅ ∠F

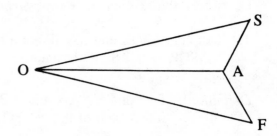

9. Given: △HRA is isosceles with vertex R
   $\overline{CH} \cong \overline{IA}$
   Prove: △CHR ≅ △IAR

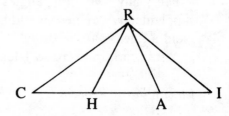

10. Given: ∠1 ≅ ∠2
    $\overline{LA} \cong \overline{AM}$
    Prove: ∠5 ≅ ∠6

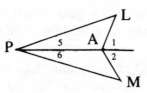

11. Given: ∠4 ≅ ∠5
    $\overline{RS} \cong \overline{RT}$
    Prove: ∠2 ≅ ∠3

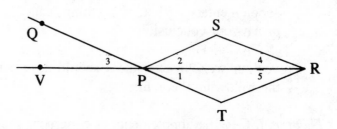

12. Given: G is midpoint of $\overline{AD}$
    $\overline{AE} \cong \overline{DB}$
    $\overline{AB} \cong \overline{DE}$
    Prove: $\overline{CD} \cong \overline{AF}$

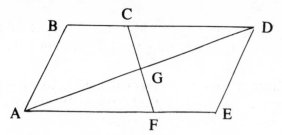

You will recall that an angle is a *right* angle if the lines containing the sides of the angle are perpendicular (or if it measures 90°). Notice that any two right angles are both congruent and supplementary; moreover, a supplement of a right angle is also a right angle. Just as we think intuitively of supplementary angles as being two angles we could "paste together" to yield a linear pair, so we might imagine two angles we could "paste together" to yield a right angle (for example, two 45° angles). Such angles are sufficiently important to deserve a special definition:

Definition: Two angles, ∠A and ∠B, are said to be *complementary* (each is called a *complement* of the other) if $\mu\angle A + \mu\angle B = 90°$.

13. Illustrate the idea of complementary angles.

If you think about it a bit, the following theorem should seem most reasonable:

Theorem (CCAC): Complements of congruent angles are congruent.

14. Prove CCAC.

Definition: An angle is said to be *acute* if it measures less than 90°; an angle is said to be *obtuse* if it measures greater than 90°. An angle with measure 180° is called a *straight* angle.

15. Illustrate the ideas in the definition just above.

16. Given: $\overline{TA} \cong \overline{EL}$
    $\overline{TA} \perp \overline{AB}$
    $\overline{EL} \perp \overline{BL}$
    $\angle T \cong \angle E$
    Prove: $\angle 1 \cong \angle 2$

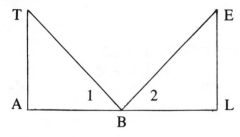

17. Given: $\overline{AB} \cong \overline{EF}$
    $\overline{BD} \cong \overline{CE}$
    $\overline{AC} \cong \overline{DF}$
    Prove: $\angle 1 \cong \angle 2$

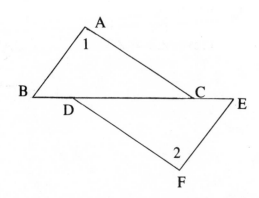

18. Given: C is midpoint of $\overline{BD}$
    $\overline{AB} \perp \overline{BD}$
    $\overline{ED} \perp \overline{CD}$
    Prove: $\triangle ABC \cong \triangle EDC$

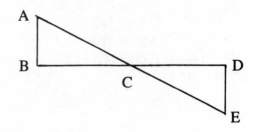

19. Given: $\angle 1 \cong \angle 2$
    $\overline{BC} \cong \overline{DE}$
    $\overline{AG} \cong \overline{FG}$
    Prove: $\angle 5 \cong \angle 6$

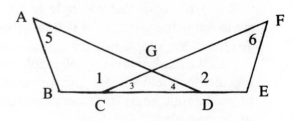

20. Given: $\overline{AB} \perp \overline{BC}$
    $\overline{DC} \perp \overline{CB}$
    $\angle 1 \cong \angle 3$
    Prove: $\angle 5 \cong \angle 6$

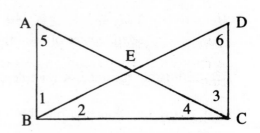

Remark: When dealing with overlapping triangles, such as those in the last two exercises, you may find it helpful to use the trick of redrawing them as **nonoverlapping** triangles (i.e., "rip them apart") to help you think about how to get the desired result.

-136-

Section 10

So far in this unit we have studied only congruent figures. Now, however, I want to take up the idea of figures of unequal size. We already have a way of comparing any two segments or any two angles. Using the idea of metric and angle measure, we can make the following:

Definition: i) $\overline{AB} < \overline{CD}$ if $AB < CD$

ii) $\angle X < \angle Y$ if $\mu\angle X < \mu\angle Y$.

It is a fairly straightforward matter to show that this definition accords well with our intuitive notion of inequality for segments and angles.

1. Prove: i) $\overline{AB} < \overline{CD}$ if and only if there is an isometry f such that $f(\overline{AB}) = \overline{CX}$ where $X \in \overset{\circ}{\overline{CD}}$;

ii) $\angle ABC < \angle XYZ$ if and only if there is an isometry f such that

$f(\angle ABC) = \angle XYP$ (or $\angle PYZ$) where P is a point in the interior of $\angle XYZ$.

While we are thinking about inequalities, we should be sure to notice that with our definitions of length and angle measure we can prove the following two *trichotomy* (cutting into 3 parts) *laws*, i.e., *theorems:*

Trichotomy Law for Segments (TLS):   Given any two segments, $\overline{AB}$ and $\overline{CD}$, one and only one of the following holds:

$$i) \; AB < CD$$
$$ii) \; AB = CD$$
$$iii) \; AB > CD.$$

Trichotomy Law for Angles (TLA): Given any two angles, $\angle X$ and $\angle Y$, one and only one of the following holds:

$$i) \;\; \mu\angle X < \mu\angle Y$$
$$ii) \;\; \mu\angle X = \mu\angle Y$$
$$iii) \;\; \mu\angle X > \mu\angle Y$$

2.   (Extra Credit) Prove the trichotomy laws for segments and angles.

Let's use our ideas about inequality to establish some very important theorems about triangles.

3.   Draw two or three fairly large triangles, e.g.:

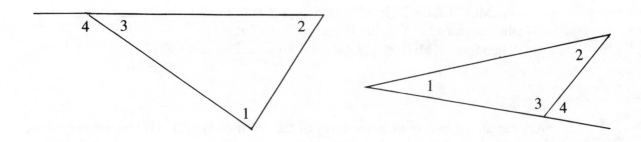

-137-

Use your protractor to measure angles 1, 2, and 4 in each. Do you notice any relation between the measures for each triangle you have drawn? Think about this before you read on.

In exercise 3, you may have conjectured that $\angle 1 + \angle 2 = \angle 4$. While this actually is valid in Euclidean geometry, we can't prove it in neutral geometry! We can, however, establish a relationship comparing angles 1, 2, and 4 in any triangle by using ideas already available to us at this stage of neutral geometry. I hope it seems reasonable to you that we should be able to prove that $\angle 4 > \angle 1$ and $\angle 4 > \angle 2$. Let's introduce some new terminology first.

Definition: An angle which forms a linear pair with one of the angles of a triangle is called an *exterior angle* of the triangle. The two angles which do *not* form a linear pair with the exterior angle are called the *remote interior angles* of the exterior angle.

4. Make a sketch illustrating the ideas in the preceding definition.

We are now in a position to state and prove the Weak Exterior Angle Theorem (WEAT).

Theorem (WEAT): For any triangle, each of its exterior angles is larger than either of the remote interior angles associated with it.

Proof: Consider the diagram:

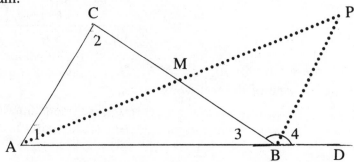

We shall prove $\angle 4 > \angle 2$; the proof that $\angle 4 > \angle 1$ is entirely analogous to this and so is omitted. Our proof follows the essential ideas of Euclid (*Elements*, Book 1, Proposition 16). Let M be the midpoint of $\overline{BC}$. (How do we know that any segment has a midpoint?) Consider the line $\overleftrightarrow{AM}$, and in particular consider that part of $\overleftrightarrow{AM}$ which consists of the ray with vertex M, opposite to $\overrightarrow{MA}$. There is a unique point P on this ray such that $\overline{AM} \cong \overline{MP}$ (why?). Draw the segment $\overline{PB}$. Then $\overline{PA}$ and $\overline{BC}$ bisect each other (why?). Thus, we can prove that $\triangle AMC \cong \triangle PMB$ (how?). Hence, $\angle 2 \cong \angle MBP$ (why?). Now the point P is in the interior of $\angle 4$. (This is correct but a bit tricky to show.) Therefore, $\angle MBP < \angle 4$ (why?). Thus, $\angle 2 < \angle 4$ (why?).

Q.E.D.

5. Answer all the questions in the body of the proof of WEAT. (If you are very clever, try to prove that $P \in Int\angle 4$.)

-138-

6. *Prove:* In △ABC, if μ∠C ≥ 90°, then both ∠A and ∠B are acute.

7. *Prove:* If P is any point in the interior of △ABC, then ∠APB > ∠C. (Hint: Draw a sketch; draw $\overrightarrow{CP}$.)

   Although the relations of inequality for segments and angles are obviously neither reflexive nor symmetric, they have two properties—transitivity and "substitutivity"—which are most important for our purposes.

8. By giving examples (called *counterexamples* since they are examples used *against* something), prove that inequality is neither reflexive nor symmetric.

   It is easy to prove the following:

Theorem: i) *Transitivity of Inequality for Segments* (TIS):
        If $\overline{AB} < \overline{CD}$ and $\overline{CD} < \overline{EF}$, then $\overline{AB} < \overline{EF}$;
      ii) *Transitivity of Inequality for Angles* (TIA):
        If ∠A < ∠B and ∠B < ∠C, then ∠A < ∠C.

9. Prove the theorem just above.

10. Prove: ∠AEB > ∠C.

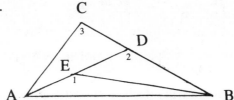

   To say that inequality has the property of "substituvity" means that we can use the:

Principle of Substitution (PS):   In "any" statement of congruence, equality, or inequality, one may substitute either one segment for another or one angle for another provided that the replacement is congruent to the original.
   E.g., ∠A < ∠B, ∠A ≅ ∠X ⇒ ∠X < ∠B.

11. Draw several fairly large triangles; use a protractor to measure each of the angles, and then compute the sum of the measures of the angles of each of your triangles. What, if anything, do you notice?

   You may already believe, perhaps on the basis of other study, that the sum of the measures of the three angles of any triangle is 180°. While this is, indeed, a fact of Euclidean geometry, it is not necessarily so in neutral geometry. As you will see, there are two classical non-Euclidean geometries in which the sum of the measures of the three angles of a triangle is *never* 180°.

12. Think of a triangle on a sphere; remember that the sides of the triangle must be segments of great circles, i.e., lines on the sphere. Is it possible to think of such a triangle in which the sum of the measures of its angles *exceeds* 180°? Indeed, must not *all* such triangles have angle sums which exceed 180°? (Hint: Draw some pictures.)

We can, however, prove a weak result analogous to the Euclidean one on the angle sum of any triangle, namely, the Weak Angle Sum Theorem:

Theorem (WAST):   The sum of the measures of any two angles of a triangle is strictly less than 180°.

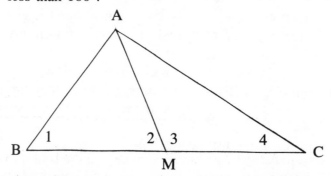

Proof: Consider △ABC as shown in the diagram above. We shall prove
μ∠B + μ∠C < 180°. Let M be the midpoint of $\overline{BC}$. Let's draw in $\overline{AM}$ and number the angles as shown.

13.   Finish the proof of WAST by explaining why μ∠4 < μ∠2 and μ∠1 < μ∠3; and thus explain why μ∠1 + μ∠4 < μ∠2 + μ∠3 = 180°. Does the fact that M is the *midpoint* of $\overline{BC}$ play any *crucial* role in the proof? Would any other randomly chosen point between B and C have worked just as well as M?

The closed segment $\overline{AM}$ in the proof of WAST is called a *median* of △ABC.

Definition: A *median* of a triangle is a closed segment having a vertex of the triangle and the midpoint of the side opposite that vertex as its endpoints.

14.   Can there exist a triangle which has two interior right angles? Explain.

15.   Prove:i) The base angles of an isosceles triangle are acute;
            ii) The angles of an equilateral triangle are acute.

In a single triangle, there is an intimate relationship between the measures of its angles and the lengths of its sides. Let's see what we can find out about this relationship. We already know that a triangle is equilateral iff (if and only if) it is equiangular. Moreover, two sides of a triangle are congruent iff the angles opposite those sides are congruent.

16.   i) What if we have △ABC with $\overline{AB} < \overline{BC}$? Draw such a triangle; can you make a conjecture about ∠A and ∠C? Do so.
      ii) What if we have △ABC with ∠A > ∠C? Draw such a triangle; can you make a conjecture about $\overline{AB}$ and $\overline{BC}$? Do so.

In the previous exercise you probably conjectured that in a single triangle the greater side is opposite the greater angle and conversely. Let's prove these conjectures. As a first step, let's prove the following *lemma*.

Lemma: The bisector of each angle of a triangle intersects the side opposite that angle.

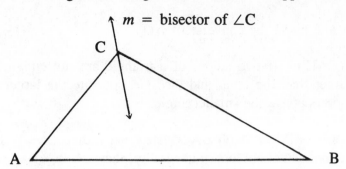

m = bisector of ∠C

Remark: If you examine the diagram accompanying the lemma, you probably will think it is silly to prove such a result. How could the angle bisector possibly fail to intersect the side opposite? Alas, we can't handwave at the diagram and wish away the difficulty. Lines are undefined, and intuition is untrustworthy. In fact, it is possible (but quite surprisingly hard) to prove that any line passing through a vertex of a triangle and containing a point in the interior of that triangle must intersect the side opposite the vertex; we shall not attempt to prove that result.

17.   Prove the lemma. (Hint: Examine the diagram; if you can explain why A and B are in opposite halfplanes of *m*, you will have the key to the whole thing. Can you do it?)

Let's get on with the proof of the main result:

Theorem (Angle Inequality Theorem (AIT)):   If two sides of a triangle are not congruent, then one is longer than the other and the angle opposite the longer side is greater than the angle opposite the shorter side.

Proof: Consider △ABC with $\overline{AC} \not\cong \overline{BC}$. Either AC > BC or AC < BC (why?). Suppose, without loss of generality, that AC < BC. (If AC > BC, we simply relabel the vertices of the triangle so that we do have AC < BC.) Consider the following diagram:

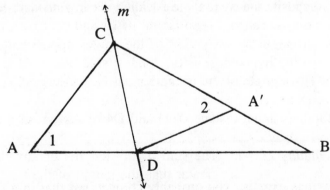

Let *m* be the angle bisector of ∠C. Then *m* intersects $\overline{AB}$ in a point D (why?). Now, $F_m(\overrightarrow{CA}) = \overrightarrow{CB}$, so there is a unique point A′ of $\overset{\circ}{CB}\!\overset{\circ}{}$ such that $F_m(A) = A'$ (why?). So, △CAD ≅ △CA′D (why?). Thus ∠1 ≅ ∠2 (why?). Now, ∠2 > ∠B (why?), and therefore ∠1 > ∠B (why?), i.e., ∠A > ∠B.
                                                          Q.E.D.

18. Answer the questions in the proof of AIT.

Let's state and prove the converse of AIT.

Theorem (CAIT):   If two angles of a triangle are not congruent, then one of them is larger than the other and the side opposite the larger angle is longer than the side opposite the smaller angle.

Proof: Consider $\triangle ABC$ with $\angle A \not\cong \angle B$. Then either $\angle A > \angle B$ or $\angle A < \angle B$ (why?). Suppose, without loss of generality, that $\angle A > \angle B$. (If $\angle A < \angle B$, then simply relabel the vertices so that $\angle A > \angle B$.) We use RAA to show that $\overline{BC} > \overline{AC}$. Suppose $\overline{BC} \not> \overline{AC}$. Then, either $\overline{BC} \cong \overline{AC}$ or $\overline{BC} < \overline{AC}$, but not both (why not?).

19. Can you produce a contradiction from the assumption that,
    i) $\overline{AC} \cong \overline{BC}$? Do so.
    ii) $\overline{AC} > \overline{BC}$? Do so.
    (Hint: Both ITT and AIT are helpful.)

Since one of the three alternatives $\overline{BC} > \overline{AC}$, $\overline{BC} \cong \overline{AC}$, or $\overline{BC} < \overline{AC}$ *must* be valid (why?) and since we have eliminated the latter two alternatives as being impossible, it must be that $\overline{BC} > \overline{AC}$.

Q.E.D.

Remark: To paraphrase Sherlock Holmes: When the impossible has been eliminated, whatever remains, however unlikely, must be so.

For convenience, we bundle AIT and CAIT into a single biconditional, the Angle-Side Inequality Theorem:

Theorem (ASIT):   In one triangle, two sides are "unequal" iff the angles opposite them are "unequal" in the same order.

Definition: A triangle which contains a right angle is called a *right* triangle. The side opposite the right angle is called the *hypotenuse*; each of the other two sides may be called a *leg*.

20. Show that the hypotenuse is the longest side of a right triangle.
    (Hint: Which angle of the triangle must be the largest?)

Our assumptions about distance (D3 and D4 of Axiom 5) yield:

Triangle Inequality $(\triangle \neq)$:   The sum of the lengths of any two sides of a triangle is greater than the length of the third side.

21. It is an easy intuitive corollary of the triangle inequality that the "shortest path" between two points A and B is the closed segment $\overline{AB}$. Explain. This fact is the reason for the saying, "The shortest distance between two points is a straight line." Of course, a straight line may not be anything like our intuitive notion of it.

While we are thinking of shortest distances, consider a line *m* and a point P. Is there a point on *m* which is closest (i.e., closer than any other point of *m*) to P? If so, where is it? We can answer both questions simultaneously. Let *p* be the unique line through P such that $p \perp m$. Then $p \cap m = X$ is the point of *m* closest to P. Thus, we have:

Theorem: Let P be a point and *m* a line. The point of *m* which is closest to P is $X = p \cap m$, where *p* is the unique line through P such that $p \perp m$.

22. Prove the theorem by showing that:
    i) If $P \in m$, then $X = P$ and so $XP = 0$. Thus, X is the point of *m* closest to P since $YP > 0$ for any other point Y of *m*.
    ii) If $P \notin m$, show that for any point Y of *m*, $PY \geq PX$ and so X is the point of *m* closest to P. (Draw a diagram!)

Definition: The *distance from a point P to a line m* is the length of the shortest segment $\overline{PX}$ connecting P to a point X of *m*.

23. Suppose you live in a farmhouse, H, near the barn, B, on a flatland alongside a gently flowing stream, *s*. Sketch the shortest path possible from the farmhouse to the barn, if you must go to the stream on the way to get a bucket of water to take along with you to the barn. Explain why the path you sketch is the shortest.

• B

H •

——————————————————————— *s*

(Hint: You want to find the point $W \in s$ such that $HW + WB$ is minimal.)

24. Given that the angles have the degree measures shown in the diagram, which is the shortest segment? Explain.

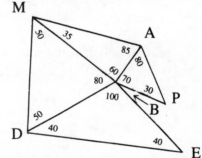

25. Given that the angles have the degree measures shown in the diagram, which is the longest segment? Explain.

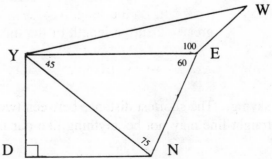

26. In each of the following, you are given AB, BC, and AC (in that order). Explain whether or not there is a triangle ABC with the side lengths given in each part.

    i) 2, 6, 9   iii) 6, 6, 3
    ii) 3, 4, 5   iv) 8, 2, 10

27. Given: CY < YP, $\overline{OY} \perp \overline{CP}$
    Prove: OC < OP.

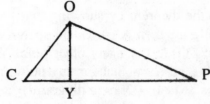

28. Given: △BAK is isosceles with vertex A
    Prove: AN > AK.

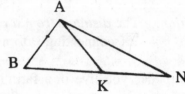

29. Given: P is any point in the interior of △ABC
    Prove: AP + PC + PB > ½(AB + BC + CA).
    (Hint: Use △≠ three times; then use algebra.)

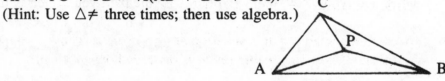

30. Given: m is the bisector of ∠C,
    Prove: AD < AC, and BD < BC.

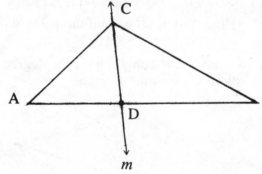

Now that you have learned ASIT, the result which details the relationship between side lengths and angle measures in a single triangle, you may wonder what can be said about two triangles.

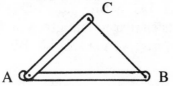 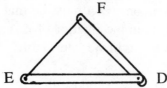

Imagine that you and a friend have identical "magic" devices. Each consists of: 1) two sticks bolted together at one end in such a way that each is free to swing like a hinge, and 2) a "magic" rubber string which is *always* stretched tightly between the other ends of the sticks. By increasing or decreasing the angle ∠BAC between the sticks, you can lengthen or shorten the "magic" rubber string. (Refer to the diagram above.)

1. i) Suppose the rubber string on your device is stretched longer than the one on the device of your friend. Can you say anything about the relative sizes of the angles included between the sticks? What?

    ii) Suppose the angle between the sticks on your device is smaller than the angle between the sticks on the device of your friend. Can you say anything about the relative lengths of the rubber strings? What?

If you correctly analyzed the situation in the exercise above, you should find the following theorem most reasonable (even if rather tedious to prove):

Theorem (Hinge Theorem (HT)): Given △ABC and △DEF with AB = DE and AC = DF. Then, ∠A > ∠D iff BC > EF.

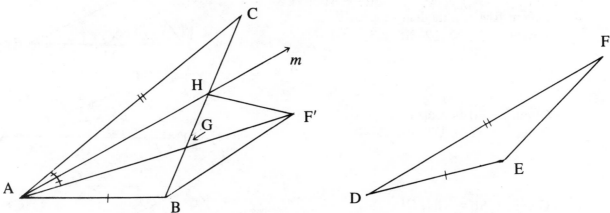

Proof: Suppose ∠A > ∠D. Since AB = DE (i.e., $\overline{AB} \cong \overline{DE}$), there is an isometry f mapping $\overline{DE}$ onto $\overline{AB}$ in such a way that f(D) = D′ = A and f(E) = E′ = B (why?). We may assume without loss of generality that f(F) = F′ is in the same halfplane of $\overleftrightarrow{AB}$ as C (why?). Now, $\overrightarrow{AF'}$ must contain a point of the interior of △CAB (why? Hint: What if not?). Suppose F′ is in the exterior of △ABC (as illustrated). Then $\overset{\circ}{AF'}$ intersects $\overline{BC}$ in a point G. Let m be the angle bisector of ∠CAG in △CAG. Then m intersects $\overset{\circ}{CG}$ at a point H (why?). Draw $\overline{HF'}$ (as illustrated). Then △CAH ≅ △F′AH (why?).

Now, BH + HC = BC (why?)

Thus, BH + HF′ = BC (why?)

Now, BH + HF′ > BF′ (why?)

Thus, BH + HF′ > EF (why?), i.e., BC > EF (why?).

If F′ is on $\overline{BC}$ it must be that B-F′-C, so that $\overline{BC} > \overline{BF′}$, i.e., BC > EF.

If F′ is in the interior of △ABC, the proof is similar to that given in the first case, where F′ is in the exterior of △ABC. So, in any case, ∠A > ∠D ⇒ BC > EF.

Conversely, suppose that BC > EF.

Now, exactly one of the following must be so: (Why?)

$$\text{i) } \angle A > \angle D$$
$$\text{ii) } \angle A \cong \angle D$$
$$\text{iii) } \angle A < \angle D.$$

If ii) is so, then △ABC ≅ △DEF (why?). Thus, BC = EF (why?). This is a direct contradiction to BC > EF. Thus, ii) cannot be so (why?).

If iii) is so, then EF > BC (why?). This is a direct contradiction to BC > EF. Thus, iii) cannot be so (why?).

Thus, we see that i) must be so, i.e., BC > EF ⇒∠ A < ∠D.

$$\text{Q.E.D.}$$

2. Answer the questions in the proof of HT.

3. Given: AB = AG
BS < SG
   Prove: ∠1 < ∠2

4. Given: $\overline{RM}$ is a median of △ORE.
   Prove: ∠1 < ∠2 iff ∠3 >∠4.

5. Given: $\overline{TH}$ is a median of △UTA.
   Prove: AT > UT iff ∠2 > ∠4.

6. Given: SI = GH, HI > SG.
   Prove: ∠ISH > ∠GHS

7. Given: $\overline{AK} \perp \overline{KE}$, $\overline{AT} \perp \overline{TE}$, AT < KA.
   Which is true: KE = ET?
   KE < ET?
   KE > ET?

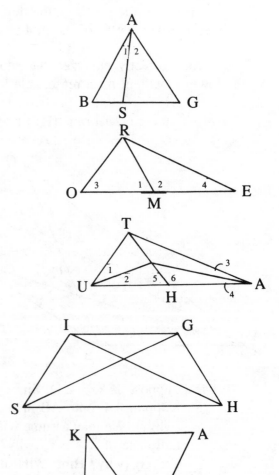

Section 12

Let's finish our rather lengthy unit on neutral geometry by establishing several more methods for proving triangles congruent.

Theorem (Side-Angle-Angle (SAA)): If two triangles contain a pair of congruent sides and two pairs of congruent angles, then the triangles are congruent.

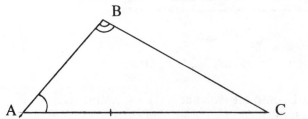 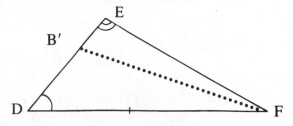

Remark: Consider the diagram above. If $\overline{AB} \cong \overline{DE}$, then $\triangle ABC \cong \triangle DEF$ (why?). Thus, we may suppose without loss of generality that $\overline{AC} \cong \overline{DF}$ and try to prove $\triangle ABC \cong \triangle DEF$.

Proof: Suppose $\overline{AC} \cong \overline{DF}$. Now exactly one of the following is so:

    i) $AB = DE$

    ii) $AB < DE$

    iii) $AB > DE$.

If i) is so, then the two triangles are congruent by ASA. Suppose ii) is so. Then there is an isometry f mapping $\overline{AC}$ onto $\overline{DF}$ such that f(B) = B' is in the same halfplane of $\overleftrightarrow{DF}$ as E and such that f(A) = A' = D and f(C) = C' = F (why?). (Refer to the diagram above.) Let f(B) = B'; then it must be that D-B'-E (why?). Of course, $\triangle ABC \cong \triangle DB'F$ (why?). Thus, $\angle B \cong \angle DB'F$ (why?). But, $\angle DB'F > \angle E$ (why?). This is a direct contradiction to the given (why?). Thus, ii) cannot be so (why?).

Suppose iii) is so. One could map $\overline{DF}$ onto $\overline{AC}$ and mimic the ideas of the proof in the previous case to get a contradiction. Hence, iii) cannot be so. Thus, i) must be so (why?). Consequently, the two triangles are congruent.

                           Q.E.D.

1. Answer the questions in the proof of SAA.

The remaining congruence theorems apply only to *right* triangles. It is trivial to prove the following Right-Triangle-Side-Angle theorem:

Theorem (RTSA): If two right triangles contain a pair of congruent sides and a pair of congruent acute angles, then the two triangles are congruent.

2. Prove RTSA.

The final congruence theorem is an Angle-Side-Side theorem for right triangles:

Theorem (Hypotenuse-Leg (HL)): If two right triangles have congruent hypotenuses and contain a pair of congruent legs (sides), then the two triangles are congruent.

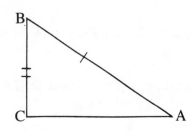
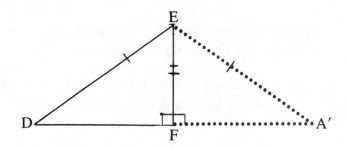

We have to show:

$$\overline{BC} \cong \overline{EF}; \ \overline{AB} \cong \overline{DE}; \ \angle C, \ \angle F \text{ right } \angle s \Rightarrow \triangle ABC \cong \triangle DEF$$

Proof: There is an isometry f mapping $\overline{BC}$ onto $\overline{EF}$ so that f(B) = E and f(C) = F, and also so that f(A) = A′ is in the halfplane of $\overleftrightarrow{EF}$ opposite to the one containing D (why?). We see that D-F-A′ (why?). Let *m* be the perpendicular bisector of $\overline{DA'}$ .Recall that the perpendicular bisector of a segment consists of all those points which are equidistant from the endpoints of the segment. Hence, E is on *m* (why?). Thus, $m = \overleftrightarrow{EF}$ (why?). But then we have that $F_m(\triangle EFA') = \triangle EFD$ (why?). Hence, $F_m \circ f$ is an isometry which maps $\triangle ABC$ onto $\triangle DEF$, i.e., $\triangle ABC \cong \triangle DEF$.

Q.E.D.

3. Answer the questions in the proof of HL.

4. List *all* the ways you know to prove that two triangles are congruent.

5. Consider the following diagram and explain why your intuition tells you that there can be no such thing as an Angle-Side-Side congruence theorem for triangles in general:

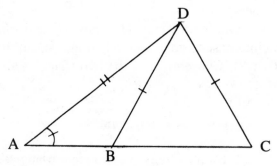

(Hint: consider $\triangle ADB$ and $\triangle ADC$.)

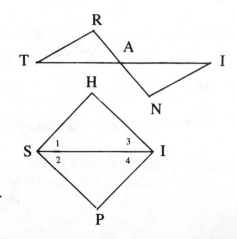

6. Given: RA = AI
      $\angle T \cong \angle I$

    Prove: RT = NI

7. Given: $\overline{SH} \perp \overline{HI}$
      $\overline{SP} \perp \overline{IP}$
      SH = SP.

    Prove: $\overleftrightarrow{SI}$ bisects both $\angle HIP$ and $\angle HSP$.

8. Given: $\overline{SH} \perp \overline{HI}$
$\overline{SP} \perp \overline{IP}$
$\angle 1 \cong \angle 2$
Prove: $HS = SP$

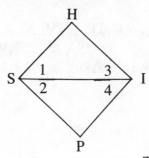

9. Given $\overline{CR} \perp \overline{TU}$
$\overline{UK} \perp \overline{TC}$
$CR = UK$
Prove: $\triangle CUT$ is isosceles with vertex T.

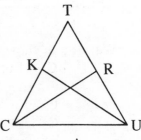

10. Given: $\triangle ABC$ is isosceles with vertex A,
$\overleftrightarrow{BD}$ bisects $\angle ABC$, $\overleftrightarrow{CE}$ bisects $\angle ACB$.
Prove: $\overline{BD} \cong \overline{CE}$.
(Hint: Let m be the bisector of $\angle A$ and show $F_m(\overline{BD}) = \overline{CE}$.)

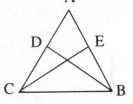

11. Given: m is the bisector of $\angle ABC$.
Prove: X is equidistant from $\overleftrightarrow{BA}$ and $\overleftrightarrow{BC}$.

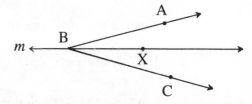

12. Given: $\overleftrightarrow{AM}$ is the perpendicular bisector of $\overline{BC}$, $\angle 1 \cong \angle 2$.
Prove: $AD = AE$

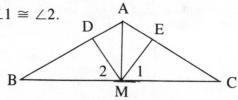

13. Given: $\angle K \cong \angle J$, $MR = NR$.
Prove: $\triangle KMN \cong \triangle JNM$.

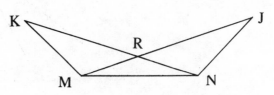

14. Given: $\angle P \cong \angle A$, $\angle 1 \cong \angle 2$.
Prove: $PE = NA$.

15. Given: $OD = OB$, $OC = OA$.
Prove: E is on the bisector of $\angle DOB$.
(Hint: let m be the bisector; show $F_m(E) = E$.)

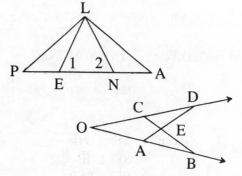

-149-

16. Given: $\overline{JT} \perp \overline{TY}$, $\overline{NI} \perp \overline{IU}$,
    $\triangle JSA \cong \triangle NKW$.
    Prove: $\triangle JTY \cong \triangle NIU$.

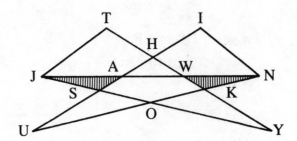

Unit IV—Review Topics

1. Axiomatic method—essential components, how it works, importance, etc.; (relatively) consistent axiom system, independent axiom system.
2. The 11 axioms for neutral geometry.
3. The theorems of neutral geometry, particularly those with special names—Pasch's theorem, the Ruler theorem, the Protractor theorem, SAS, SAA, ASA, SSS, RTSA, HL, TRT, ITT, LPT, SCAC, VAT, CCAC, TLS, TLA, WEAT, TIS, TIA, 'PS', WAST, AIT, CAIT, ASIT, Triangle Inequality ($\triangle \neq$), HT.
4. Definitions: consistency and independence of axioms; collinear and non-collinear points; betweenness; open, closed segments; perpendicular bisector and midpoint of segment; triangle, sides, vertices; formal definition of congruence of two figures; ray, endpoint; angle, sides, vertex, interior, bisector; perpendicular lines; right angle; isosceles triangle, vertex, vertex angle, base angles; equilateral and equiangular triangles; equidistance; adjacent angles; linear pair of angles; supplementary angles; vertical angles; complementary angles; acute, obtuse, and straight angles; inequality of segments and angles; exterior angle of a triangle, remote interior angles associated with an exterior angle; median of a triangle; right triangle, hypotenuse, legs; distance from point to line.

Unit V
Parallels: None, One, or Many?

> "Euclid alone has looked on beauty bare."
> –Edna St. Vincent Millay–

> ". . . whatever else this postulate may be, self-evident it is not."
> –J. L. Coolidge–

As you doubtless remember, Euclid's *Elements* set a standard for excellence in axiomatization which endured, essentially unchanged, for over two thousand years. It came to be accepted almost universally that Euclid had captured the very essence of idealized space in his axioms and postulates for geometry. Everyone "knew" not only that there was no geometry other than Euclid's but also that the human mind was so constituted that any other geometry was literally inconceivable! We shall see in this unit how far from accurate such beliefs were.

Let's begin by examining Euclid's axioms and postulates. You should remember from our prior study of axiomatization that it is considered "elegant" to assume as few things as possible and then to tease out, by deduction, the logical consequences of those minimal assumptions. As you will soon see, Euclid was most economical—too much so, in fact—in his assumption of only five axioms and five postulates, viz.:

The Euclidean Axioms and Postulates

A1: Things which are equal to the same thing are also equal to each other.
A2: If equals be added to equals, the wholes are equal.
A3: If equals be subtracted from equals, the remainders are equal.
A4: Things which coincide with one another are equal to one another.
A5: The whole is greater than the part.

P1: It is possible to draw a straight line from any point to any other point.
P2: It is possible to extend a finite straight line segment continuously in a straight line.
P3: It is possible to draw a circle with any point as center and any length as radius.
P4: All right angles are equal.
P5: If a straight line falling on two straight lines makes the interior angles on the same side less than two right angles, the two straight lines, if extended indefinitely, meet on the side on which the angles are less than two right angles.

Did you recognize that P5 refers to parallel lines without explicitly saying so? It is giving a characterization of the conditions under which two lines are *not* parallel, viz., the two interior angles on the same side of the "transversal" are less than two right angles. Euclid is saying that under this condition the lines are not parallel, i.e., they meet at a common point. Let's remind ourselves of the definition of parallelism for lines:

Definition: Two distinct coplanar lines, *m* and *n*, are said to be *parallel*, denoted by
$m \parallel n$, if $m \cap n = \varnothing$, i.e., if *m* and *n* have no point in common; we also
say that any line is parallel to itself.

Before we go on, let's learn some handy new terminology. Consider the diagram:

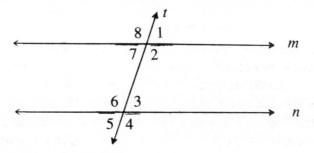

1. The line *t* crossing both *m* and *n* is a *transversal;*
2. Angles 2, 3, 6, 7 are *interior angles;* 2 and 3 are *consecutive interior angles*—so are
   6 and 7; 2 and 6 are *alternate interior angles*—so are 3 and 7;
3. Angles 1, 4, 5, 8 are *exterior angles;* 1 and 4 are *consecutive exterior angles*—so are
   5 and 8; 4 and 8 are *alternate exterior angles*—so are 1 and 5;
4. Angles 1 and 3 are *corresponding angles*—so are 2 and 4, 6 and 8, and 5 and 7.

Euclid's P5 says, then, that if the sum of the angle measures of either pair of consecutive
interior angles is less than 180, then *m* is not parallel to *n*. In fact, P5 tells us even more
by specifying in which halfplane of the transversal the lines will intersect if they are
sufficiently extended. Euclid probably phrased P5 in a somewhat obscure way to avoid
criticism from the philosophers and others who would never have accepted a condition
for parallelism such as: "Two coplanar lines are parallel if they never meet no matter
how far they are extended." Such a "direct" definition of parallelism would have raised
a storm of protest on the grounds that no one can reasonably assert on the basis of limited
experience what may or may not happen to two lines if they are prolonged *infinitely far!*
In condensed form, Euclid's P5 says:

● The sum of 2 consecutive interior angles $< 180 \Rightarrow m \parallel n$.

We can prove the *converse* of P5 as a theorem of neutral geometry.

1.   State the converse of the condensed form ● of P5.

2.   Answer the questions in the following proof of the converse of ●:
     Suppose $m \nparallel n$. (Refer to the diagram below.) Then $m \cap n \neq \varnothing$ (why?). Thus, *m*
     and *n* have exactly one point R in common (why?). Thus, we have △PQR. Hence,
     $\mu\angle 2 + \mu\angle 3 < 180$ (why?).
                                                            Q.E.D.

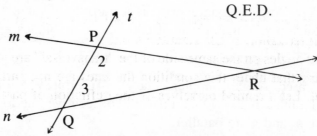

-153-

3. Each of the following results is easy to prove. Taken together, they establish an interesting chain of logically equivalent conditions on the angles in the diagram:

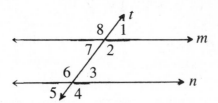

The fact that $\angle 2 \cong \angle 6$ is the first hypothesis and also the last conclusion in the long chain of implications below means that all 11 conditions on the angles in the diagram are logically equivalent, i.e., they are all either valid or invalid simultaneously in neutral geometry; prove each of the following:

i) $\angle 2 \cong \angle 6 \Rightarrow \angle 7 \cong \angle 3$
ii) $\angle 7 \cong \angle 3 \Rightarrow \angle 5 \cong \angle 1$
iii) $\angle 5 \cong \angle 1 \Rightarrow \angle 8 \cong \angle 4$
iv) $\angle 8 \cong \angle 4 \Rightarrow \angle 2 \cong \angle 4$
v) $\angle 2 \cong \angle 4 \Rightarrow \angle 8 \cong \angle 6$
vi) $\angle 8 \cong \angle 6 \Rightarrow \angle 7 \cong \angle 5$

vii) $\angle 7 \cong \angle 5 \Rightarrow \angle 2$ supp $\angle 3$
viii) $\angle 2$ supp $\angle 3 \Rightarrow \angle 6$ supp $\angle 7$
ix) $\angle 6$ supp $\angle 7 \Rightarrow \angle 1$ supp $\angle 4$
x) $\angle 1$ supp $\angle 4 \Rightarrow \angle 5$ supp $\angle 8$
xi) $\angle 5$ supp $\angle 8 \Rightarrow \angle 2 \cong \angle 6$

Note: $\angle A$ supp $\angle B$ means $\angle A$ and $\angle B$ are supplementary.

4. Suppose any one of the above 11 conditions on angles is valid, say $\angle 2$ supp $\angle 3$. (Then as you have seen, all 10 of the other conditions are also valid, in particular $\angle 6$ supp $\angle 7$.)
Prove that $m \parallel n$ if $\angle 2$ supp $\angle 3$.
(Hint: Suppose $m \nparallel n$ and try to derive a contradiction.)

5. Prove or disprove: Two coplanar lines which are perpendicular to the same line are parallel to one another.

The outcome of exercises 3 and 4 means that we have several ways of proving that lines are parallel in neutral geometry; *each* of the following is a theorem of neutral geometry:

Theorem (Alt.-Int.): If a transversal t cuts two coplanar lines m and n in such a way that a pair of alternate-interior angles are congruent, then m and n are parallel.

Theorem (Alt.-Ext.): If a transversal t cuts two coplanar lines m and n in such a way that a pair of alternate-exterior angles are congruent, then m and n are parallel.

Theorem (Corr. Angles Congruent): If a transversal t cuts two coplanar lines m and n in such a way that a pair of corresponding angles are congruent, then m and n are parallel.

Theorem (Consec. Angles Supplementary): If a transversal t cuts two coplanar lines m and n in such a way that a pair of consecutive interior angles are supplementary, then m and n are parallel.

In short, *each* of the eleven logically equivalent conditions in exercise 3 implies that the lines *m* and *n* are parallel.

You must be *extremely* careful not to confuse Alt.-Int., Alt.-Ext., etc. with their converses! Because Alt.-Int., Alt.-Ext., etc. depend only upon the eleven axioms we have so far introduced, they are part of *neutral geometry*—the collection of all the theorems which depend solely upon those eleven axioms.

As you will see in the rest of this unit, we have arrived at a crucial divide in the path of our development of geometry. The choice we make for our next axiom will determine whether we go on to study Euclidean or non-Euclidean geometry. All that has gone before forms neutral geometry, the common core of both Euclidean and one of the non-Euclidean geometries. We shall travel down the Euclidean path, but with due consideration paid to the non-Euclidean paths.

In particular, then, you should note that the converses of Alt.-Int., etc. are theorems only in *Euclidean* geometry. They are *not* valid in any non-Euclidean geometry we shall study.

We now know that there were flaws in the logical foundations of the *Elements*. For example, Euclid overlooked the necessity to postulate the *uniqueness* of the line, the extension, and the circle mentioned in P1, P2, and P3, respectively. Moreover, Euclid unconsciously assumed that lines are *infinitely* long in his P2 (he meant to say that a line could be extended indefinitely without overlapping itself). So, Euclid's foundations for the *Elements* were seriously incomplete in that his assumptions were insufficient for him to be able to prove all the theorems which he wanted to have. Despite the flaws which made some of the *proofs* invalid, Euclid never fell into the error of stating a totally invalid result as a theorem of Euclidean geometry. Around 1900, various mathematicians—notably David Hilbert—succeeded in giving complete sets of axioms for Euclidean geometry and thus secured its logical foundations forever. To consider such axiom systems in detail would take us far from where we want to go, and so we shall not do so. (You, however, might be interested in pursuing advanced study of the foundations of geometry—in particular, Hilbert's axioms. If so, you may *start* by consulting pages 1727 and 1728 of volume 3 of *The World of Mathematics*, ed. by J.R. Newman.)

Even in antiquity, Euclid's set of geometric postulates was not above cricism. A casual glance at the postulates reveals that the fifth postulate lacks the easy, intuitive immediacy of the others. A more penetrating investigation would raise questions about other postulates as well. For example, P4 asserts something wholly non-obvious—the *homogeneous* nature—of the very thing Euclid was attempting to describe abstractly: physical space itself.

Let's focus our attention on P5. As far as we know, P5 seems to have been an original product of Euclid's genius. Even so, this postulate generated much controversy among geometers; many of them felt that it had no place in a list of supposedly self-evident principles. Indeed, it was proposed that since the converse of P5 is a theorem, one should be able to prove P5 itself as a theorem dependent on Euclid's other assumptions. Failing that, it was thought best to try to replace P5 with another "obviously self-evident" postulate which would, along with the other 9 assumptions, yield the same results in a more psychologically satisfying way. Prodigious efforts were made along these lines. Despite many erroneous attempts, no one was able to prove P5 dependent. Thereby hangs a most important tale in the history of the development of mathematics and, indeed, in the story of the intellectual maturation of the human race. However, a particularly nice logical alternative to P5 (related to Proposition 31, Book I of the *Elements*) was known already to Proclus (c. 300 AD; commentator on Euclid's *Elements*) and was much later "popularized" by the Scot mathematician John Playfair. It became known as Playfair's postulate; it is this postulate which is used in most modern geometry books as a replacement for Euclid's P5. We shall assume:

A12: Given a line m and a point P not on m there is one and only one line n which passes through P and is parallel to m.

A bit later, we shall see that, in neutral geometry, we can prove the existence of *at least one* line such as the n mentioned in A12. Thus, the force of the axiom is that it asserts that there is *only one* such line n, i.e., it asserts the *uniqueness* of the line n through P and parallel to m. It is the addition of this axiom to our system for geometry which marks the dividing line between neutral and Euclidean geometry, i.e., theorems which depend on A12 are *not* theorems of neutral geometry. Euclid himself seems to have been somewhat hesitant to use P5 since he postponed any use of it for as long as possible in his *Elements*. Remember that *all* the geometry we did in Unit IV is independent of A12.

It will be of great use to us in developing our study of parallelism to be able to use halfturns and to know their basic properties. You should recall from your prior study that products such as $F_h \circ F_v$ and also $F_p \circ F_n$ are halfturns around the origin. What is it about the mirror lines of the reflections in these products which results in their products being halfturns? It is simply the fact that the mirror lines are perpendicular to one another at the point which is the center of the halfturn. As you may recall, it turns out that the image X' of a point X ($X \neq C$) under the halfturn with center C is determined by the fact that the center C must be the midpoint of the closed segment joining the point X and its image X'. This leads us to make the following:

Definition: Let C be a point. The *halfturn*, H_C, around the *center* C is a mapping of the plane to itself such that for any point $X \neq C$, C is the midpoint of the closed segment joining X and $H_C(X)$. Moreover, $H_C(C) = C$.

Theorem: For any point C there is a halfturn H_C with center C.

Proof: Let C be a point, For any point $X \neq C$, let $m = \overleftrightarrow{CX}$. On the ray of m which is opposite to $\overrightarrow{CX}$ there is a unique point X' such that $CX' = CX$ (why?). Let $H_C(X) = X'$. Then C is the midpoint of $\overline{XX'}$ (why?). The map so defined is the halfturn with center C, provided that we define $H_C(C) = C$.

Q.E.D.

1.   Answer the questions in the proof above.

2.   Explain why one would want to require that $H_C(C) = C$, i.e., that C be fixed under H_C. Explain why the point C is the *unique* fixed point of H_C, i.e., explain why $H_C(X) = X$ iff $X = C$.

The remark we made above—that the perpendicularity of the mirror lines is the key to why the composite of two reflections turns out to be a halfturn—can be verified as follows:

Theorem: Let C be a point and let m and n be any two lines which are perpendicular at C. Then $F_m \circ F_n = H_C$.

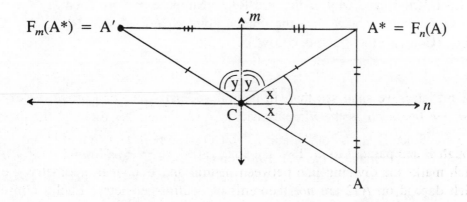

Proof: Let A be any point except C. Suppose that $F_n(A) = A^*$ and let $F_m(A^*) = A'$. (Refer to the diagram above.) The angles and segments are congruent as marked in the diagram (why?). Thus, AC = CA′ (why?). Moreover, we have A-C-A′ (why? Hint: x + y = 90). Thus, C is the midpoint of the closed segment $\overline{AA'}$ where $A' = F_m \circ F_n(A)$. Hence, $F_m \circ F_n = H_C$.

Q.E.D.

3.   Answer the questions in the proof above. Explain why $F_m \circ F_n(C) = C$.

Remark: Since H_C may be represented as a product of two reflections, it is an isometry and thus, of course, a similarity; hence, it has all the properties associated with such maps.

4.   Consider the diagram for the proof above. What is $H_C(A')$? Verify your conjecture. What does this mean about $H_C(H_C(X))$ for any point X?

If you worked exercise 4 correctly, you saw that the following theorem is true:

Theorem: For any point C, $H_C \circ H_C$ = Identity, i.e., H_C is an involution.

5. Consider the line *m* and the point C shown below:

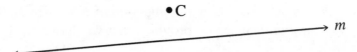

Copy this diagram and complete it by sketching the image *n* of *m* under H_C. Do you notice any special relationship between *m* and *n*? Make a conjecture about the relationship between any line *m* and its image *n* under a halfturn around a point. What happens if the center of the halfturn is on the line *m*? Is your conjecture still valid? Can you prove your conjecture? Try to before you read on.

Your thoughts on exercise 5 should make the following theorem seem most reasonable:

Theorem: Let *m* be a line and C a point. Then $m \parallel H_C(m)$.

Proof: If C is on *m*, then $H_C(m) = m$ (why?). Thus, the desired result is true in this case (why?). Suppose C is not on *m*. Let $n = H_C(m)$. Then $H_C(n) = m$ (why?). We use RAA. Suppose $m \nparallel n$. Then $m \cap n \neq \varnothing$; let's say that *m* and *n* have the unique point X in common. Now, X ≠ C (why?). (Consider the diagram below.)

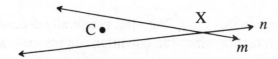

Since X is on both *m* and *n*, $H_C(X)$ is on both $H_C(m)$ and $H_C(n)$, i.e., $H_C(X)$ is on both *n* and *m* (why?). But then $H_C(X) = X$ (why?). Thus, X = C (why?). This is a direct contradiction to the fact that X ≠ C. Hence, by RAA, we have that $m \parallel n$.

Q.E.D.

6. Answer the questions in the proof above.

We can use the theorem above to prove the converse of P5, i.e., to prove half of our Axiom 12, and thereby show that Axiom 12 could be weakened to guarantee only the uniqueness of the parallel. It is important to note that it is the uniqueness assumption in Axiom 12 which makes neutral geometry into Euclidean geometry. Let's prove:

Theorem   (Existence of Parallels (EP)): Given a line m and a point P, there exists a line n containing P and parallel to m.

Proof: If P is on m, we may choose $n = m$ and the desired result is true (why?). Suppose P is not on m. Let Q be any point on m, and let M be the midpoint of $\overline{PQ}$.

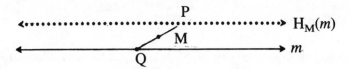

Then $H_M(Q) = P$ (why?). Thus, we see that $H_M(m)$ is a line with the desired property (why?).

Q.E.D.

7. Answer the questions in the proof above.

8. State the converse of Alt.-Int.; prove the converse as a theorem of *Euclidean* geometry (i.e., you may use Axiom 12).
   (Hint: In terms of the diagram below, you wish to prove that $\angle 2 \cong \angle 6$. Let M be the midpoint of $\overline{PQ}$ and show that $H_M(m) = n$, etc.)

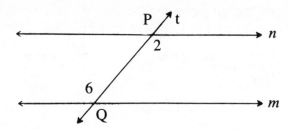

If you did exercise 8 correctly, you have already proved the following:

Theorem (Conv. Alt.-Int.):   If t is a transversal crossing two parallel lines, the pairs of alternate interior angles are congruent.

Let me remind you again that Conv. Alt.-Int. essentially depends on A12, but Alt.-Int. does *not* so depend. Moreover, since the conditions on alt.-int., alt.-ext., etc. angles are all equivalent, we see that in *Euclidean* geometry parallelism implies *all* 11 of those conditions. Now that we have the converses of Alt.-Int., Corr. Angles Congr., etc., we can prove the Strong Exterior Angle Theorem of Euclidean geometry:

Theorem (SEAT):   The measure of an exterior angle of a triangle is the sum of the measures of its remote interior angles, i.e.:

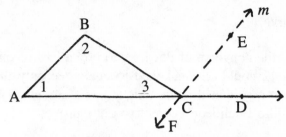

$$\mu\angle BCD = \mu\angle 1 + \mu\angle 2.$$

Proof: We phrase our proof in terms of the diagram above. Let *m* be a line passing through C and parallel to $\overleftrightarrow{AB}$. (How do we know, even in *neutral* geometry, that there is such a line *m*?) Then, $\angle 2 \cong \angle BCE$ and $\angle 1 \cong \angle ECD$ (why?). Thus, $\mu\angle BCD = \mu\angle BCE + \mu\angle ECD = \mu\angle 2 + \mu\angle 1$ (why?).

Q.E.D.

9. Answer the questions in the proof of SEAT.

10. Prove the following corollary of SEAT (in Euclidean geometry):
   The sum of the measures of the angles in any triangle is 180.
   (Hint: Look back at the diagram for SEAT and notice that $\angle 3$ and $\angle BCD$ are supplementary.)

Solve the following problems in Euclidean geometry:

11. Given: $m \parallel n$, $\mu\angle 3 = 40$.
   Find the measure of each of the numbered angles.

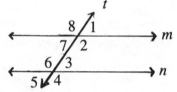

12. Given: $m \parallel n$.
   Find the measure of the smaller of the two angles whose measures are given as indicated.

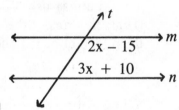

13. If the angles have the measures indicated, are *m* and *n* parallel? Explain.

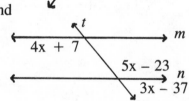

14. Let *t* be a transversal crossing two parallel lines *m* and *n*. Prove that the angle bisectors of a pair of consecutive interior angles are perpendicular. (Draw a diagram!)

15. Prove that parallelism is a transitive relation on the set of lines.

16. Let *m*, *n*, and *o* be three lines such that $m \perp n$, and $n \parallel o$.
   Prove: $m \perp o$. (Draw a diagram!)

17. Given: $\overleftrightarrow{AC}$ bisects $\angle DAB$,
   $\overleftrightarrow{BC} \parallel \overleftrightarrow{AD}$.
   Prove: $\triangle ABC$ is isosceles with vertex B.

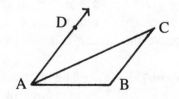

18. Given: △ABC is isosceles with vertex B,
    $\overleftrightarrow{DE} \parallel \overleftrightarrow{AC}$.

    Prove: i) △DBE is isosceles with vertex B,
    ii) The perpendicular bisector of $\overline{AC}$ is also
    the perpendicular bisector of $\overline{DE}$.

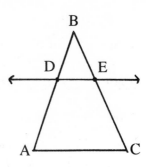

19. Given: $\overleftrightarrow{AE}$ bisects ∠A, AD = DE.
    Prove: $\overleftrightarrow{DE} \parallel \overleftrightarrow{AB}$

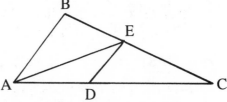

20. Given: $\overline{NF}$ and $\overline{RU}$ are medians of △RAN, U is the midpoint of $\overline{RL}$,
    F is the midpoint of $\overline{NH}$.

    Prove: H, A, and L are collinear.

    (Hint: Show they are all on the unique parallel to $\overleftrightarrow{RN}$ passing through A.)

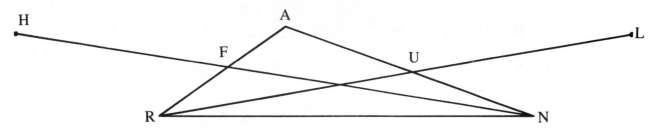

21. Given: $m \parallel n$, E and Q are any two points on m.

    Prove: The distance from E to n equals the distance from Q to n,
    i.e., prove EI = QU in the diagram.

    (Hint: Let p be the perpendicular bisector of $\overline{IU}$. Show that $F_p(\overline{QU}) = \overline{EI}$.)

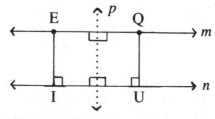

If you did exercise 21 correctly, you proved:

Theorem (PLE):   In Euclidean geometry, parallel lines are everywhere equidistant.

PLE is the reason your intuition pictures parallel lines as being like railroad tracks (or any other equidistant lines).

The problem of parallels, i.e., the controversy over P5, was regarded as a scandal of geometry and a blot on the perfection of Euclid's work. This problem is, as we shall soon see, intimately bound to the value of the sum of the measures of the angles of a triangle.

Definition: The sum of the measures of a triangle will be called its *angle sum* and will be denoted by the Greek letter sigma Σ.

Let's focus our attention on angle sums and begin by proving a powerful result of *neutral* geometry—the Neutral Angle Sum Theorem (NAST).

Theorem (NAST): For any triangle, $\Sigma \leq 180$.

To prove NAST we shall need:

Lemma: Given $\triangle ABC$, there exists $\triangle DEF$ having the same angle sum as $\triangle ABC$ and also having $\mu\angle D \leq \frac{1}{2} \mu\angle A$.

Proof: Let $\triangle ABC$ be given. Let M be the midpoint of $\overline{BC}$. Consider $H_M(\triangle ABC)$. (Refer to the diagram below.)

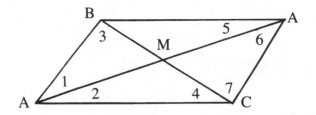

We know $H_M(B) = C$ and $H_M(C) = B$ (why?). Also if $H_M(A) = A'$, we can say that A-M-A' with M the midpoint of $\overline{AA'}$ (why?). Now, $H_M(\angle 1) = \angle 6$ and $H_M(\angle 3) = \angle 7$. So, $\angle 1 \cong \angle 6$ and $\angle 3 \cong \angle 7$. The angle sum of $\triangle ABC$ is $\mu\angle 1 + \mu\angle 2 + \mu\angle 3 + \mu\angle 4 = \Sigma$. But $\Sigma = \mu\angle 6 + \mu\angle 2 + \mu\angle 7 + \mu\angle 4$ (why?). This is the angle sum of $\triangle ACA'$. I claim that as a result of our construction we have either $\mu\angle 2 \leq \frac{1}{2}\mu\angle BAC$ or $\mu\angle 6 \leq \frac{1}{2}\mu\angle BAC$. If $\mu\angle 2 \leq \frac{1}{2}\mu\angle BAC$, we may choose $\angle DEF$ to be $\triangle ACA'$ since $\triangle ACA'$ has the desired properties. If $\mu\angle 2 > \frac{1}{2}\mu\angle BAC$, then $\mu\angle 1 < \frac{1}{2}\mu\angle BAC$ (why?). Since $\mu\angle 1 = \mu\angle 6$, we may choose $\triangle DEF = \triangle A'CA$ in this case since $\triangle A'CA$ has the desired properties. In any case, we have shown the existence of $\triangle DEF$ having the same angle sum as $\triangle ABC$ and having $\mu\angle D \leq \frac{1}{2}\mu\angle A$.

Q.E.D.

1. Answer the questions in the proof of the lemma above.

Note that the intuitive idea of obtaining $\triangle DEF$ from $\triangle ABC$ is that we "cut off" $\triangle AMB$ and "paste" $\overline{MB}$ onto $\overline{MC}$ to form the "slimmer" $\triangle ACA'$ which has the properties desired for $\triangle DEF$.

2. Explain how, given $\triangle ABC$, we could show the existence of a triangle having the same angle sum as $\triangle ABC$ and containing an angle with measure less than or equal

to ¼ of the measure of ∠A. If we repeat this procedure over and over again we could produce a triangle with the same angle sum as △ABC, containing an angle with measure less than or equal to ⅛ (or 1/16, 1/32, etc.) of the measure of ∠A. Does this mean that for any positive number ε (epsilon) we could produce a triangle with the same angle sum as △ABC, containing an angle with measure less than ε? Think carefully about this and give the most plausible explanation which you can.

Remark: The last part of the exercise above depends on the so-called *Archimedean property* of the real numbers. You may wish to find out what this property is and how it can be used to justify the claim in the exercise. See page 99 of volume 1 of *The World of Mathematics*.

Using the lemma, we can prove NAST; we use RAA:

Proof: (NAST) Consider △ABC. Suppose μ∠A + μ∠B + μ∠C > 180. Then, we can say that μ∠A + μ∠B + μ∠C = 180 + ε for some ε > 0. By using the lemma repeatedly (as you saw in the exercise above), we see that there is a triangle, say △XYZ, having the same angle sum as △ABC and containing an angle, say ∠X, such that μ∠X < ε. But this means that μ∠Y + μ∠Z > 180. This is a direct contradiction to the fact that the sum of the measures of any two angles of a triangle must be ≤ 180. Hence, by RAA, we have
μ∠A + μ∠B + μ∠C ≤ 180.
　　　　　　　　　　　　　　　　　　　　　　　　　Q.E.D.

3.　State the meaning of NAST in your own words.

4.　How many right angles may a triangle contain? Explain.

Having proved NAST, we are faced with the thorny problem of refining our knowledge about the angle sum of a triangle. Notice, for example, that NAST does *not* say that the angle sum Σ is a constant, i.e., the same for every triangle. In fact, Σ is *not* a constant in non-Euclidean geometry; the angle sum of a triangle in non-Euclidean geometry depends on the *size* of the triangle! In Euclidean geometry, however, as you saw in exercise 2.10, Σ is a constant 180. This result is important enough to be stated as the Euclidean Angle Sum Theorem (EAST).

Theorem (EAST):　Σ = 180 for any triangle in Euclidean geometry.

Just in case you didn't get exercise 2.10, here is a proof of EAST which points out the clear connection between parallelism and angle sum:

Proof:

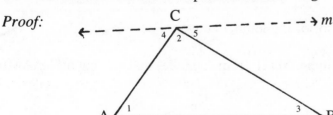

Let m be the line through C parallel to $\overleftrightarrow{AB}$. By Conv. Alt.-Int., $\angle 1 \cong \angle 4$ and $\angle 3 \cong \angle 5$. Since $\mu\angle 4 + \mu\angle 2 + \mu\angle 5 = 180$, we have that $\mu\angle 1 + \mu\angle 2 + \mu\angle 3 = 180$.

Q.E.D.

To pursue the question of angle sums further would take us far from where we should be going. Here, however, are two important results which are theorems of neutral geometry:

Theorem 1: If there is one triangle with $\Sigma < 180$, then $\Sigma < 180$ for every triangle.

Theorem 2: If there is one triangle with $\Sigma = 180$, then $\Sigma = 180$ for every triangle.

5. What can you say about the sum of the angle measures of the four angles in any quadrilateral in *neutral* geometry?
     (Hint: Any quadrilateral can be split up into two triangles, e.g., 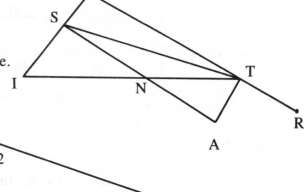 can be split up into 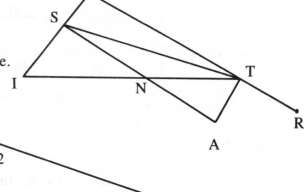 .)

    What can you say about the sum of the measures of the angles of any quadrilateral in *Euclidean* geometry?

If you worked the exercise above correctly, you should know that,

Theorem: i) In neutral geometry, the sum of the angle measures of any quadrilateral does not exceed 360;
    ii) In Euclidean geometry, the sum of the angle measures of any quadrilateral is 360.

    Do the following 4 exercises in Euclidean geometry:

6. Suppose $\triangle ABC$ has a right angle, $\angle C$. How are the acute angles of $\triangle ABC$ related to one another? Explain.

7. Suppose $\triangle ABC$ and $\triangle DEF$ contain two pairs of congruent angles. What, if anything, may be said about the third pair of angles? Explain.

8. Given: $\overleftrightarrow{TS}$ bisects $\angle OTI$
    $\overrightarrow{TA}$ bisects $\angle ITR$
    $\overleftrightarrow{AS} \parallel \overleftrightarrow{OR}$
    Prove: a) SN = TN = NA
    b) $\triangle STA$ is a right triangle.

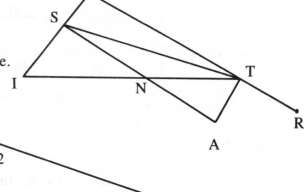

9. Given: $\overline{AT} \perp \overline{ES}$
    AS > AE.
    Prove: $\angle 1 < \angle 2$.

-164-

As you have learned, the controversy over Euclid's P5 was regarded as a lamentable blemish on the luster of the *Elements*. Over the course of 2000 years, many geometers tried in vain to prove P5 dependent on the other Euclidean assumptions. We now know that such efforts were doomed to fail since they eventually yielded the amazing result that there is a consistent geometry (hyperbolic geometry) in which all the Euclidean axioms and postulates *except* P5 are valid and in which P5 fails! Thus, there is a non-Euclidean geometry. In fact, there are two classical non-Euclidean geometries: hyperbolic geometry and elliptic geometry (sometimes called Lobachevskian and Riemannian in honor of Nikolai Ivanovich Lobachevsky and Bernhard Riemann); and we shall examine a few of the key ideas of each of them. There are, indeed, many other non-Euclidean geometries but the classical two are the only ones in which the geometrical space is homogeneous and isotropic, i.e., the same everywhere and in every direction—just as in Euclidean geometry. (If you are interested in learning more about non-Euclidean geometries you will surely want to consult some of the references listed at the end of this Unit.) In order not to obscure the main ideas of non-Euclidean geometry, we shall relax our standards of rigor enough to accept reasonably plausible explanations in place of strict proofs whenever it is convenient to do so.

One geometer who toiled to prove P5 and thereby remove the "flaw" from Euclid used a strategy which you can understand easily now. He was Girolamo Saccheri (1667 – 1733), an Italian Jesuit priest, the author of the first known text to contain theorems of a truly non-Euclidean geometry. That text, *Euclid Freed from Every Flaw (Euclides ab omni naevo Vindicatus)*, was published just prior to Saccheri's death in 1733.

Saccheri's strategy was to prove P5 by using RAA. He made certain assumptions (which he was intuitively certain were false) about a special type of quadrilateral (a four-sided figure) and hoped to derive from those assumptions the contradictions which would *force P5 to be* the only viable logical alternative and, thus, the *necessarily true* alternative. The special figure on which Saccheri based his work is now named in his honor, a Saccheri quadrilateral (SQ). It is an isosceles, birectangular quadrilateral. Consider the diagram of an SQ below:

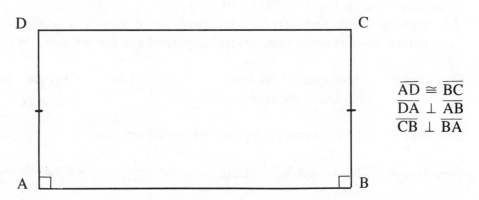

Some useful terminology:
1. $\overline{AB}$ is the *base*
2. $\overline{AD}$ and $\overline{BC}$ are the *legs*
3. $\overline{CD}$ is the *summit*
4. $\angle A$ and $\angle B$ are the *base angles*
5. $\angle C$ and $\angle D$ are the *summit angles*.

N.B. Until further notice, all exercises are to be done in *neutral geometry* unless it is specifically stated otherwise.

1. Prove that the legs of an SQ are parallel.

The obvious symmetry of an SQ may lead you to suspect that the summit angles are nicely related to one another. They are, as you probably guessed, congruent to one another.

2. Before you read on, try to prove that the summit angles of an SQ are congruent to one another.

If you didn't get the exercise above, read the following:

Theorem: The summit angles of an SQ are congruent to one another.

Proof: Consider the SQ ABCD with *m* the perpendicular bisector of the base $\overline{AB}$ as diagrammed below:

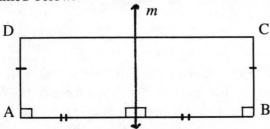

Let's consider the effect of F_m on ABCD. We know that $F_m(A) = B$ and also that $F_m(B) = A$ (why?). We also know that $F_m(\overline{BC}) = \overline{AD}$ and $F_m(\overline{AD}) = \overline{BC}$ (why?). Thus, we have that $F_m(C) = D$ and $F_m(D) = C$ (why?). Moreover, it is true that $F_m(\overline{CD}) = \overline{DC}$ (why?). Hence finally, we have that $\angle C \cong \angle D$ (why?).

Q.E.D.

3. Answer the questions in the proof above.

The proof above easily yields several important corollaries about SQ's:

Corollary 1: The perpendicular bisector of the base of an SQ is also the perpendicular bisector of the summit.

Corollary 2: The base and the summit of an SQ are parallel.

Corollary 3: The diagonals of an SQ are congruent, i.e., $\overline{AC} \cong \overline{BD}$.

4. Prove the three corollaries.

Saccheri established many properties of SQ's, but the major result concerning the congruence of the summit angles will suffice to give us a way of getting the flavor of his work.

Using the trichotomy law for angles, Saccheri set up three possibilities for the summit angles of an SQ. He named them:

The Hypothesis of the Acute Angle (HAA):
    The summit angles of an SQ are acute angles.
The Hypothesis of the Right Angle (HRA):
    The summit angles of an SQ are right angles.
The Hypothesis of the Obtuse Angle (HOA):
    The summit angles of an SQ are obtuse angles.

Of course, one and only one of these hypotheses can be valid since Saccheri succeeded in proving that if *one* SQ satisfied one of his hypotheses, then *every* SQ satisfied that same hypothesis. Therefore, the summit angles of all SQ's are of the same type.

Now Saccheri knew that in Euclidean geometry the summit angles of any SQ must be right angles.

5.   Prove that in Euclidean geometry the summit angles of any SQ must be right angles. (Hint: The base and summit of any SQ are parallel.) Thus, P5 implies HRA.

Moreover, Saccheri had proved with great effort that HRA implies P5. Thus, he knew that *P5 is equivalent to HRA.* Saccheri set out to show, by using RAA, that the Hypotheses of the Acute and Obtuse Angle are false in neutral geometry. Successful completion of the task would have justified Saccheri in asserting that he had proved that HRA, and thus P5, *had* to be true, i.e., geometry *had* to be Euclidean. Thus Euclid would have been freed from every flaw. Let's take a brief look at what really happened. In the spirit of Saccheri's own wonderfully expressive phrasing:

Theorem: The Hypothesis of the Obtuse Angle is absolutely false because it destroys itself.

Our proof is not the same as Saccheri's, but it shows an easy way to get the desired result.

Proof: Let ABCD be an SQ. Suppose the Hypothesis of the Obtuse Angle is valid. Then the summit angles of ABCD are obtuse. Thus, the angle sum of ABCD exceeds 360 (why?). This is a direct contradiction (to what?). Thus, the Hypothesis of the Obtuse Angle is not valid (why?).

                                                                    Q.E.D.

6.   Answer the questions in the proof above.

Having demolished the Hypothesis of the Obtuse Angle, Saccheri hopefully set out to do the same to the Hypothesis of the Acute Angle. He labored long and hard at this task, but despite deriving many very odd results, he was unable to arrive at an actual contradiction. He concluded his work by declaring that the Hypothesis of the Acute Angle must be false because he had, in one instance, made an error which led him to believe that he had found a contradiction, and in another instance, had proved results which he felt were "repugnant to the nature of straight lines." These results wrongly convinced him that he had demolished the Hypothesis of the Acute Angle. In fact, he had proved some significant theorems of what later came to be called hyperbolic (Lobachevskian) geometry. There are some historians of mathematics who speculate that Saccheri was well aware that he had found a new, non-Euclidean geometry, but that he piously denied it to ensure that he would get the approval of his religious superiors to publish his work. He got the approval, his work was published, but his "pious denial" is interpreted by most as showing that although he had opened the gate to a marvellous non-Euclidean wonderland, he gazed uncomprehending at the strange, new landscape.

7. Explain why Saccheri's religious superiors would probably have denied him permission to publish if he had claimed to have found a new, non-Euclidean geometry. (Hint: Remember that Euclidean geometry was thought to be an absolute truth; denial of it would possibly have opened the way for attacks on other so-called absolute truths. Refer to an encyclopedia to remind yourself of the fate of Galileo who did challenge an accepted, "absolute truth".)

Although Saccheri's work attracted considerable attention when it was first published, it was quickly forgotten—only to be rediscovered in 1889. But by then, all that Saccheri had found had been recreated by others, most notably Carl Friedrich Gauss, Janos Bolyai, and Nicolai Ivanovich Lobachevsky. We now honor these mathematicians as the Fathers of non-Euclidean geometry.

8. Write a brief essay on the development of non-Euclidean geometry. As a start, you may refer to the Mathematical Games column of the *Scientific American* for October, 1981; then look into an encyclopedia or history of mathematics for further information and leads to other references.

Let's examine one of the important theorems of hyperbolic geometry to see again the close connection between the type of geometry and the angle sum of any triangle. Recall that EAST tells us that the angle sum of any triangle in Euclidean geometry is 180.

9. Prove: If the angle sum of any triangle is 180, then The Hypothesis of the Right Angle is valid. (Hint: Show that the hypothesis implies that the angle sum of any quadrilateral is 360. What does that imply about the summit angles of any SQ?)

10. (Extra Credit) Prove the converse of the conditional in the previous exercise. Combine the two conditionals and state the resulting biconditional.

We shall see that the angle sum of any triangle in hyperbolic geometry is strictly less than 180.

Theorem (Hyperbolic Angle Sum Theorem (HAST)):   In hyperbolic geometry, i.e., under the Hypothesis of the Acute Angle, the angle sum of any triangle is strictly less than 180.

Proof: Recall that it is possible to show that if the angle sum of even one triangle is less than 180, then the angle sum of *every* triangle is less than 180. Thus, without loss of generality, we may examine a very special triangle to establish the general result. Let's use an isosceles triangle ABC with vertex C. Consider the diagram below:

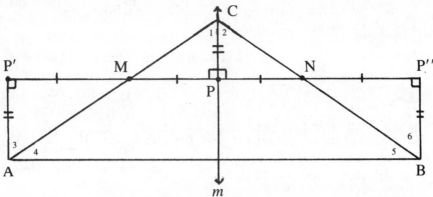

Let M and N be the midpoints of $\overline{AC}$ and $\overline{BC}$, respectively. Draw $\overline{MN}$. Then $\triangle MNC$ is isosceles with vertex C (why?). Let m be the bisector of angle C. Then m is also the perpendicular bisector of $\overline{MN}$ (why?). Let $P = m \cap \overline{MN}$; then P is the midpoint of $\overline{MN}$ (why?). Now $H_M(\triangle CMP) = \triangle AMP'$ and $H_N(\triangle CNP) = \triangle BNP''$ as shown in the diagram (why?). We know that $\angle P'$ and $\angle P''$ are right angles and $\overline{AP'} \cong \overline{BP''}$ (why?). Hence, we can see that $\angle P'AB$ and $\angle P''BA$ are acute angles (why?) (Hint: Is $P'P''BA$ an SQ?). Thus, we have $\mu\angle 3 + \mu\angle 4 + \mu\angle 5 + \mu\angle 6 < 180$ (why?). We know $\mu\angle 3 = \mu\angle 1$ and $\mu\angle 2 = \mu\angle 6$ (why?). Hence, $\mu\angle 1 + \mu\angle 4 + \mu\angle 5 + \mu\angle 2 < 180$ (why?). But $\mu\angle 1 + \mu\angle 4 + \mu\angle 5 + \mu\angle 2$ is the angle sum of the original triangle ABC. Thus, any triangle has angle sum less than 180.

Q.E.D.

11. Answer the questions in the proof of HAST.

12. Prove: If every triangle has angle sum less than 180, then the Hypothesis of the Acute Angle is valid.

Thus, the Hypothesis of the Acute Angle is valid if and only if the angle sum of any triangle is less than 180. It is possible to show that the angle sum of triangles in hyperbolic geometry is *not* a constant (remember that it *is* a *constant* 180 in Euclidean geometry). In fact, the amount by which the angle sum of a triangle falls short of 180 varies directly with the area of the triangle—the smaller the triangle, the closer its angle sum is to 180; the larger the triangle, the further its angle sum is from 180. Amazingly enough, it turns out that there is, in some sense, a *largest* hyperbolic triangle which has angle sum zero!

Of course, the wonderfully odd results of the realm of hyperbolic geometry would be of no interest at all if we did not know that hyperbolic geometry is consistent. We can model hyperbolic geometry inside Euclidean geometry. Thus, if Euclidean geometry is consistent, so is hyperbolic geometry. Before we briefly describe such a model of hyperbolic geometry, let's see that Axiom 12, (i.e., Euclid's P5) fails in hyperbolic geometry.

Theorem: Axiom 12 is false in hyperbolic geometry.

Proof: Let m be a line and P a point not on m.

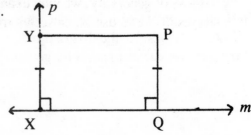

Let $\overleftrightarrow{PQ}$ be the line through P and perpendicular to m at Q. (How do we know that there is such a perpendicular?) Let X be a point on m different from Q. (How do we know there is such a point?) Let p be the line through X which is perpendicular to m. (How do we know that there is such a perpendicular?) On the ray of p in the same halfplane of m as P, there is a unique point, say Y, such that XY = PQ (why?). Draw $\overline{YP}$. I claim that XQPY is an SQ. (Why is it an SQ?) Now $\overleftrightarrow{YP} \parallel m$ (why?). Let n be the line through P which is perpendicular to $\overleftrightarrow{PQ}$. (How do we know that there is such a perpendicular?) Since $\angle QPY$ is known to be acute (why?), it must be that $n \neq \overleftrightarrow{YP}$ (why?). But $n \parallel m$ (why?). Thus, we have at least two lines both parallel to m and passing through P. Hence, Axiom 12 is false in hyperbolic geometry.

Q.E.D.

13.   Answer the questions in the proof above.

We have now seen that Axiom 12 (i.e., P5) fails in hyperbolic geometry. In particular, what fails is the *uniqueness* of the parallel whose existence is asserted in Axiom 12. it is possible to prove in hyperbolic geometry that, given a line m and a point P not on m, there are *infinitely* many lines passing through P and parallel to m! This is terribly strange indeed! We can not wonder at the fact that Gauss, the Prince of Mathematicians, refrained from publishing his results in hyperbolic geometry lest he be ridiculed by those incapable of understanding his work.

Moreover, the Euclidean theorem PLE also fails in hyperbolic geometry.

Theorem: In hyperbolic geometry, parallel lines are *not* everywhere equidistant.

14.   Prove the theorem above.
      Given: $m \parallel n$ in hyperbolic geometry.
      Prove: m and n are not equidistant.
      (Hint: Assume m and n are everywhere equidistant. Then (see the diagram below) AD = BE = CF. What sort of angles are $\angle 1$ and $\angle 2$? (Look for SQ's!) Does this yield a contradiction?)

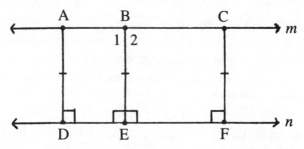

It is possible to give a model for hyperbolic geometry inside Euclidean geometry. How can hyperbolic geometry be modelled in Euclidean geometry? There are several such models; I shall give a brief description of one due to the French lawyer-mathematician Poincare'. Consider the diagram below to help yourself understand the vocabulary of the Poincare' model of hyperbolic geometry:

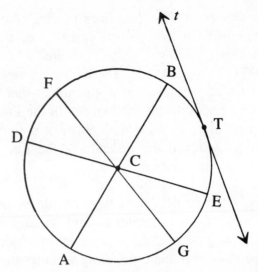

Circle C is denoted by ⊙C; C is the *center* of ⊙C. The segments $\overline{AB}$, $\overline{DE}$, and $\overline{FG}$ are *diameters* of ⊙C. Pieces of ⊙C such as $\overarc{BE}$ or $\overarc{AG}$ are *arcs* with endpoints B and E or A and G, respectively. A line such as *t* which touches ⊙C at a single point is a *tangent* to ⊙C.

Poincare''s Model of Hyperbolic Geometry

1. The *plane* consists of all the Euclidean points strictly inside a Euclidean circle, ⊙C.
2. The *points* are the same as Euclidean points.
3. The *lines* are either of the following types:
   i) any Euclidean diameter of ⊙C, minus its endpoints, or
   ii) the arc inside ⊙C of any Euclidean circle, ⊙O, which intersects ⊙C in two points at each of which the tangent to ⊙C is perpendicular to the tangent to ⊙O.

Consider the figures sketched below; they illustrate some of the main ideas of the Poincare' model of hyperbolic geometry:

1. Any diameter is a line.

2. Special arcs are lines.

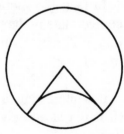

3. A triangle.

4. An SQ.

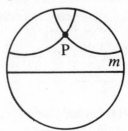

5. Axiom 12 fails

6. A largest triangle —$\Sigma = 0$.

In figure 5 above, we see at least two lines passing through P parallel to *m*. Thus, Axiom 12 fails in this model in exactly the way desired, i.e., the assertion of the *uniqueness* of the parallel fails. It is possible to verify that Poincare''s model satisfies all the Euclidean assumptions except P5 (i.e., Axiom 12). The metric (distance function) usually defined in this model is not easy to explain—but it guarantees that the lines are infinitely long in the sense intended by Euclid in his P2. Angles in the Poincare' model are measured in the usual way; in particular, an angle with either or both of its sides being the second sort of "straight" line is assigned the measure of the Euclidean angle formed by the tangent(s) to the side(s) at the vertex of the angle.

Poincare' gave a very interesting "physical" interpretation of his model of hyperbolic geometry. Imagine yourself to be living on a large circular metal plate which gets uniformly colder as one moves away from its center toward its edge which has a temperature of absolute zero. Further imagine that the size of every object in this "universe" varies directly with its temperature and that everything assumes the temperature of its location instantaneously and imperceptibly.

Then, from the point of view of the inhabitants, the cooled plate universe is infinitely large. If you set out walking steadily in a given direction, you could never reach the edge of the plate. In fact, since you would get smaller and smaller as you moved away from the center, your steps would get shorter and shorter. You would be totally unaware of these changes since they occur in a uniform and imperceptible fashion. In particular, if you were to measure the length of your steps, they would all seem to be of the same length since your measuring instruments also shrink in the same imperceptible way as you do. Thus, it would seem to you that you could walk on forever in any given direction.

A "straight" line in the cooled plate universe corresponds to the shortest path between two points. If you wish to walk to a point which is on the same diameter as you are on, then you simply move along that diameter toward your destination (this results in your minimizing the length of your journey from point to point). If you wish to walk to a point not on the same diameter as you are on, your shortest path would bend toward the center of the plate.

15.   Think about the claim in the last sentence above and try to explain why it is so.

In fact, the shortest path in the latter case would be an arc of a circle overlapping the cooled plate in the special way specified in the description of the second sort of "straight" line in Poincaré's model of hyperbolic geometry. This completes our study of Poincaré's model.

It is interesting to note that Euclidean geometry can be modelled in hyperbolic geometry. (It is not at all easy to understand the model, however.) Thus,

> Euclidean geometry is consistent
> if and only if
> hyperbolic geometry is consistent.

The curious and ironic upshot of all this modelling is that if poor Saccheri had succeeded in his attempt to prove Euclid's P5 as a theorem, he would have demolished Euclidean geometry since his proof would have implied that Euclidean geometry is self-contradictory!

The model of Euclidean geometry inside hyperbolic geometry would then be an interpretation in which Axiom 12 is simultaneously true and false. This is surely not what Saccheri had in mind!

Section 5

We might be led to wonder if there is a non-Euclidean geometry in which Axiom 12 fails because its assertion of the *existence* of parallels is false. By now, it should be no surprise to you that the answer is yes, there is such a geometry. We shall very briefly consider a model of this geometry, known as *elliptic* geometry (actually *double elliptic* geometry), or Riemannian geometry, in honor of the German mathematician Riemann.

Elliptic geometry must in some sense be even more wildly non-Euclidean than hyperbolic geometry since we proved long ago (recall theorem EP) that parallel lines exist in neutral geometry. Hence, we can understand that some Euclidean assumption in addition to P5 must fail to be valid in elliptic geometry; e.g., P2 fails because all lines are not infinitely long in the sense which Euclid intended them to be.

Elliptic geometry was developed in the latter part of the 19th century by Riemann and Schlafli. Because it is so radically non-Euclidean, we shall not attempt any detailed study of it. It does, however, deserve a quick glance to acquaint us with a few of its main features. We shall examine a particularly appealing intuitive model of elliptic geometry.

Suppose you are a "spherelander" living *in* (not just on) the surface of a very large sphere. Let's investigate what your ideas of the geometry of your universe might be like.

1. You may believe that a "straight" line should be the shortest path between two points, but by now you know that this idea does not always lead to lines that are "straight" in the intuitive sense. For example, suppose you were to stretch a string tightly between two points on the sphere where you live. What would the resulting line segment be like? (You may already have done this as an experiment in Unit I.) What would the resulting line be like if you were to continue to stretch the string all the way around the surface of the sphere? Sketch a sphere and draw in several such lines on its surface. Imagine cutting the sphere along such a line; must anything in particular be true about the two pieces resulting from such a cut? Explain. What, if anything, does this tell you about the line along which you cut? Would this spherical universe seem infinite to you?

By doing the previous exercise, you should have discovered or remembered that the straight lines on the surface of the sphere are so-called "great circles" of the sphere, i.e., the largest circles which can be drawn on its surface. Such circles have the same center as the sphere itself. A particular example of a great circle is the equator of the globe. If you cut the sphere along such a line, you obtain two hemispheres, i.e., congruent half-spheres.

Now in this model the plane is obviously the surface of the sphere while the lines are the great circles of the sphere. What , then, are we to think of as being the points?

2. What do you think a point should be in this model? Most students, probably including you, tend to say that a point in this model is simply a normal Euclidean point of the sphere (visualized as a tiny dot on the sphere. With this interpretation of point, how many distinct points do any two lines have in common? (Hint: This is why it's called *double* elliptic geometry.) Are there any parallel lines in this model? Explain. If you take any pair of these points, is there a unique line passing through them? (Hint: Use the North and South poles as the pair of points.) If there is even one pair of points which has two or more distinct lines passing through them, then what Euclid intended as his first postulate fails to be true. Is P1 true in this model? Is P2 true? Is P5 true?

Although we shall not do so, it is possible to give another interpretation of this model in which an elliptic "point" is thought of as being a *pair* of Euclidean points at opposite ends of a diameter of the sphere (such points are called *polar* points since they are related to one another in the same way as the North and South poles of the sphere). The procedure of identifying polar points with one another as a single point can be used to rescue Euclid's first postulate, but many other results still fail even in this modified model—which is called *single* elliptic geometry since now two lines intersect in exactly one point. For example, the lines are all the same finite length and so are not infinitely long in the sense intended by Euclid in his second postulate.

3. Suppose you began a journey at the North pole and travelled due South until you reached the equator. Having turned due West, you walked one-fourth of the way around the sphere along the equator. Having turned due North, you walk straight back up to your starting point. Sketch a diagram of your trip on the surface of a sphere. Your path is a spherical triangle. Answer the following questions:

   i)   How many right angles are contained in the triangle you sketched?
   ii) What is the angle sum of this triangle?
   iii) Draw a few more triangles on the surface of a sphere and then make a conjecture about the angle sum of any triangle in spherical geometry. Note that angle sums are not constant (as in Euclidean geometry) but are variable (as in hyperbolic geometry). What is the relationship to 180 of the angle sum of any triangle in spherical geometry?
   iv) Is the following statement valid in elliptic geometry? "Two coplanar lines which are both perpendicular to the same line are parallel."
   v)   Is either exterior angle theorem (weak or strong) valid in elliptic geometry?
   vi) Can you think of any other ways in which the model on the surface of the sphere shows elliptic geometry to be different from Euclidean geometry?

In this Unit, we have seen some of the ideas of the two classic non-Euclidean geometries as well as some important ideas of Euclidean geometry. You may wonder why anyone should be interested in strange non-Euclidean geometries. Well, recall that the ancient Greek geometers, when doing geometry, were trying to give a faithful abstraction of the nature of physical space, i.e., in some sense they were actually doing theoretical physics! The aura of infallibility which came to surround Euclid and his geometry led people to believe not only that space was necessarily Euclidean, but also that it was literally impossible for the human mind even to imagine any other possibility for the geometry of space.

Euclidean geometry was thought to be an *absolute truth*. With this in mind, you may perhaps begin to appreciate the revolutionary character of the non-Euclidean geometries. They utterly demolished the smug illusion that mathematics is a pipeline into absolute truth. Indeed, they cast grave doubt upon whether there can be any such thing as an absolute truth.

"'What is truth?' said jesting Pilate; and would not stay for an answer."
–Francis Bacon–

4.   Do you see now why poor Saccheri may have been hesitant to announce to the world that he had produced a non-Euclidean geometry even if he had believed that he had done so?

The advent of non-Euclidean geometry opened the gateway onto the path leading to the Riemannian differential geometry underlying Einstein's theory of relativity—a theory which assumes the geometry of the universe to be highly non-Euclidean. But, even more important, the realization that there are consistent non-Euclidean geometries led both to a radical restructuring of the ways mathematicians think about mathematics and also to a far-reaching change in the ways all people think about the universe and their relation to it.

Below you will find a chart which should be useful for comparing and contrasting the properties of the three geometries studied in this Unit. In addition, I have included references for further reading for those of you who may find this constellation of ideas as intriguing as I do.

Properties of the Three Plane Geometries			
	Riemannian Elliptic	Euclidean Parabolic	Lobachevskian Hyperbolic	
1. Given a line m and a point $P \notin m$, there is/are	no	exactly one	infinitely many	line(s) through P parallel to m.
2. For any $\triangle$	$\Sigma > 180$	$\Sigma = 180$	$\Sigma < 180$	
3. WEAT	fails	holds	holds	
4. Two lines perpendicular to the same line	are not	are	are	parallel.
5. Two lines meet in	1 or 2	$\leqslant 1$	$\leqslant 1$	point(s)
6. Parallel lines	do not exist	are always equidistant	are not equidistant	
7. Parallelism	——	is	is not	transitive
8. The valid Saccheri Hypothesis is that of the	Obtuse	Right	Acute	Angle.

References and Suggested Reading

Beck, A., Bleicher, M.N., and Crowe, D.W., *Excursions into Mathematics*. New York: Worth Publishers, Inc. 1969.

    This is a most interesting, easy to read textbook. Particularly relevant to this Unit is Chapter 4, "Some Exotic Geometries."

Gray, J., *Ideas of Space*. Oxford: Oxford University Press. 1979.

    While parts of this book are heavy going, it is worth it. Gray stresses his idea that the controversy over P5 was not simply a wrangling over axiomatic "purity" but was fueled by the desire to capture the true nature of physical space.

Greenberg, M.J., *Euclidean and Non-Euclidean Geometries* (2d edition). San Francisco: W.H. Freeman and Company. 1974.

    This is a very complete text with a most helpful bibliography.

Harrison, E.R., *Cosmology*. Cambridge: Cambridge Univ. Press. 1981.

    This is a fascinating introductory text which covers its topics in a most readable way.

Kauffmann, III, W.J., *Relativity and Cosmology*. New York: Harper and Row. 1973.

    This is an inexpensive paperback which gives a popular introduction to such topics as black holes, white holes, etc.

Kline, M., *Mathematical Thought from Ancient to Modern Times*. New York: Oxford Univ. Press. 1972.

    A very comprehensive history of mathematics which does not shy away from the technical aspects of the subject. I highly recomend this book to you.

    Mathematics—The Loss of Certainty. New York: Oxford Univ. Press. 1980.

    This book is less polemical than most of Kline's works and gives the careful reader real insight into the somewhat sorry state of the foundations of mathematics.

Krause, E.F., *Taxicab Geometry*. Reading, MA.: Addison-Wesley. 1975.

    This is an inexpensive paperback which is extremely easy to read. It gives an overview of a non-classical non-Euclidean geometry which arises from one of the non-Euclidean metrics which we studied.

Lockwood, J.R. and Runion, G.E., *Deductive Systems: Finite and Non-Euclidean Geometries*. Reston,VA: NCTM. 1978.

    Another inexpensive paperback produced by the National Council of Teachers of Mathematics; an easy introduction.

Martin, G.E., *The Foundations of Geometry and The Non-Euclidean Plane*. New York: Intext Educational Publishers. 1975.

    A very thorough introductory text with excellent exercises and student projects.

Rucker, R.v.B., *Geometry, Relativity and The Fourth Dimension*. New York: Dover Publications. 1977.

    This is a wonderful little paperback from the Dover treasurehouse. It is fascinating reading and has a very good bibliography.

Steen, L.A. (ed.), *Mathematics Today*. New York: Springer-Verlag. 1978.

    This book is now available in paperback. It is sometimes very challenging, but a thoroughly worthwhile text. The section, "The Geometry of The Universe," by Penrose is, all-in-all, quite heavy going. Worth the effort if you can do it!

Unit V—Review Topics

1. Euclidean assumptions—especially P5 and the controversy surrounding it.
2. Definition of parallelism; terminology associated with parallels.
3. The 11 logically equivalent conditions sufficient to show that lines are parallel in neutral geometry, and whose converses are valid only in Euclidean geometry.
4. The logical flaws in the foundations of Euclid's *Elements*.
5. Axiom 12 (Playfair's Postulate); what is the crucial assumption? Why does it mark the boundary between neutral and Euclidean geometry? How is it related to the two classical non-Euclidean geometries?
6. The definition and properties of a halfturn around a central point; e.g., the only fixed point of a halfturn is its center, a halfturn is an isometry and involution, the halfturn image of a line is another line parallel to the original line, halfturns preserve parallelism, etc.
7. The Strong Exterior Angle Theorem of Euclidean geometry.
8. Parallel lines are equidistant in Euclidean geometry.
9. The relation of P5 with the angle sum of triangles; NAST; EAST.
10. Saccheri—his goal, method, and results; Saccheri quadrilaterals—definition, properties, and Saccheri's hypotheses concerning them.
11. Non-Euclidean geometries—hyperbolic and elliptic; the philosophical and mathematical consequences of the existence and consistency of non-Euclidean geometries; HAST; how Axiom 12 fails to be true; parallel lines are not equidistant in hyperbolic geometry; models of hyperbolic and elliptic geometries.

Unit VI
Quadrilaterals: Trapezoids, Parallelograms, and All That

"In mathematics the art of posing problems is easier than that of solving them."

–Georg Cantor–

"There are things which seem incredible to most men who have not studied mathematics."

–Archimedes–

Note carefully that *all* the geometry from here on is assumed to be *Euclidean* geometry.

You may recall that a quadrilateral is a four-sided figure. For our purposes here, however, we shall need a more exact definition and some additional technical vocabulary:

Definition: Let A, B, C, and D be four points, no three of which are collinear. The *quadrilateral* ABCD consists of four closed line segments, $\overline{AB}$, $\overline{BC}$, $\overline{CD}$, and $\overline{DA}$, called the *sides* of ABCD; two sides must not intersect except at their common endpoint, if any exists. Two sides sharing a common endpoint are said to be *adjacent* sides; non-adjacent sides are called *opposite* sides. The points A, B, C, and D are called the *vertices* of the quadrilateral. If two vertices are endpoints of the same segment, they are said to be *adjacent* vertices; non-adjacent vertices are said to be *opposite* vertices. A line segment joining two opposite vertices is called a *diagonal* of the quadrilateral. Two angles of the quadrilateral are said to be *adjacent* angles if their vertices are adjacent; non-adjacent angles are said to be *opposite* angles.

1. Illustrate the new technical terms in the definition above by sketching several examples of quadrilaterals and labelling their key parts.

Definition: A quadrilateral ABCD is said to be *convex* if no two points of it lie in different halfplanes of the unique line which contains any two of its adjacent vertices.

2. Specify whether or not each of the figures below is a quadrilateral. Specify whether or not each quadrilateral is convex. Explain your answers.

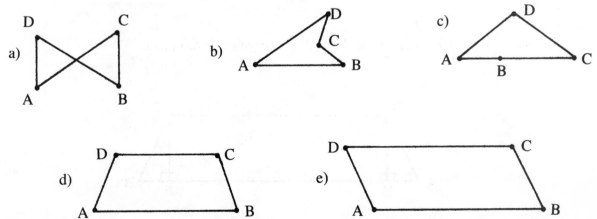

We shall limit our study to convex quadrilaterals, and we shall begin by examining those with exactly one pair of parallel sides.

Definition: A quadrilateral with exactly one pair of parallel sides is called a *trapezoid*. Each of the parallel sides is called a *base* of the trapezoid; the non-parallel sides are called the *legs* of the trapezoid. Two angles of the trapezoid which have their vertices at the endpoints of the same base are called *base angles* of the trapezoid.

3.   Sketch a few examples of trapezoids.

4.   Prove that any trapezoid contains exactly two pairs of supplementary angles. Sketch a trapezoid and indicate in your sketch which two pairs of angles must be supplementary.

In keeping with our interest in symmetry, let's consider what sort of symmetry may be found in trapezoids.

5.   Is it possible for a trapezoid to have any allowable symmetry motion other than the identity? Illustrate your answer.

Definition: A trapezoid is said to be *isosceles* if its legs are congruent.

6.   Sketch an example of an isosceles trapezoid. What sort of symmetry group is associated with an isosceles trapezoid? (Hint: Can you prove that an isosceles trapezoid has a line or point of symmetry? Try to do so before you read further.)

On the grounds of its symmetry, and by analogy with isosceles triangles, you may suspect that the base angles of an isosceles trapezoid are congruent.

7.   Try to prove your suspicion about the base angles of an isosceles trapezoid. (Hint: Draw a perpendicular to the "bottom" base from each vertex of the "top" base and argue that the right triangles thus formed are congruent, etc.)

The proof of the next theorem yields some other interesting facts about isosceles trapezoids.

Since we shall need to use the fact that the base angles of an isosceles trapezoid are congruent, we prove the following lemma (just in case you didn't get the preceding exercise):

Lemma: The base angles of an isosceles trapezoid are congruent.

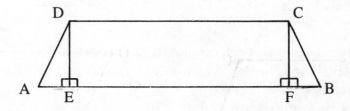

Proof: Let ABCD be an isosceles trapezoid (see the diagram above). Construct $\overline{DE}$ perpendicular to $\overline{AB}$ and $\overline{CF}$ perpendicular to $\overline{AB}$ as shown. Then DE = CF (why?). Thus, $\triangle ADE \cong \triangle BCF$ (why?). So, $\angle A \cong \angle B$ by cpcfc. Hence, $\angle ADC \cong \angle BCD$ (why?).

Q.E.D.

8.   Answer the questions in the proof of the lemma.

Theorem: The perpendicular bisector of either base of an isosceles trapezoid is the perpendicular bisector of the other base and is also a line of symmetry for the trapezoid.

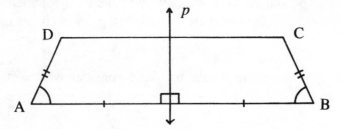

Proof: Consider the isosceles trapezoid ABCD diagrammed above. Recall that the base angles of such a trapezoid are congruent, in particular, $\angle A \cong \angle B$. Let p be the perpendicular bisector of the base $\overline{AB}$. Then $F_p(A) = B$ and $F_p(B) = A$. Moreover, $F_p(\overline{BC}) = \overline{AD}$ and $F_p(\overline{AD}) = \overline{BC}$ (why?). Thus, $F_p(C) = D$ and $F_p(D) = C$ (why?). Hence, we have $F_p(ABCD) = (BADC)$. So, p is the perpendicular bisector of $\overline{CD}$ and a symmetry line for trapezoid ABCD (why?). The proof is essentially the same if we assume p to be the perpendicular bisector of $\overline{CD}$.

Q.E.D.

9.   Answer the questions in the proof above.

Corollary: The diagonals of an isosceles trapezoid are congruent.

10.   Prove the corollary above; state and prove or disprove its converse.

11.   Prove that if one pair of base angles of a trapezoid are congruent, then the trapezoid is isosceles.

12.   The diagonals of a trapezoid ABCD meet at E and AE = BE.
      Prove: trapezoid ABCD is isosceles.

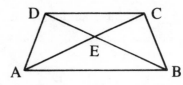

13.   Given: The diagonals of trapezoid ABCD intersect at E.
      Prove: ABCD is isosceles if and only if $\triangle AEB$ and $\triangle CED$ are isosceles with vertex E.
      (Hint: Refer back to exercise 12.)

Section 2

We turn our attention to quadrilaterals with two pairs of parallel sides.

Definition: A *parallelogram* ABCD, denoted by □ABCD, is a quadrilateral with two pairs of parallel sides.

1. Sketch a few examples of parallelograms. What allowable symmetry motion(s) does a parallelogram seem to have? Can you prove your conjecture?

Your results from exercise 1 should make the following theorem and its corollaries seem most reasonable:

Theorem (Point Symmetry of a Parallelogram (PSP)): Let M be the midpoint of a diagonal of □ABCD. Then H_M(□ABCD) = □CDAB.

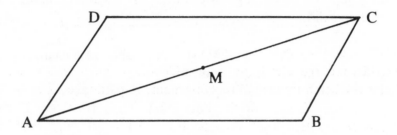

Proof: Suppose that M is the midpoint of $\overline{AC}$. (See the diagram above.) Then we know $H_M(A) = C$ and $H_M(C) = A$ (why?). Thus, we see that $H_M(\overleftrightarrow{AB})$ is the line passing through C and parallel to $\overleftrightarrow{AB}$ (why?). Hence, $H_M(\overleftrightarrow{AB}) = \overleftrightarrow{CD}$ (why?). Similarly, $H_M(\overleftrightarrow{AD}) = \overleftrightarrow{BC}$. Now, $D = \overleftrightarrow{CD} \cap \overleftrightarrow{DA}$.
Therefore, $H_M(D) = H_M(\overleftrightarrow{CD}) \cap H_M(\overleftrightarrow{DA}) = \overleftrightarrow{AB} \cap \overleftrightarrow{BC} = B$.
Moreover, $H_M(B) = H_M(H_M(D)) = D$ (why?).
Thus, H_M(□ABCD) = □CDAB.

Q.E.D.

2. Answer the questions in the proof of PSP.

Corollary 1. The opposite sides of a parallelogram are congruent.
Corollary 2. The opposite angles of a parallelogram are congruent.
Corollary 3. A diagonal of a parallelogram splits it into two congruent triangles.
Corollary 4. The diagonals of a parallelogram bisect each other.

3. Ponder the proof of PSP and then show how the four corollaries follow easily from that proof.

4. Prove: If the opposite sides of a quadrilateral are congruent, then the quadrilateral is a parallelogram.

5. Prove or disprove: If a pair of the sides of a quadrilateral are both congruent and parallel, then the quadrilateral is a parallelogram.

6. Prove: If the opposite angles of a quadrilateral are congruent, then the quadrilateral is a parallelogram.

7. Prove or disprove: If a diagonal of a quadrilateral splits it into two congruent triangles, then the quadrilateral is a parallelogram.

8. Prove: If the diagonals of a quadrilateral bisect each other, then the quadrilateral is a parallelogram.

9. Prove or disprove: If the diagonals of a quadrilateral are perpendicular to each other, then the quadrilateral is a parallelogram.

10. Prove: The pairs of consecutive angles in a parallelogram are supplementary.

Definition: A line segment which connects the midpoints of two sides of a triangle (or the midpoints of the legs of a trapezoid) is called a *midline* of the triangle (or trapezoid).

Theorem (Triangle Midline Theorem (TMT)): A midline of a triangle is parallel to and half as long as the side it does not intersect.

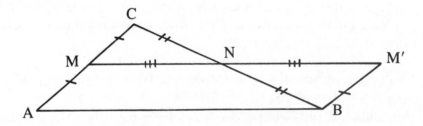

Proof: In terms of the diagram above, we must show $\overline{MN} \parallel \overline{AB}$ and MN = ½AB, given that M and N are midpoints of $\overline{AC}$ and $\overline{BC}$, respectively. Consider the effect of H_N on $\triangle MCN$. Under this half-turn, $\triangle MCN \cong \triangle M'BN$. Thus, MC = M'B and $\overline{M'B} \parallel \overline{CM}$ (why?). Hence, ABM'M is a parallelogram (why?). Therefore, we have that $\overline{MN} \parallel \overline{AB}$ and MN = ½AB.

Q.E.D.

11. Answer the questions in the proof above.

12. Given: M is the midpoint of $\overline{BC}$, $m \parallel \overline{AB}$.
    Prove: $m \cap \overline{AC}$ is the midpoint of $\overline{AC}$.

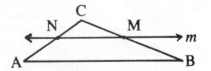

13. Let ABCD be a quadrilateral. Let MNOP be the quadrilateral whose vertices are the midpoints of the sides of ABCD. Prove: MNOP is a parallelogram. (Hint: Draw the diagonals of ABCD.)

14. Given: $\overleftrightarrow{AF} \parallel \overleftrightarrow{BE} \parallel \overleftrightarrow{CD}$, AB = BC.
    Prove: FE = ED.
    (Hint: Draw $\overline{AD}$ and argue that AX = XD, etc.)

-184-

The previous exercise may be rephrased (and generalized) as the following:

Theorem: If three (or more) parallel lines cut off congruent segments on one transversal, then they cut off congruent segments on any transversal.

Analogous to the Triangle Midline Theorem is the Trapezoid Midline Theorem:

Theorem (Trap. MT):   The midline of a trapezoid is parallel to the bases and half as long as the sum of their lengths.

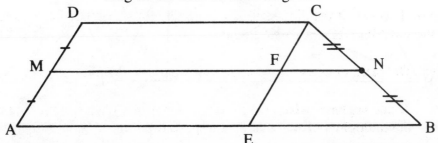

Proof: In terms of the diagram above, we must show both that $\overline{MN}$ is parallel to $\overline{AB}$ and $\overline{CD}$ and also that MN = ½(AB + CD), given that $\overline{MN}$ is the midline of trapezoid ABCD. The unique line through M parallel to $\overline{AB}$ cuts off congruent segments on $\overline{AD}$ (why?). Hence, it must also cut off congruent segments on $\overleftrightarrow{BC}$(why?). Therefore, it must pass through N (why?), i.e., it is $\overrightarrow{MN}$. Thus, we see that $\overline{MN}$ is parallel to $\overline{AB}$ and also to $\overline{CD}$. Now, draw $\overline{CE}$ parallel to $\overline{AD}$ and let F be its point of intersection with $\overline{MN}$.
Then, FN = ½EB and MF = EA = CD (why?).
Thus, MN = MF + FN = ½(AE + CD) + ½EB = ½(AE + EB + CD) = ½(AB + CD) (why?).
Hence, $\overline{MN}$ is parallel to and half as long as the sum of the lengths of the trapezoid ABCD.

Q.E.D.

15.   Answer the questions in the proof of Trap. MT.

16.   Prove that the bisector of an exterior angle at the vertex of an isosceles triangle is parallel to the base.

17.   Given: AMCD is a parallelogram, M is the midpoint of $\overline{AB}$, △CMD is isosceles with vertex M.
      Prove: ABCD is an isosceles trapezoid.

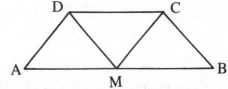

18.   Given: ▱HALF, $\overline{FT} \perp \overline{HL}$, $\overline{AU} \perp \overline{HL}$.
      Prove: FT = AU and FTAU is a parallelogram.
      (Hint: If M is the midpoint of $\overline{HL}$, what is H_M ($\overline{FT}$)? Then draw $\overline{UF}$ and $\overline{AT}$. So?)

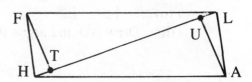

19. Given: $\square$HLFU, $\overline{UR} \perp \overline{HF}$, $\overline{LN} \perp \overline{HF}$, $\overline{RT} \perp \overline{UF}$, $\overline{NA} \perp \overline{HL}$.
   Prove: RANT is a parallelogram.

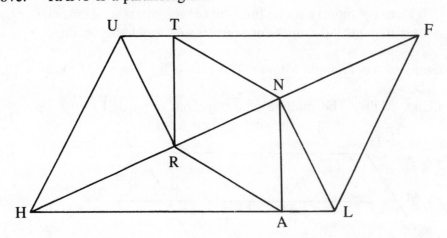

Section 3

1. Consider a figure ABCD which consists of two coplanar non-congruent isosceles triangles "pasted together" along their common base, say △ABD and △BCD. The resulting quadrilateral is called a *kite*. Sketch a kite. What are the allowable symmetry motions for a kite? What does this imply about the relationships either between the sides or between the angles of the kite? What does it imply about the relationship between the diagonals of the kite?

Now, what would happen if we were to "paste together" two congruent isosceles triangles so that they were coplanar and shared the same base? Make a sketch of such a figure and refer to it as you think about the next exercise.

2. Prove that the resulting quadrilateral is a parallelogram having a pair of adjacent sides congruent (and hence prove that all four of its sides are congruent to one another).

Definition: A *rhombus*, ABCD, is a parallelogram containing a pair of adjacent congruent sides.

3. Prove that a rhombus, ABCD, may be split into two congruent coplanar isosceles triangles. (Hint: Draw a diagonal.)

Since a rhombus is a parallelogram, it has all the properties of a parallelogram—e.g., its diagonals bisect each other, its opposite angles are congruent, its adjacent angles are supplementary, etc..

4. What are the allowable symmetry motions for a rhombus? What does this imply about how the diagonals are related to one another? How are the diagonals related to the angles?

If you did the previous exercise correctly, you should have discovered:

Theorem: In a rhombus, the diagonals are perpendicular to one another and each diagonal bisects the angles whose vertices it contains.

5. Prove: If the diagonals of a parallelogram are perpendicular to each other, the parallelogram is a rhombus.

6. Prove or disprove: If each diagonal of a quadrilateral bisects the angles whose vertices it contains, then the quadrilateral is a rhombus.

If we "paste together" two congruent right triangles so that they are coplanar and share the same hypotenuse, the resulting quadrilateral is a rectangle.

Definition: A *rectangle* is a parallelogram which contains a right angle.

7. What are the allowable symmetry motions for a rectangle? What does this imply about the relationship between the diagonals or about the relationship between the angles?

8. Show that the diagonals of a rectangle are congruent to one another.

9. Show that a rectangle contains four right angles.

10. (Extra Credit) Explain why a rectangle can not exist in either hyperbolic or elliptic geometry.

11. Show that a rectangle may be split up into two congruent coplanar right triangles sharing the same hypotenuse.

12. Prove or disprove: If the diagonals of a parallelogram are congruent to one another, then the parallelogram is a rectangle.

13. Prove: The median drawn to the midpoint of the hypotenuse of a right triangle is half as long as that hypotenuse, i.e., the midpoint of the hypotenuse of a right triangle is equidistant from the vertices of the triangle.

What if a quadrilateral is both a rectangle and a rhombus, i.e., what if we "paste together" two congruent isosceles right triangles so they are coplanar and have the same hypotenuse?

Definition: A *square* is a parallelogram which is both a rectangle and a rhombus.

14. What are the allowable symmetry motions for a square? What does this imply about the relationships among its various parts? List all the important properties of a square. (Hint: Since a square is both a rectangle and a rhombus, it has all the properties of each of those types of parallelograms.)

15. List the various conditions which are sufficient to imply that a quadrilateral is a: i) trapezoid, ii) parallelogram, iii) rhombus, iv) rectangle, v) square.

The diagram below should help you remember the organizational classification of quadrilaterals.

Quadrilaterals

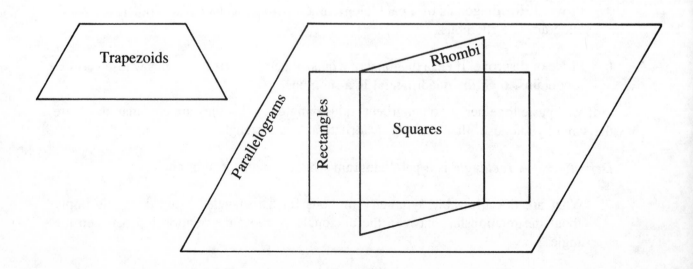

Unit VI—Review Topics

1. Definition and classification of the various quadrilaterals; sides, angles, vertices—adjacent and opposite; diagonal; convex quadrilateral.
2. Definition of trapezoid—bases, legs, and base angles; midline of a trapezoid and its relation to the bases; isosceles trapezoid—definition and properties.
3. Definition of parallelogram; Point Symmetry of a Parallelogram theorem and its corollaries.
4. The Triangle Midline Theorem.
5. Definition and properties of rhombus, rectangle, and square.

Unit VII

Similarity

"I have multiplied visions, and used similitudes."
–Hosea (12:10)–

"To every figure there exists a similar figure of arbitrary magnitude."
–J. Wallis–

We extend our study of geometry to include similarity transformations.

You will probably recall that a similarity map S with scale factor k (a positive real number) is a map which stretches or shrinks all distances in a uniform way, i.e., if A and B are two points, the length of $S(\overline{AB})$ is k times the length of $\overline{AB}$. In our previous study of such maps, we used coordinates and considered the map S_k such that $S_k(x, y) = (kx, ky)$. By using the Euclidean distance formula, we verified that this map is a similarity. We also found that, if $k \neq 1$, then the only point fixed by S_k is the origin $(0, 0)$.

1. a) Show that, if $k = 1$, $S_k(x, y) = (x, y)$ for every point (x, y). What sort of mapping is S_1?

   b) Verify that, if $k \neq 1$, the only point fixed under S_k is $(0, 0)$, i.e., prove that if $k \neq 1$, and $S_k(x, y) = (x, y)$, then $x = 0$ and $y = 0$. (Hint: $(kx, ky) = (x, y)$ iff $kx = x$ and $ky = y$.)

The unique point left fixed by a similarity S_k with scale factor $k \neq 1$ is called the *center* of the similarity.

We wish now to study the idea of similarity without using coordinates, i.e., *synthetically*. Recall that a similarity is a type of mapping of the plane to itself, and one may define such a mapping by specifying the image of each point of the plane. We shall begin to define a similarity map by describing a size change with center O and scale factor k (those special maps are analogous to the S_k's we studied before).

Definition: Let O be a point in the plane and k a positive real number. The *size change* $S_{O, k}$ *with center O and scale factor k* is defined as follows:
i) $S_{O, k}(O) = O$,
ii) If $A \neq O$, then $S_{O, k}(A) = A'$ where A' is on the ray $\overrightarrow{OA}$ and is such that $OA' = k \cdot OA$.

Example: Suppose that $k = 3$ and O and A are as shown below. Then A' is the point indicated on the ray $\overrightarrow{OA}$ such that $OA' = 3 \cdot OA$. (The existence of such a unique image of A is guaranteed by the Ruler Theorem.)

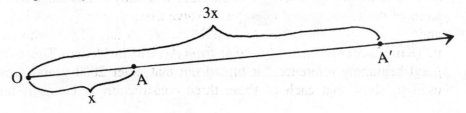

Remark: You may be surprised to learn that our axioms do not guarantee the existence of an image under $S_{O,k}$ for each point A unless k is carefully chosen! It is not entirely easy to understand why this is so, but let's try to figure it out. Recall the Ruler Theorem:

> Given a segment $\overline{RS}$ and a ray $\overrightarrow{PX}$, there is one and only one point Q on $\overrightarrow{PX}$ such that $\overline{PQ} \cong \overline{RS}$, i.e., PQ = RS.

We were able to prove the Ruler Theorem only because we *assumed the existence* of the segment $\overline{RS}$ which we mapped into $\overrightarrow{PX}$ by an isometry carrying R onto P. The image of S under this isometry was the unique point Q of $\overrightarrow{PX}$ which was at the specified distance (i.e., the distance RS) from P. We are, however, not guaranteed by our axioms that, given any length, we can produce a segment having that given length! Our axioms are stated in such a way that we can produce only "constructible" segments and angles. What does that mean? Well, the ancient Greek geometers gave the word "constructible" a definite, technical meaning. A segment or angle is called "constructible" iff it can (in theory) be produced by using the geometrical tools of the ancients:

A. An *unmarked straightedge* (not a ruler with distance markings), which was used for drawing segments, and
B. A *compass*, a pair of "sticks" hinged at one end, which was used for drawing circles or parts of circles called arcs.

2. Look up compass (or compasses) and find out what a modern geometric compass is.

Amazingly enough, it turns out that there are lengths and angle measures which do not correspond to any "constructible" segment or angle! Be sure to skim the following extra credit project whether or not you decide to work on it.

3. (Extra Credit Project) A great deal of geometry was "created" in futile attempts to solve the three famous construction problems of antiquity:

> 1. The Problem of Doubling a Cube.
> 2. The Problem of Trisecting an Angle.
> 3. The Problem of Squaring a Circle.

These problems may be thought of as follows:
1. Given any cube, *construct* the edge of a cube with double the volume of the given cube.
2. Given any angle, *construct* an angle with one-third the measure of the given angle.
3. Given any circle, *construct* a square with the same area as the circle.

Of course, the constructions *had* to be done using only straightedge and compass. The Greeks discovered how to do them if other drawing tools were allowed, but were baffled in their attempts to do them with only straightedge and compass. The story of the unsuccessful attempts to solve these three problems is quite interesting and would make a very good research project for any of you who might like to try it. (Kline's *Mathematical Thought from Ancient to Modern Times*, pp. 38–42 is a good beginning reference.) It turned out that, after 2000 years, group theory was used to show that each of these three construction problems is unsolvable! For example, it is impossible to construct a segment with length $\sqrt[3]{2}$, and so a cube with side length 1 can not be doubled. thus, it is impossible to solve problem 1. Moreover, it is impossible to construct an angle with measure 20, and so an angle with measure 60 (which *is* constructible—any equilateral triangle contains three angles with measure 60) can not be trisected. Thus, it is impossible to solve problem 2. Finally, it is also impossible to construct a segment with length π, and so one can not square a circle with radius 1. Thus, it is impossible to solve problem 1.

The unsolvability of the problem of doubling the cube implies that it is impossible to construct images for some points under the map $S_{O, \sqrt[3]{2}}$. We can "wipe out" the difficulties indicated above by assuming that the metric and angle measure maps of Axioms 5 and 9 are surjective! That is, we assume in effect that there is a segment with any desired length and an angle with any desired measure. While it is possible to do a great deal of geometry without making such an assumption, we shall not follow that path. It will enrich our geometry and ease our work if we assume that Axioms 5 and 9 have been modified to guarantee that:

> The metric and angle measure maps are surjections.

Having made this assumption, we have a well-defined map $S_{O, k}$ for any O and *any* k.

4. a) Show that for any k, if A ≠ O, then $S_{O, k}(A) \neq O$;
    b) Show that, if k ≠ 1 and A ≠ O, then $S_{O, k}(A) \neq A$. Thus conclude that only O is left fixed by $S_{O, k}$ if k ≠ 1.

5. Let O, A be given as in the diagrams below; sketch in, as precisely as you can, $S_{O, 2}(A)$, $S_{O, .5}(A)$, and $S_{O, 1.5}(A)$. Do the same for the point B.

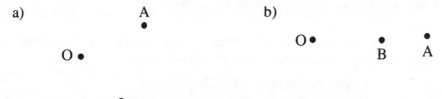

Look back at what you did in the previous exercise. Does it seem reasonable to say that if A ≠ B, then $S_{O, k}(A) \neq S_{O, k}(B)$? I hope that you agree that it is quite reasonable. In fact, we can prove a theorem verifying our most reasonable conjecture:

Theorem: Any size change is injective.

Proof: Suppose A ≠ B. We must prove that $S_{O, k}(A) \neq S_{O, k}(B)$ (why?). If either A or B is O result is the trivial (why?). Hence, we shall assume that neither A nor B is O. Consider the diagrams below:

-192-

In the first case, since $S_{O,k}(A)$ is on the ray $\overrightarrow{OA}$ while $S_{O,k}(B)$ is on ray $\overrightarrow{OB}$, they can not be the same point (why?). (Hint: What is the *only* point common to the two rays?) Of course, if O, A, and B are on the same ray, as in the second case, it is easy (using an argument about distances) to show that $S_{O,k}(A) \neq S_{O,k}(B)$ (why?) Hence, $S_{O,k}$ is injective.

Q.E.D.

6. Answer the questions in the proof above.

7. "Prove" that a size change $S_{O,k}$ is a surjection, i.e., "prove" that for any point $P = (a, b)$ in the plane, there is a point Q such that $S_{O,k}(Q) = P$. (Hint: Draw a picture!)

We may summarize by saying that any size change is both injective and surjective, i.e., *size changes are bijections*.

8. Let $S_{O,k}$ and $S_{O,m}$ be size changes with the same center O. What do you think $S_{O,k} \circ S_{O,m}$ and $S_{O,m} \circ S_{O,k}$ are? Are these two products of size changes nicely related to one another? (Hint: Think carefully about the effect of doing one size change followed by another with the *same* center.)

9. Let $S_{O,k}$ be a size change with center O. Does this map have an inverse? If so, what is it? Can you prove your conjecture? (Hint: Remember that f and g are inverse mappings iff each "undoes" the other, i.e., $f \circ g = g \circ f =$ Identity.)

10. Does the collection of all size changes with center O form a group under the operation of composition of mappings? Explain your answer.

Let's consider the effect of $S_{O,k}$ on a segment, $\overline{AB}$. It is very easy to do this if O, A, and B are collinear, so let's examine such a situation first. Consider the diagram below; let $A' = S_{O,k}(A)$ and $B' = S_{O,k}(B)$.

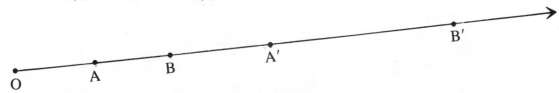

By the definition of size change we have $OB' = k \cdot OB$ and $OA' = k \cdot OA$. Thus, we can see that the following computation is correct:
$$\begin{aligned} A'B' &= OB' - OA' \\ &= k \cdot OB - k \cdot OA \\ &= k \cdot (OB - OA) \\ &= k \cdot AB. \end{aligned}$$
In short, for this special situation we have $A'B' = k \cdot AB$.

11. Let O and $\overline{AB}$ be as indicated in the diagram below. $S_{O,2}$ maps $\overline{AB}$ to a segment $\overline{A'B'}$ which is twice as long as and parallel to $\overline{AB}$. Give a reasonable explanation of why this is so. (Hint: The triangle midline theorem will be helpful.) Thus, in this special situation, $A'B' = 2 \cdot AB$.

These special cases, combined with our intuition for what is going on here, should make it most reasonable to suppose that the effect of $S_{O,k}$ on any segment $\overline{AB}$ is to multiply its length by k, i.e., to suppose that $S_{O,k}$ is a *similarity mapping* with scale factor k. Recall the definition of a similarity mapping of the plane, E, to itself.

Definition: A *similarity*, S, with scale factor $k > 0$ is a mapping of the plane E to itself such that for any two points A and B we have $d(S(A), S(B)) = k \cdot d(A, B)$.

Axiom 13: Each size change $S_{O,k}$ is a similarity mapping with scale factor k.

It is possible to prove, having assumed Axiom 13, that any similarity mapping is a composite of isometries and size changes. We shall not prove this result. Remember, however, that:

Any similarity map is a composite of a finite number of isometries and size changes.

Any similarity is a collineation, i.e., any similarity preserves lines. The proof was given in Unit III.

Theorem: Any similarity is a collineation.

Proof: See Unit III.

So, the image of a line under any similarity is a line. Thus, the image of any segment is also a segment; moreover, the image of $\overline{AB}$ has length $k \cdot AB$ where k is the scale factor of the similarity. Since size changes are similarities, they act on segments as we had guessed they did.

Section 2

1. Given O and m as shown in the diagram below, sketch the image of m under $S_{O,2}$, i.e., sketch $S_{O,2}(m) = m'$.

Are m and m' nicely related to one another? Explain. Make a bold conjecture about the relationship between any line and its image under a size change. Can you prove your conjecture?

In exercise 1, you may have conjectured the following:

Theorem: The image under a size change of a line m is another line, m', which is parallel to m.

Proof: We already know that the image of m is a line (how?). Hence we need to prove only that m' is parallel to m. Let the size change be $S_{O,k}$. Now, if $k = 1$, then $S_{O,k}$ is the identity map (why?), and so $m' = m$; thus, m' is parallel to m since every line is, by definition, parallel to itself. Suppose $S_{O,k}$ is a size change and $k \neq 1$. One and only one of the following is valid: 1) O is on m, or 2) O is not on m. We shall show that the desired result holds in either case, and so holds in general.

Case 1. O is on m. In this case $m' = m$ (why?). Thus, m' is parallel to m by definition.

Case 2. O is not on m. Consider the diagram below:

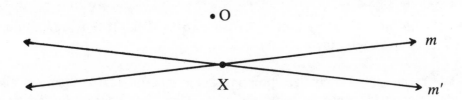

We proceed by RAA. Suppose $S_{O,k}(m)$ is not parallel to m. Then there is a unique point X common to m and m' (why?). Now, since X is on m', X is the image of some point Z on m, i.e., $S_{O,k}(Z) = X$ for some Z on m. We must have O, Z and X collinear (why?). This forces Z = X since, if Z $\neq$ X, then $m = \overset{\leftrightarrow}{ZX}$ and so O is on m, which is absurd (why?). But Z = X is impossible since this would mean that X $= S_{O,k}(X)$, which is absurd (why?) (Hint: What point is fixed by $S_{O,k}$?). Hence, m is parallel to m'. Since the desired result is true in any case, it is true in general.

Q.E.D.

2. Answer the questions in the proof above.

The result above should make the following theorem seem quite reasonable.

Theorem: $S_{O,k}$ preserves parallelism, i.e., if *m* is parallel to *n*, then $S_{O,k}(m)$ is parallel to $S_{O,k}(n)$.

3. Prove the theorem just above. (Hint: It should be an easy consequence of the preceding theorem and of other things you already know about parallelism.)

4. Given O and △ABC as shown in the diagram below, carefully sketch the image of △ABC under $S_{O,2}$ (Hint: The fact that corresponding segments must be parallel will help a lot.) Then use a protractor to measure the sizes of the pairs of corresponding angles. What seems to be true about the measures of corresponding angles?

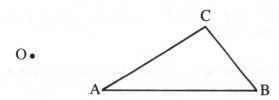

Your answer to the exercise just above (or your recollection of previous work with similarities) probably led you to conjecture that size changes preserve angle measure; in fact, since a similarity is a composite of isometries and size changes, one might conjecture more generally that any similarity mapping preserves angle measure.

Theorem: Size changes preserve angle measure, i.e., if $S_{O,k}$ is a size change and ∠A is any angle, then $S_{O,k}(\angle A) \cong \angle A$.

5. Prove the theorem just above. (Hint: The corresponding rays of the angle and its image must be parallel (why?). The desired result follows from things you know about parallels and the angles associated with them.)

Corollary (Similarities Preserve Angle Measure (SPAM)): If S is any similarity and ∠A is any angle, then $S(\angle A) \cong \angle A$.

Proof: We know that size changes preserve angle measure. Of course, we also know that isometries preserve angle measure. Thus, any composite of size changes and isometries also preserves angle measure, i.e., any similarity preserves angle measure.

Q.E.D.

Recall that we say that two figures $\mathbf{F}_1$ and $\mathbf{F}_2$ are *similar* (denoted by $\mathbf{F}_1 \sim \mathbf{F}_2$) iff there is a similarity mapping $\mathbf{F}_1$ onto $\mathbf{F}_2$. From the results above we have:

Theorem: Corresponding angles of similar figures are congruent.

Recall that a relation such as similarity is said to be an equivalence relation on a set iff it is reflexive, symmetric, and transitive. It is not too difficult to see that similarity must be an equivalence relation on the set of all figures.

6. Prove that similarity is an equivalence relation on the set of all figures.

In order to discuss the situation for corresponding distances in similar figures, we introduce some handy notation and terminology.

Definition: The *ratio* of two real numbers a and b (b ≠ 0) is a/b (sometimes written a:b). We say that two ratios a/b and c/d are *equal* if ad = bc. A statement of equality of ratios such as a/b = c/d is called a *proportion*. The numbers whose ratios are equal are said to be *proportional*, i.e., a, b is proportional to c, d means a/b = c/d (sometimes written as a:b::c:d, which is read as "a is to b as c is to d"). In the proportion a/b = c/d, the numbers a and d are called the *extremes* while the numbers b and c are the *means*.

Remark: Thus, one would say that a/b = c/d iff the product of the extremes equals the product of the means, i.e., ad = bc.

Since a similarity mapping multiplies each length by the same scale factor, k, we see that:

Theorem: Corresponding distances in similar figures are proportional.

Remark: Thus, if we form the ratio A'B'/AB for any segment $\overline{AB}$ and its image $\overline{A'B'}$ under a similarity, we must get k, the scale factor of the similarity.

Examples:

1. 2/3, (1.5)/(12.3), and $\sqrt[3]{2}$ / $\sqrt{5}$ are all examples of ratios;
2. Since 2 · 6 = 3 · 4, we may say that 2/3 = 4/6 is a proportion;
3. In the figure below, $S_{O,2}(\triangle ABC) = \triangle A'B'C'$. Since the size change $S_{O,2}$ doubles lengths, we know that the corresponding distances are all proportional, in fact they are in the ratio 2/1 (or 2:1, i.e., two to one).

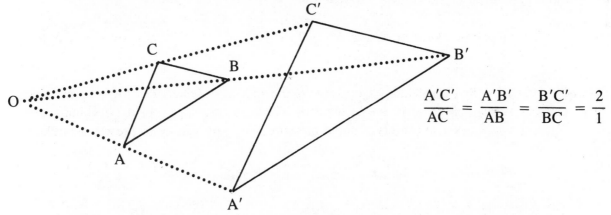

$$\frac{A'C'}{AC} = \frac{A'B'}{AB} = \frac{B'C'}{BC} = \frac{2}{1}$$

7. Suppose $\triangle ABC \sim \triangle A'B'C'$. Refer to the diagram below. State the scale factor of the similarity mapping $\triangle ABC$ onto $\triangle A'B'C'$ and fill in the missing lengths.

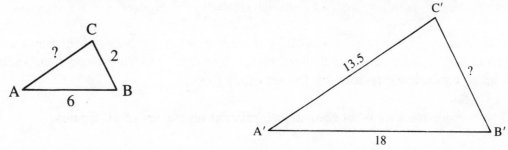

8. Explain why all the figures in each of the following collections are similar to one another: 1. all equilateral triangles, 2. all squares, 3. all cubes, 4. all circles, and 5. all spheres.

We are now in a position to prove the three big theorems which pertain to the similarity of triangles.

Theorem (Angle-Angle Similarity Theorem (AA~)):   If two angles of one triangle are congruent to two angles of another triangle, then the two triangles are similar to one another.

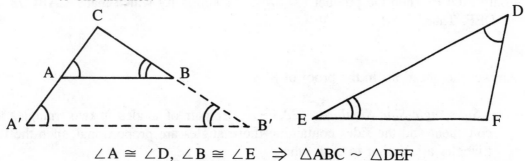

$$\angle A \cong \angle D, \ \angle B \cong \angle E \ \Rightarrow \ \triangle ABC \sim \triangle DEF$$

Remark: The idea of the proof is to make use of the ASA congruence theorem to help us see that we can combine a simple size change with an isometry to get the desired similarity mapping. Refer to the diagram above as you read the proof.

Proof: Let $k = DE/AB$. Then $S_{C,k}(\triangle ABC) = \triangle A'B'C'$ where we have $\angle A' \cong \angle A$, $\angle B' \cong \angle B$, and $A'B' = k \cdot AB = (DE/AB) \cdot AB = DE$ (why?). Thus, we have $\triangle A'B'C' \cong \triangle DEF$ (why?). Let f be the isometry which maps $\triangle A'B'C'$ onto $\triangle DEF$. Then, the product $f \circ S_{C,\ k}$ is a similarity which maps $\triangle ABC$ onto $\triangle DEF$. Thus, $\triangle ABC \sim \triangle DEF$.

Q.E.D.

1.   Answer the questions in the proof of AA~.

Theorem (Side-Side-Side Similarity (SSS~):   If the three pairs of sides of two triangles are proportional, then the two triangles are similar to one another.

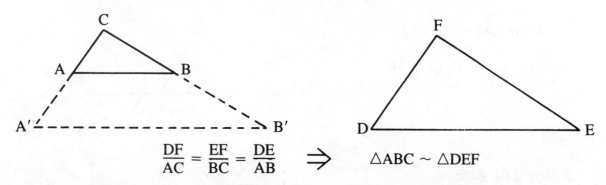

$$\frac{DF}{AC} = \frac{EF}{BC} = \frac{DE}{AB} \ \Rightarrow \ \triangle ABC \sim \triangle DEF$$

Remark: The idea of the proof is to make use of the SSS theorem for congruence to show that we can combine a simple size change with an isometry to get a similarity which maps the one triangle onto the other. Refer to the diagram above as you read the proof.

Proof: Let $k = DE/AB$. Then, $S_{C,\ k}(\triangle ABC) = \triangle A'B'C$ where we have:

$$1. A'B' = k \cdot AB = (DE/AB) \cdot AB = DE$$
$$2. B'C = k \cdot BC = (EF/BC) \cdot BC = EF$$
$$3. A'C = k \cdot AC = (DF/AC) \cdot AC = DF$$

(Why?)

Thus, $\triangle A'B'C \cong \triangle DEF$ (why?). Let f be the isometry which maps $\triangle A'B'C$ onto $\triangle DEF$. Then the product $f \circ S_{C,\,k}$ is a similarity which maps $\triangle ABC$ onto $\triangle DEF$. Thus, $\triangle ABC \sim \triangle DEF$.

Q.E.D.

2. Answer the questions in the proof of SSS~.

Theorem (Side-Angle-Side Similarity (SAS~)): If pair of angles in two triangles are congruent and the sides containing those angles are proportional, then the two triangles are similar to each other.

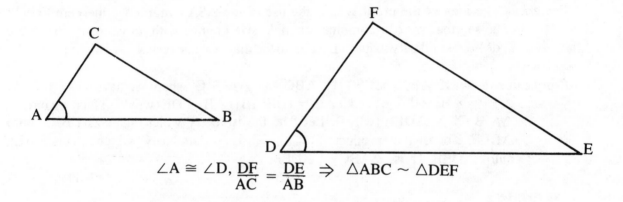

$$\angle A \cong \angle D, \frac{DF}{AC} = \frac{DE}{AB} \Rightarrow \triangle ABC \sim \triangle DEF$$

Remark: The idea of the proof is to make use of the SAS theorem for congruence to help us see that we can combine a simple size change with an isometry to get a similarity which maps the one triangle onto the other. Refer to the diagram above as you write up the proof.

3. Prove SAS~

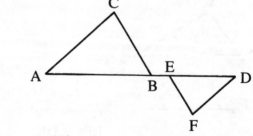

4. Given: $\overline{AC} \parallel \overline{DF}$, $\overline{BC} \parallel \overline{EF}$
   Prove: $\triangle ABC \sim \triangle DEF$.

5. Given: $\overline{BC} \parallel \overline{DE}$
   Prove: $\triangle ABC \sim \triangle ADE$

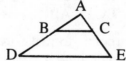

6. Given: BD/AB = CE/AC
   Prove: $\overline{BC} \parallel \overline{DE}$
   (Hint: Begin by proving $\triangle ABC \sim \triangle ADE$.)

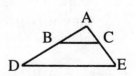

7. Given: ABCD is a trapezoid.

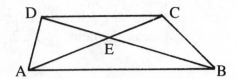

Are any triangles in the diagram similar? Prove it.

8. Given: Right triangles ABC and DEF as shown.
   Are these triangles similar to one another?
   Prove it.

 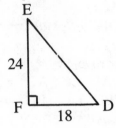

9. Given: L, M, N are midpoints in △ABC.
   Prove: △ABC ~ △MLN.

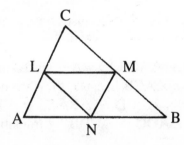

Section 4

This section is devoted to establishing what is perhaps the most famous theorem of Euclidean geometry: the Pythagorean theorem. In so doing, we shall also establish the converse of the theorem.

1. Given the diagram:
$$\overline{AC} \perp \overline{BC}$$
$$\overline{CD} \perp \overline{AB}$$

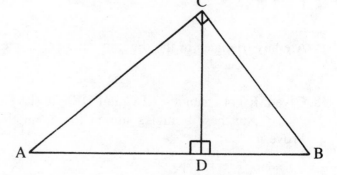

Prove: i) $\triangle ADC \sim \triangle ACB$
      ii) $\triangle BCD \sim \triangle BAC$
      iii) $\triangle ADC \sim \triangle CDB$

Using these results, prove:
iv) $AD/AC = AC/AB$, i.e., $AC^2 = AD \cdot AB$
v) $BC/AB = BD/BC$, i.e., $BC^2 = AB \cdot BD$
vi) $AC^2 + BC^2 = AB^2$

Thus, the Pythagorean theorem is proved.

If you didn't get the exercise just above, read the following (refer to the diagram above):

Proof: i) $\triangle ADC \sim \triangle ACB$ by AA~ since each of these triangles contains $\angle A$ and $\angle ADC \cong \angle ACB$ because they are both right angles.
    ii) Similarly, $\triangle BCD \sim \triangle BAC$.
    iii) Thus, $\triangle ADC \sim \triangle CDB$ by transitivity of similarity.

Since corresponding sides of similar triangles are proportional, we have from i) $AD/AC = AC/AB$, i.e., $AC^2 = AD \cdot AB$, so iv) is proved. For the same reason, ii) yields $BC/AB = BD/BC$, i.e., $BC^2 = BD \cdot AB$, so v) is proved. Finally, by adding the equations in iv) and v), we get the desired result
$AC^2 + BC^2 = AD \cdot AB + BD \cdot AB = (AD + BD) \cdot AB =$
$(AD + DB) \cdot AB = AB \cdot AB = AB^2$

                                      Q.E.D.

Thus, we have proved the Pythagorean theorem.

Pythagorean Theorem: If a triangle is right, then the square of the length of the longest side equals the sum of the squares of the lengths of the other two sides.

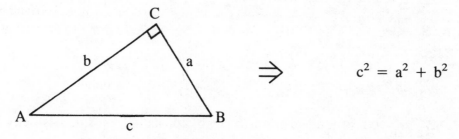

2. Explain why the hypotenuse (the side opposite the right angle) is the longest side of a right triangle.

3. State the converse of the Pythagorean theorem.

   Let's prove the converse of the Pythagorean theorem.

Proof: Suppose we are given a triangle, $\triangle ABC$, with $c^2 = a^2 + b^2$ (refer to the diagram below). We must prove that $\triangle ABC$ is a right triangle with hypotenuse $\overline{AB}$.

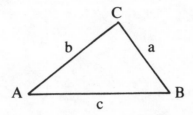

Construct a right triangle with leg lengths a and b as shown below. (Explain how this could be done.)

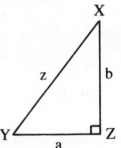

Thus, $a^2 + b^2 = z^2$ (why?).
By the given, $a^2 + b^2 = c^2$.
Hence, $z^2 = c^2$, and so $z = c$.
Thus, $\triangle ABC \cong \triangle XYZ$ (why?).
So, $\triangle ABC$ is a right triangle with hypotenuse $\overline{AB}$ (why?).
                                                            Q.E.D.

4. Answer the questions in the proof of the converse of the Pythagorean theorem.

5. In each of the following, verify that a triangle having the given side lengths is a right triangle:

   1. $3, 4, 5$ 2. $3k, 4k, 5k$
   3. $5, 12, 13$ 4. $8, 15, 17$
   5. $1, \sqrt{3}, 2$ 6. $\sqrt{2}/2, \sqrt{2}/2, 1$

6. Suppose $\triangle ABC$ is an acute triangle, i.e., all 3 of its angles are acute. Suppose further that side $\overline{AB}$ is the "longest" side of $\triangle ABC$, i.e., $AB \geq BC$ and $AB \geq AC$. Make a conjecture about the relative sizes of the numbers AB^2 and $AC^2 + BC^2$.

7. Suppose $\triangle ABC$ is an obtuse triangle with $\angle C$ being the obtuse angle. Explain why side $\overline{AB}$ is the longest side of $\triangle ABC$. Make a conjecture about the relative sizes of the numbers AB^2 and $AC^2 + BC^2$.

   Your conjectures in the two exercises above should lead you to believe:

Theorem: $\triangle ABC$ is acute iff the square of the length of its longest side is strictly less than the sum of the squares of the lengths of its other sides.

Theorem: △ABC is obtuse iff the square of the length of its longest side is strictly greater than the sum of the squares of the lengths of its other sides.

8. (Extra Credit) Present a talk to your class on Pythagorean triples. Be sure to show how to generate *primitive* triples.

Section 5

Among all right triangles there are two special types which merit particular attention because of the patterns which relate their side lengths, and also because they will appear often in your later study of mathematics. They are:

 i) Right triangles obtained by slicing a square in half along an angle bisector, i.e., isosceles right triangles, and

 ii) Right triangles obtained by slicing an equilateral triangle in half along an angle bisector.

Let's consider triangles of type i):

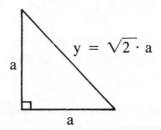

It follows from the Pythagorean theorem that $y^2 = a^2 + a^2 = 2 \cdot a^2$. Hence, $y = \sqrt{2} \cdot a$.

Thus, the pattern which relates the side lengths in such a triangle is a, a, $\sqrt{2} \cdot a$, where the hypotenuse, the longest side, has length $\sqrt{2} \cdot a$.

1. Prove that a triangle with side lengths a, a, $\sqrt{2} \cdot a$ is an isosceles right triangle.

2. What are the measures of the angles in an isosceles right triangle? (Hint: Recall that the acute angles of a right triangle are complementary.)

Let's consider triangles of type ii). Suppose $\triangle ABC$ is equilateral with side length a as shown below:

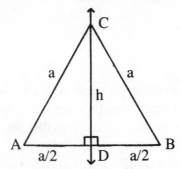

By the ITT, we know that the angle bisector of $\angle C$ is also the perpendicular bisector of the base, $\overline{AB}$. Thus, the angle bisector m splits $\triangle ABC$ in half. Now, it follows from the Pythagorean theorem that $a^2 = (a/2)^2 + h^2$. Thus, $h^2 = a^2 - (a/2)^2 = 3 \cdot a^2/4$.

Hence, $h = \sqrt{3} \cdot a/2$. Thus, the pattern which relates the side lengths in such a triangle is: a/2, $\sqrt{3} \cdot a/2$, a, where the hypotenuse, the longest side, has length a.

3. Prove that a triangle with side lengths a/2, $\sqrt{3} \cdot a/2$, a is a right triangle.

4. What are the measures of the angles in a triangle of type ii)?

Thus, we have the following two theorems:

Theorem (45-45-90):   A triangle is an isosceles right triangle iff its side lengths follow the pattern a, a, $\sqrt{2} \cdot$ a.

Theorem (30-60-90):   A triangle is a 30-60-90 triangle iff its side lengths follow the pattern a/2, $\sqrt{3} \cdot$ a/2, a.

Remark: Note that the 30-60-90 triangle theorem tells us that in a 30-60-90 triangle the side opposite the 30 degree angle is just exactly half as long as the hypotenuse while the side opposite the 60 degree angle is $\sqrt{3}$ / 2 times as long as the hypotenuse, i.e., it is $\sqrt{3}$ times as long as the shortest side.

5.   Suppose $\angle$A is acute. Prove or disprove: All *right* triangles containing an angle congruent to $\angle$A are similar to one another.

6.   Suppose $\triangle$ABC is an isosceles right triangle with hypotenuse $\overline{AB}$. In each of the following, find the missing lengths:

   i)   AB = 10, BC = ?, AC = ?
   ii)   BC = 2, AB = ?, AC = ?

7.   Do the preceding exercise over again, but this time suppose that $\triangle$ABC is a 30-60-90 triangle with hypotenuse $\overline{AB}$.

8.   Prove or disprove: The diagonals of a rhombus split it into 4 congruent isosceles right triangles.

9.   Let $\triangle$ABC be a 45-45-90 right triangle with hypotenuse $\overline{AB}$. Compute the exact value of each of the following (trigonometric) ratios:

   i) BC/AB   ii) BC/AC   iii) AB/AC
   iv) AB/BC   v) AC/BC   vi) AC/AB

Remark: The ratios computed in the previous exercise are the same for *any* isosceles right triangle. As we shall see, the fact that one can compute the *exact* value of these trigonometric ratios is what gives this sort of triangle its importance.

10.   Let $\triangle$ABC be a 30-60-90 triangle with hypotenuse $\overline{AB}$. Do each of the parts of the previous exercise for such a triangle.

Remark: Of course, 30-60-90 triangles are of special interest principally because one can compute the exact values of the trigonometric ratios for such a triangle.

Unit VII—Review Topics

1. Definition of size change; center, scale factor.
2. Properties of size changes—bijectivity, preserves lines, angles, parallelism, etc., maps lines to images which are parallel to the pre-images.
3. How and why we changed Axioms 5 and 9.
4. Definition of similarity mapping.
5. Axiom 13.
6. Any similarity mapping is a composite of a finite number of isometries and size changes.
7. SPAM.
8. Corresponding angles of similar figures are congruent.
9. Definitions of ratio, proportion, means, and extremes.
10. Corresponding distances in similar figures are proportional.
11. AA~, SSS~, SAS~.
12. The Pythagorean Theorem and its converse.
13. The 45-45-90 and the 30-60-90 triangle theorems.

Unit VIII
Circles

"God is a circle whose center is everywhere and whose circumference is nowhere."
–Empedocles–

"All things from eternity are of like forms and come round in a circle."
–Marcus Aurelius Antoninus–

We turn our attention to circles and their principal properties. We already know that any circle is so enormously rich in symmetry that it has:
  - i) infinitely many lines of symmetry, each passing through its center, and
  - ii) allowable rotations through angles of arbitrary measure and hence infinitely many rotational symmetries.

It was this great symmetry which led the ancients to regard the circle as the "perfect" plane figure (and the sphere as the "perfect" space figure). So strong was their conviction of the perfection of the circle and sphere that many of the earliest astronomical theories held that the moon, planets, and stars moved in circles around the Earth because they were somehow carried along on rotating spheres of "solid ether" in which they were embedded.

1. (Extra Credit) Research the ancient explanations of celestial harmony, i.e., the orderly movements of the heavenly bodies. Try to find out the main ideas of such models of the universe as i) the Pythagorean, ii) the Aristotelian, and iii) the Ptolemaic. Investigate how these ideas were swept away by later scientific revolutions. A *careful* study of the latter topic will enlighten you concerning the nature of scientific revolutions in general.

Before we can talk in detail about circles, we need some new terminology and notation:

Definition: The *circle* with *center O and radius* r, denoted by $\odot_r O$, is the set of all points X in the plane such that OX = r, i.e., the set of all points in the plane which lie at a fixed distance, the radius, from a fixed point, the center. The *interior* of $\odot_r O$ is the set of all points X in the plane such that OX < r; the *exterior* of $\odot_r O$ is the set of all points X of the plane such that OX > r. Two circles with the same center are said to be *concentric*.

Remark: Note that the center, O, is *not* a point of $\odot_r O$. Note also that we shall feel free to denote the circle with center O and radius r simply by $\odot O$ whenever it is convenient to do so.

2. Using the Euclidean distance formula, show that an equation for the circle with center (h, k) and radius r is $(x - h)^2 + (y - k)^2 = r^2$.

Refer to the diagram below as you read on:

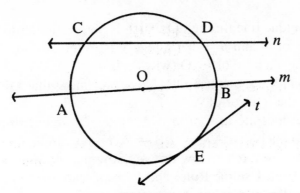

Definition: A line (such as *m* or *n*) which intersects a circle in two points is called a *secant line of the circle* (or simply a *secant*). A line (such as *t*) which intersects the circle in exactly one point is called a *tangent*; *t* is said to be tangent to the circle at E, the *point of tangency*. A segment (such as $\overline{CD}$ or $\overline{AB}$) which connects two points of the circle is called a *chord* of the circle. A chord (such as $\overline{AB}$) which contains the center of the circle is called a *diameter* of the circle. A segment (such as $\overline{AO}$ or $\overline{OB}$) connecting the center of the circle to a point of the circle is called a *radius* of the circle.

Remark: By a standard abuse of langauge (which we shall follow) the words "radius" and "diameter" have dual meanings. The word "radius" is used to refer both to the *distance* from the center of the circle to any point on the circle and to a *segment* such as $\overline{OA}$ or $\overline{OB}$. Thus, "radius" may refer to a length or to a segment. Similarly, the word "diameter" is used to refer both to the *distance* which is twice the length of the radius (distance) and to a *segment* such as $\overline{AB}$. The appropriate one of the dual meanings should always be clear from the context in which the word "radius" or "diameter" is used.

Your intuition should tell you that a straight line can intersect a circle in at most two points. Can we, indeed, prove that such is the case? Do we, in fact, need to prove it? Yes, we do—precisely because intuition is not to be trusted too far when we are dealing with abstractions about ultimately undefined terms. So, as a first step, let's prove:

Theorem: A line *m* which contains a point P of the interior of $\odot_r O$ intersects $\odot_r O$ in exactly two points.

Proof: Suppose P is on *m* and in the interior of $\odot_r O$. Consider the diagram below:

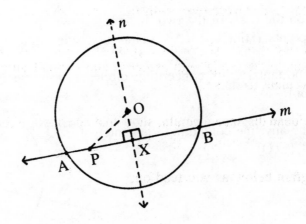

Let n be the unique line through O which is perpendicular to m; let X be the point of intersection of m and n. I claim that X is in the interior of $\odot_r$O. If X = P, X is surely in the interior of $\odot_r$O (why?). If X ≠ P, consider $\triangle$OXP which is a right triangle with hypotenuse $\overline{OP}$. Now, we know that OX < OP < r (why?). Thus, X is in the interior of $\odot_r$O. Let h = OX. Then there is exactly one point on each of the opposite rays of m with vertex X which is on the circle, viz., the points A and B such that AX = XB = $\sqrt{r^2 - h^2}$. (Why? How do we know that A and B are on the circle? How do we know that no other points of m could be on the circle? Hint: Use the Ruler and Pythagorean theorems.) Thus, m intersects $\odot_r$O in exactly the two points A and B.

Q.E.D.

3. Answer the questions in the proof above.

Theorem: A line which contains two points of $\odot_r$O must also contain a point of the interior of $\odot_r$O.

Proof: Let m be a line which contains two points, say A and B, of $\odot_r$O. If O is on m, then we have the desired result (why?). So, suppose O is not on m. Then let n be the unique line through O which is perpendicular to m; let X be the point of intersection of m and n. (Refer to the diagram below.)

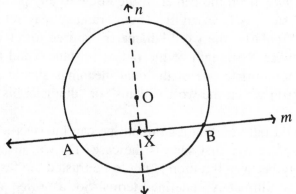

Now, X is in the interior of $\odot_r$O since OX < OB = r (why?).
Thus, in any case, m contains a point in the interior of the circle.

Q.E.D.

4. Answer the questions in the proof above.

5. Explain why, on the basis of the two theorems above, no line can intersect a circle in more than 2 points. (Hint: Use RAA.) Thus, no circle contains three collinear points.

Many of the important results concerning circles follow easily from the following theorem and its proof:

Theorem: Let m be any line containing the center of $\odot_r$O.
Then $F_m(\odot_r O) = \odot_r O$.

Proof: (Refer to the diagram above as you read through this proof.) Let X be a point of $\odot_r O$ and let $X' = F_m(X)$. I claim that X' is also a point on the circle. Since F_m is an isometry, $OX' = OX = r$. Thus, X' is on $\odot_r O$. Moreover, since F_m is an involution, we can easily see that for any point X of the circle there is a point, viz. $F_m(X)$, of the circle which maps onto X (why?).
Thus, $F_m(\odot_r O) = \odot_r O$.

Q.E.D.

6. Answer the questions in the proof.

Remark: Refer to the diagram for the proof above and note that $\triangle OXX'$ is *isosceles* and also that m is the perpendicular bisector of $\overline{XX'}$.

7. Prove the following theorem: Let m be a line which passes through the center of circle O. Then m is perpendicular to chord $\overline{AB}$ of circle O iff m bisects $\overline{AB}$.

8. i)   Chord $\overline{AB}$ is 6 units from O, the center of $\odot_{10} O$. Find AB.
    ii) Chord $\overline{AB}$ of $\odot_r O$ is 12 units from O and AB = 10. Find r.
    iii) How far from the center of $\odot_{30} O$ is chord $\overline{AB}$ if AB = 12?

9. Prove the following theorem: The perpendicular bisector of any chord $\overline{AB}$ of circle O contains O, the center of the circle.

While we have *defined* the notion of a line tangent to a circle, we have not *proved* the existence of such lines. Let's do so:

Theorem: Let A be any point of $\odot_r O$. Then the line t which is perpendicular to the radius $\overline{OA}$ at A is tangent to $\odot_r O$ at A.

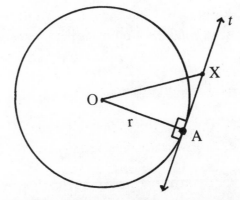

Proof: Let t be a line as described in the statement of the theorem. (Refer to the diagram above.) Let X be any point of t other than A. Then we have that $OX > OA = r$ (why?). Thus, X is in the exterior of the circle. So t contains only one point, viz. A, of the circle; thus, t is tangent to the cirle at A (why?).

Q.E.D.

10. Answer the questions in the proof just above.

Theorem: Suppose t is tangent to $\odot_r O$ at A. Then t is perpendicular to $\overline{OA}$ at A.

Proof: Suppose t is *not* perpendicular to $\overline{OA}$ at A. Let n be the unique line through O which is perpendicular to t, and let X be the intersection of n and t.
Then, OA > OX > r (why?).
   But this is a direct contradiction (why?). Thus, by RAA, t is perpendicular to $\overline{OA}$ at A.

Q.E.D.

11.   Answer the questions in the proof above. (Hint: draw a diagram!)

Corollary: There is exactly one line tangent to $\odot O$ at any point of $\odot O$.

12.   Prove the above corollary.

13.   Prove the following theorem: Let $\overline{AB}$ be a diameter of $\odot O$. Then the lines tangent to $\odot O$ at A and B are parallel.

14.   Prove that two chords, $\overline{EF}$ and $\overline{GH}$, of a circle are the same distance from the center of the circle iff EF = GH. (Hint: HL may be helpful. Remember that the distance from a point to a line is measured along a perpendicular.)

Section 2

We need just a few more new terms before we go on with our study of circles. Refer to the diagram below as you read the definition:

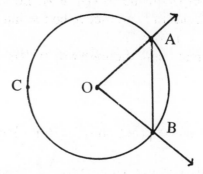

Definition: A *central angle* of a circle is an angle (such as $\angle AOB$) which has its vertex at the center of the circle. An *arc* of a circle is either:

i) The part of the circle which has its endpoints on the sides of a central angle but which otherwise lies in the *interior* of that angle (e.g., $\overarc{AB}$), or

ii) The part of the circle which has its endpoints on the sides of a central angle but which otherwise lies in the *exterior* of that angle (e.g., $\overarc{ACB}$).

A chord (such as $\overline{AB}$) is said to *subtend* the central angle $\angle AOB$; an angle is said to *intercept* an arc which has its endpoints on the sides of the angle but otherwise lies in the interior of the angle, e.g., $\angle AOB$ intercepts $\overarc{AB}$.

We can define two different types of "measure" on arcs. We could define the length of an arc, but we shall postpone such matters until Unit IX. Now, however, we shall define the so-called "angle-measure" of an arc:

Definition: We assign to each arc $\overarc{AB}$ a degree measure, denoted by $\mu\overarc{AB}$, which is either:

i) The same number as the degree measure of the central angle which intercepts $\overarc{AB}$ if $\overarc{AB}$ is an arc of type i) in the definition of arc, or

ii) 360 minus the measure of the central angle associated with $\overarc{AB}$ if $\overarc{AB}$ is an arc of type ii) in the definition of arc.

Remark: In effect, we are saying that an entire circle is assigned the degree measure 360. This is in keeping with a tradition established by the ancient Babylonians; in our later work on trigonometry, we shall see that one may also assign a measure of 2π "radians" to an entire circle.

Definition:

A *major* arc is an arc with degree measure > 180,

A *minor* arc is an arc with degree measure < 180,

A *semicircle* is an arc with degree measure $= 180$.

1. Explain as well as you can why two arcs (possibly of different circles) have the same degree measure iff they are similar to one another. Thus, the degree measure of an arc is related to, but not in general the same as, its length. In particular, it is possible

to prove that two arcs of the same circle are congruent iff they have the same degree measure.

2. (Extra Credit) Explain as well as you can why two arcs of the same circle are congruent iff they have the same degree measure.

Our definition of the degree measure of an arc makes the following theorems "obvious":

Theorem: $\mu\overset{\frown}{ACB} = \mu\overset{\frown}{AC} + \mu\overset{\frown}{CB}$.

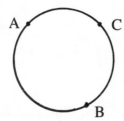

Theorem: $\overset{\frown}{AB} \cong \overset{\frown}{CD}$ iff $\mu\overset{\frown}{AB} = \mu\overset{\frown}{CD}$.

3. Draw a diagram to illustrate each of the theorems just above and convince yourself that they are indeed obvious.

Consider the following diagram as you attempt to prove the theorem in the next exercise:

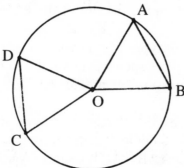

4. Prove:
     i) $\overline{AB} \cong \overline{CD} \Rightarrow \overset{\frown}{AB} \cong \overset{\frown}{CD}$
     ii) $\overset{\frown}{AB} \cong \overset{\frown}{CD} \Rightarrow \angle AOB \cong \angle COD$
     iii) $\angle AOB \cong \angle COD \Rightarrow \overline{AB} \cong \overline{CD}$.

Thus, all 3 of the conditions above are logically equivalent to one another.

5. i) Find AB if OB = 10
  ii) Find OB if AB = 12

6. i) Find AB if OB = 7
  ii) Find OB if AB = 8

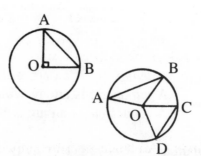

7. Use the Hinge Theorem to prove:
  AB > CD iff $\mu\angle AOB > \mu\angle COD$.

8. Prove: AB < CD iff $\overline{AB}$ is further from O than $\overline{CD}$ is. (Hint: The Pythagorean Theorem may be helpful.) (Compare this result with that of exercise 1.14.)

-214-

Definition: We say than an angle is *inscribed* in a circle if its vertex is on the circle and each of its sides contains 2 points of the circle.

9. Draw several examples of angles inscribed in rather large circles. Measure each angle, say $\angle ABC$, and the central angle which intercepts the same arc as $\angle ABC$. (Refer to the figure below.)

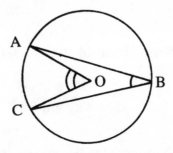

What relationship, if any, do you notice between the angle measures of such pairs?

Your results in exercise 9 should make the following theorem seem most reasonable:

Theorem: The degree measure of an angle inscribed in a circle is half the degree measure of its intercepted arc, i.e.,

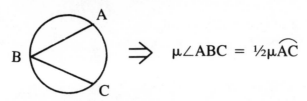

$$\Rightarrow \quad \mu\angle ABC = \tfrac{1}{2}\mu\overset{\frown}{AC}$$

10. Fill in the missing steps in each of the following cases to complete the proof.

Proof: Case 1. Suppose O is on a side of $\angle ABC$. Use ITT and SEAT to show that $\mu\angle AOC = 2 \cdot \mu\angle ABC$, and so $\mu\angle ABC = \tfrac{1}{2} \cdot \mu\overset{\frown}{AC}.$

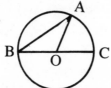

Case 2. Suppose O is in the interior of $\angle ABC$. Use the result of Case 1 to deduce the desired result.

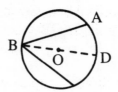

Case 3. Suppose O is in the exterior of $\angle ABC$. Use the result of Case 1 to deduce the desired result.

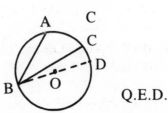

Q.E.D.

Corollary: An angle inscribed in a semicircle is a right angle.

Corollary: Inscribed angles which intercept congruent arcs are congruent.

11. Prove the two corollaries just above.

Theorem; Parallel lines intercept congruent arcs of $\odot_r O$.

$$\overline{AD} \parallel \overline{BC} \implies \widehat{AB} \cong \widehat{CD}$$

12. Prove the theorem just above. (Hint: Sketch in, say, $\overline{AC}$ and use alt.-int. to help you deduce the desired result.)

13. Prove: $\widehat{AB} \cong \widehat{CD} \implies \overline{AD} \parallel \overline{CB}$. (See diagram for 12.)

14. Prove: A parallelogram whose vertices lie on a circle (i.e., a parallelogram which is *inscribed* in a circle) must be a rectangle. (Hint: Remember that the degree measure of an entire circle is 360.)

Let's investigate the degree measure of other types of angles associated with circles. We begin by considering angles formed by two intersecting secants, *m* and *n*. There are three cases which depend on the location (with respect to the circle) of the point of intersection, X, of the secants.

Case 1: X is on the circle.

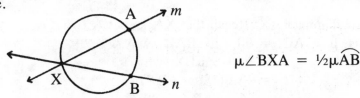

$$\mu\angle BXA = \tfrac{1}{2}\mu\widehat{AB}$$

Case 2: X is in the interior of the circle. What is, for example, $\mu\angle BXC$?

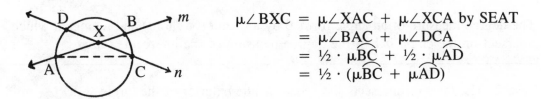

$$\mu\angle BXC = \mu\angle XAC + \mu\angle XCA \text{ by SEAT}$$
$$= \mu\angle BAC + \mu\angle DCA$$
$$= \tfrac{1}{2}\cdot\mu\widehat{BC} + \tfrac{1}{2}\cdot\mu\widehat{AD}$$
$$= \tfrac{1}{2}\cdot(\mu\widehat{BC} + \mu\widehat{AD})$$

So, $\mu\angle BXC$ is the average of the degree measures of the arcs intercepted by $\angle BXC$ and its vertical angle, $\angle DXA$. Thus,

---

The degree measure of an angle formed by two secants which intersect in the interior of a circle is the average of the degree measures of the arcs intercepted by the angle and its vertical angle.

Case 3: X is in the exterior of the circle.
How can we express $\mu\angle DXB$? Draw in, say, $\overline{AD}$. Then,

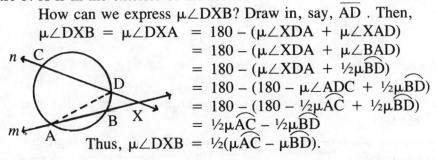

$$\mu\angle DXB = \mu\angle DXA = 180 - (\mu\angle XDA + \mu\angle XAD)$$
$$= 180 - (\mu\angle XDA + \mu\angle BAD)$$
$$= 180 - (\mu\angle XDA + \tfrac{1}{2}\mu\widehat{BD})$$
$$= 180 - (180 - \mu\angle ADC + \tfrac{1}{2}\mu\widehat{BD})$$
$$= 180 - (180 - \tfrac{1}{2}\mu\widehat{AC} + \tfrac{1}{2}\mu\widehat{BD})$$
$$= \tfrac{1}{2}\mu\widehat{AC} - \tfrac{1}{2}\mu\widehat{BD}$$

Thus, $\mu\angle DXB = \tfrac{1}{2}(\mu\widehat{AC} - \mu\widehat{BD})$.

The degree measure of an angle formed by two secants which intersect in the exterior of a circle is half the difference of the degree measures of the larger intercepted arc and the smaller intercepted arc.

Let's consider an angle formed by a tangent and a secant. There are two cases:

Case 1: the tangent intersects the secant on the circle.

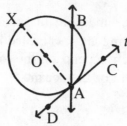

Draw diameter $\overline{AX}$. Recall that $\overline{XA} \perp t$ at A (why?).

Thus, $\mu\angle BAC = 90 - \mu\angle BAX$ (why?)

$= 90 - \frac{1}{2}\mu\widehat{BX}$ (why?)

$= \frac{1}{2} \cdot (180 - \mu\widehat{BX})$ (why?)

$= \frac{1}{2} \cdot \mu\widehat{AB}$ (why?)

Similarly, $\mu\angle BAD = \frac{1}{2} \cdot \mu\widehat{BXA}$.

Thus:

The degree measure of an angle formed by a secant (or chord) and a tangent which intersect on the circle is half the degree measure of the intercepted arc.

Case 2. The tangent intersects the secant in the exterior of the circle.

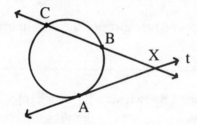

$\mu\angle BXA = 180 - (\mu\angle XBA + \mu\angle XAB)$ (why?)

$= 180 - (180 - \mu\angle CBA + \mu\angle XAB)$ (why?)

$= 180 - (180 - \frac{1}{2}\mu\widehat{AC} + \frac{1}{2}\mu\widehat{AB})$ (why?)

$= \frac{1}{2}\mu\widehat{AC} - \frac{1}{2}\mu\widehat{AB}$ (why?)

$= \frac{1}{2}(\mu\widehat{AC} - \mu\widehat{AB})$ (why?)

1. Answer the questions in the proofs above.

Notice that this result is identical to that of the case of two secants which intersect in the exterior of a circle.

To finish our consideration of angles, let's consider the case of an angle formed by two intersecting tangents.

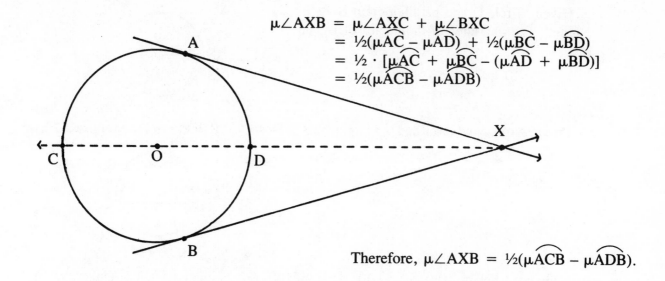

$$\mu\angle AXB = \mu\angle AXC + \mu\angle BXC$$
$$= \tfrac{1}{2}(\mu\overset{\frown}{AC} - \mu\overset{\frown}{AD}) + \tfrac{1}{2}(\mu\overset{\frown}{BC} - \mu\overset{\frown}{BD})$$
$$= \tfrac{1}{2} \cdot [\mu\overset{\frown}{AC} + \mu\overset{\frown}{BC} - (\mu\overset{\frown}{AD} + \mu\overset{\frown}{BD})]$$
$$= \tfrac{1}{2}(\mu\overset{\frown}{ACB} - \mu\overset{\frown}{ADB})$$

Therefore, $\mu\angle AXB = \tfrac{1}{2}(\mu\overset{\frown}{ACB} - \mu\overset{\frown}{ADB})$.

Again, the result is identical to that of the case of two secants intersecting in the exterior of a circle. (Why do you suppose this is so?)

2. Refer to the diagram above and prove: i) $\overleftrightarrow{OX}$ bisects $\angle AXB$ and ii) $AX = BX$.

3. Given the diagram, find x.

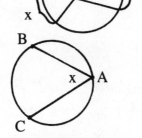

4. Given the diagram,
$\mu\overset{\frown}{AB} = 100$, $\mu\overset{\frown}{AC} = 120$.
Find: $\mu\angle A$.

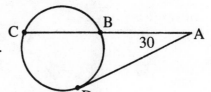

5. Given the diagram,
$\overleftrightarrow{AD}$ tangent to the circle at D; $\mu\overset{\frown}{CD} = 140$.
Find: $\mu\overset{\frown}{BD}$.

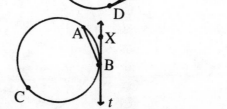

6. Given: $\mu\overset{\frown}{ACB} = 310$; t tangent at B.
Find: $\mu\angle ABX$

7. Given: $\overleftrightarrow{DB}$ and $\overleftrightarrow{DA}$ are tangent to the circle at B and A, respectively.
Find: $\mu\overset{\frown}{ACB}$ and $\mu\overset{\frown}{AB}$.

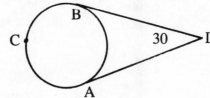

8. Given: Circle O and parallelogram BOYS.
   Find: The measures of the angles of BOYS.

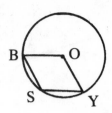

9. Prove: A trapezoid inscribed in a circle must be isosceles. (Hint: Refer to exercise 2.12.)

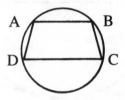

10. Given: μ$\widehat{SN}$ = 80, μ$\widehat{SE}$ = 30, μ$\widehat{EL}$ = 100, $\overleftrightarrow{GA}$ tangent at N, $\overleftrightarrow{GL}$ tangent at L.
    Find: μ∠1, μ∠ANS, μ∠3, μ∠ENG, μ∠5, μ∠6, μ∠7, μ∠ALG

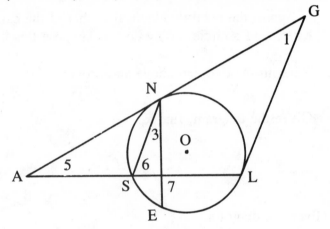

11. Given: $\overleftrightarrow{TN}$ tangent at A; μ$\widehat{AS}$ = 70, μ$\widehat{SQ}$ = 60, μ$\widehat{QR}$ = 80.
    Find: μ∠TAQ, μ∠2, μ∠3, μ∠4, μ∠5, μ∠6, μ∠7, μ∠8, μ∠9

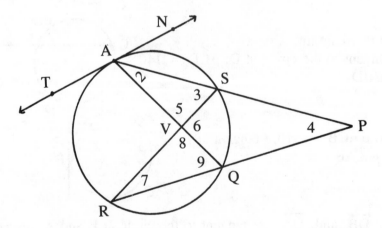

-220-

12. Given: $\overline{AX}$ and $\overline{CX}$ are congruent chords of $\odot O$.
    Prove: $\overleftrightarrow{OX}$ bisects $\angle AXC$

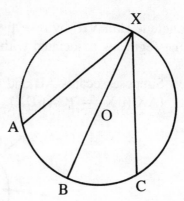

13. Given: $\overline{AB}$ and $\overline{CD}$ are congruent chords of $\odot O$.
    Prove: $\overleftrightarrow{OX}$ bisects $\angle AXC$
    (Hint: Refer to exercise 1.14. Draw $\overline{OM} \perp \overline{AB}$ and $\overline{ON} \perp \overline{CD}$.)

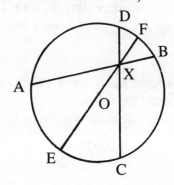

We conclude Unit VIII by investigating the relationships between the lengths of various line segments associated with circles:

Theorem: Suppose secants $\overleftrightarrow{AB}$ and $\overleftrightarrow{CD}$ intersect at X in the interior of circle O. Then $(AX)(BX) = (CX)(DX)$.

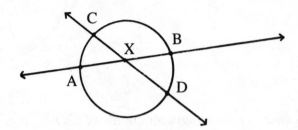

1. Prove the theorem above. (Hint: Draw $\overline{AC}$ and $\overline{BD}$ and prove that $\triangle AXC \sim \triangle DXB$ by using AA$\sim$; then deduce the desired result.)

2. Suppose you have many secants intersecting at X in the interior of circle O. (Refer to the diagram below.)
Generalize the theorem above to show that:

$$(A_1X)(B_1X) = (A_2X)(B_2X) = \ldots = (A_nX)(B_nX).$$

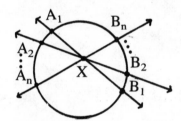

Theorem: Suppose secants $\overleftrightarrow{AB}$ and $\overleftrightarrow{CD}$ intersect at X in the exterior of circle O. Then $(AX)(BX) = (CX)(DX)$.

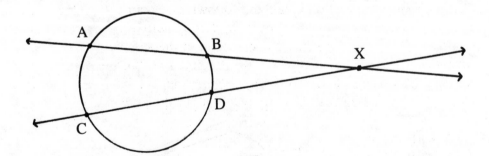

3. Prove the theorem above. (Hint: Draw $\overline{AD}$ and $\overline{BC}$ and prove $\triangle XBC \sim \triangle XDA$; then deduce the desired result.)

4. Suppose you have many secants intersecting at a point X in the exterior of circle O. (Refer to the diagram below.)
Generalize the theorem above by showing that:

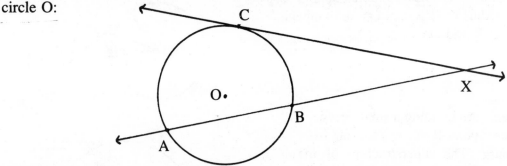

$$(A_1X)(B_1X) = (A_2X)(B_2X) = \ldots = (A_nX)(B_nX).$$

5. Would the theorem analogous to the previous two, but now involving secants which intersect at X, a point *on* the circle, be valid? State the theorem and explain your answer. Is the result particularly interesting?

The fact that all the products in the previous exercises are the same justifies the following definition:

Definition: Let X be a point on $\overleftrightarrow{AB}$ which is a secant cutting circle O at A and B. Then $(AX)(BX)$ is called the *power of the point* X with respect to the circle O.

Finally, consider the case of the segments formed by a tangent and a secant to circle O:

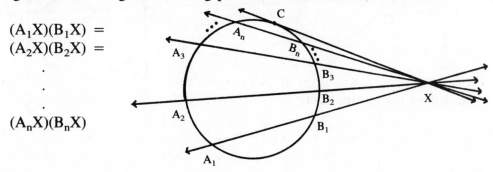

Theorem: $(CX)^2 = (AX)(BX)$, i.e., $(CX)^2 = $ the power of X with respect to $\odot O$.

6. Prove the theorem above. (Hint: Draw in $\overline{BC}$ and $\overline{AC}$ and prove that $\triangle XCA \sim \triangle XBC$; then deduce the desired result.)

7. (Extra Credit) Prepare to explain the following to your class: One might have "discovered" the previous theorem by considering *many* secants intersecting at X such that the "limit" of the points of intersection of the secants with the circle is C, i.e., such that the secants "approach" the tangent line "in the limit" (intuitively, the secants are getting closer and closer to the tangent line, so we can think of the tangent line as being the "limiting position" of the secants). We have:

$(A_1X)(B_1X) = $
$(A_2X)(B_2X) = $

.
.
.

$(A_nX)(B_nX)$

and, moreover, as n gets bigger and bigger, both A_nX and B_nX are getting closer and closer to CX. Thus, it is reasonable to expect that "in the limit" we would get (CX)(CX), i.e., $(CX)^2$ as the value of the product.

8. Given: the figure.
   Find: x, AX, BX, CX, DX.

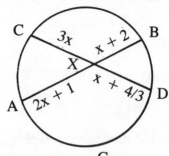

9. Given: $\overleftrightarrow{XC}$ is tangent to $\odot O$ at C,
   CX = x + 2, AB = x – 3, BX = x – 1
   Find: x, CX, AX, BX, AB.

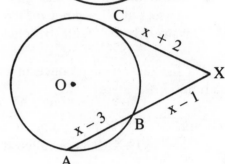

10. Given: Circles O and O′ have a common tangent
    line at T; $\odot O$ has radius 5, $\odot O'$ has
    radius 4; $\overleftrightarrow{O'X}$ and $\overleftrightarrow{OY}$ are tangents.
    Find: O′X and OY

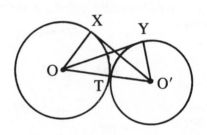

11. Engineers are building a small bridge
    over the Spoon River not too far from
    Galesburg. The superstructure of the
    bridge is in the form of a circular arc
    which is 20 feet high at its highest point.
    The bridge span is 50 feet. Find the
    radius of the circle of which the
    superstructure is a part.

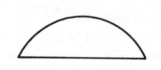

12. Given: The radius of $\odot O$ is 8;
    m and n are tangent to the circle
    at P and Q, respectively; $\overline{PQ}$ is
    a diameter of $\odot O$ $m\overarc{QX}$ = 120.
    Find: PS and QS.

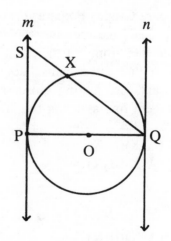

13. Given: Circles O and O′ have a common tangent $\overleftrightarrow{PT}$ at T; $\overleftrightarrow{PQ}$ and $\overrightarrow{PR}$ are tangents.
    Prove: $\overline{PQ} \cong \overline{PR}$.

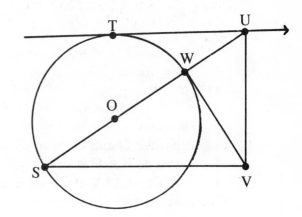

14. Given: $\overline{AB} \cong \overline{CD}$
    Prove: $\overline{BX} \cong \overline{DX}$.

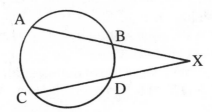

15. Given: $\overleftrightarrow{TU}$ is tangent to $\odot O$ at T;
    $\overleftrightarrow{VW}$ is tangent to $\odot O$ at W;
    $\overline{UV} \perp \overline{VS}$; S, O, W, U are collinear.
    Prove: UV = UT
    (Hint: Prove $\triangle WUV \sim \triangle VUS$ and combine that result with the relationship between $\overline{UT}$ and the segments of the secant $\overline{US}$.)

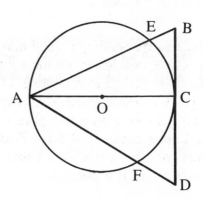

16. Given: $\overleftrightarrow{BD}$ is tangent to $\odot O$ at C;
    $\overline{CA}$ is a diameter of $\odot O$;
    $\overline{AB}$ and $\overline{AD}$ are secants as shown.
    Prove: $(AB)(AE) = (AD)(AF)$
    (Hint: Draw $\overline{CE}$ and $\overline{CF}$ and use similar triangles.)

17. Given: $\overline{CD} \parallel \overline{BF}$ in the figure.
    Prove: $(CD)^2 = (AD)(ED)$
    (Hint: Look for congruent angles and use similar triangles.)

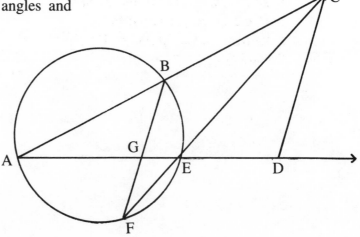

-225-

Unit VIII—Review Topics

1. Definition of circle: center, radius, interior, exterior; symmetry of circle; secant line; tangent line, point of tangency; chord, diameter.
2. No line can intersect a circle in more than two points.
3. For any line m containing O, $F_m(\odot O) = \odot O$
4. A line passing through the center of a circle is perpendicular to a chord of that circle iff it bisects that chord.
5. The perpendicular bisector of any chord of a circle contains the center of that circle.
6. A line m is tangent to $\odot O$ iff m is perpendicular to a radius of $\odot O$ at the endpoint of the radius on $\odot O$.
7. There is exactly one line tangent to $\odot O$ at each point of $\odot O$.
8. Two chords of $\odot O$ are equidistant from O iff they are congruent.
9. Definition: central angle; arcs; chord subtends angle; angle intercepts arc; degree measure of arcs; major, minor arcs; semicircle.
10. Two arcs of $\odot O$ are congruent iff they have the same degree measure.
11. $\mu \overset{\frown}{ACB} = \mu \overset{\frown}{AC} + \mu \overset{\frown}{CB}$; $\overset{\frown}{AB} \cong \overset{\frown}{CD}$ iff $\mu \overset{\frown}{AB} = \mu \overset{\frown}{CD}$.
12. $\overline{AB} \cong \overline{CD}$ iff $\overset{\frown}{AB} \cong \overset{\frown}{CD}$ iff $\angle AOB \cong \angle COD$.
13. Definition: inscribed angle.
14. Rules for finding the measures of central and inscribed angles.
15. An angle inscribed in a semicircle is a right angle.
16. Inscribed angles which intercept congruent arcs of $\odot O$ are congruent.
17. Parallel lines intercept congruent arcs of a circle.
18. If two lines intercept congruent arcs of a circle, they are parallel.
19. Rules for measuring angles formed by intersecting secants, secant and tangent, and two tangents.
20. Relationships between the lengths of segments associated with circles, e.g., intersecting chords, secants, and secant and tangent.
21. The power of a point with respect to a circle.

Unit IX
Perimeter, Area, and Volume

In this Unit we shall make a brief study of the main results concerning perimeter, area, and volume. We begin by examining "simple" results about the perimeter and area of certain special regions of the plane. Our approach in this Unit will no longer be *strictly* axiomatic since a rigorous treatment, particularly of volume, would be far from straightforward—not to say tiresomely tedious. Nevertheless, we shall at least begin on an axiomatic note, and we lay the foundations for doing so by giving the following:

Definition: A *triangular region*, **R**, consists of a triangle and its interior (which is the intersection of the interiors of the angles of the triangle); the triangle itself is called the *boundary* of **R**.

Definition: Given three or more distinct coplanar points, denoted by P_1, P_2, P_3, . . . , P_n, (called the *vertices*), we say that the union of the n line segments $\overline{P_1P_2}$, $\overline{P_2P_3}$, . . . , $\overline{P_{n-1}P_n}$, $\overline{P_nP_1}$ (called the *edges* or *sides*) is a *closed n-gon* (or a *closed polygon with n sides*) provided that:
i) the intersection of any two sides is either empty or a common vertex, and
ii) no two sides having a common vertex are collinear.
Two sides which have a common vertex are said to be *adjacent* sides. The endpoints of each side are *adjacent* vertices. The union of all the sides is called the *boundary* of the n-gon. The *perimeter* of the n-gon is the sum of the lengths of its sides (i.e., the perimeter is the total length of the boundary). An *angle of a polygon* is an angle whose sides contain a pair of adjacent sides of the polygon and whose vertex is the vertex common to those adjacent sides, e.g., $\angle P_nP_1P_2$, $\angle P_1P_2P_3$, etc.

Remark: The following terminology is standard:

Number of Sides	Name	
3	triangle	(3-gon)
4	quadrilateral	(4-gon)
5	pentagon	(5-gon)
6	hexagon	(6-gon)
7	heptagon	(7-gon)
8	octagon	(8-gon)
9	nonagon	(9-gon)
10	decagon	(10-gon)
.	.	
.	.	
.	.	
n	n-gon	

1. Sketch some examples of polygons of various types and label the vertices, edges, and angles. Give the standard name of each polygon.

In this section we shall study the areas of polygonal regions, which are generalizations of triangular regions.

Definition: A *polygonal region*, **R**, is the union of finitely many triangular regions T_1, T_2, . . . , T_n such that the intersection of any two of the triangular regions is either:

> i) the empty set,
> ii) a single point, or
> iii) a common edge.

The *interior* of the polygonal region **R**, denoted by Int **R**, is **R** minus those sides *NOT* common to two of the triangular regions which make up **R** (see the various examples diagrammed below). The *boundary* of **R** is **R** minus Int **R**; i.e., the boundary of **R** is what's left of **R** after you remove all of the interior of **R**.

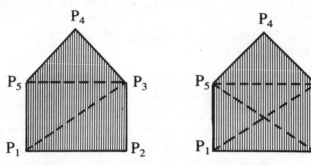

The dotted lines help show two different representations of a polygonal region as the union of finitely many triangular regions.

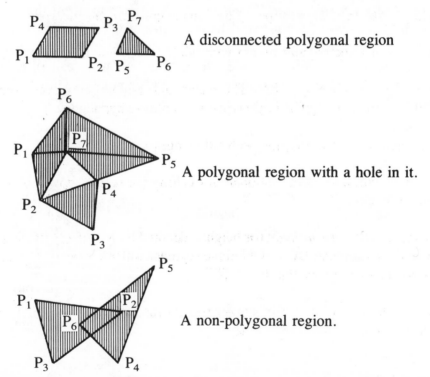

A disconnected polygonal region

A polygonal region with a hole in it.

A non-polygonal region.

2. Sketch your own examples of regions which are polygonal; also sketch examples of regions which are *not* polygonal and explain why they are not.

3. Explain how an n-gon may be thought of as being the boundary of a polygonal region. What is the *smallest* number of triangular regions which may be thought of as forming a polygonal region having an n-gon as its boundary? (Hint: Examine the situation for n = 3, 4, 5, 6, . . . and look for a pattern in your answers.)

Here is the area axiom which will enable us to pursue our study of the area of polygonal regions:

Let $\mathbb{P}$ be the collection of all polygonal regions in the plane. (The Greek letter α, which you will find used below, is alpha—read al-fa.)

Axiom 14: There exists a mapping α: $\mathbb{P} \to \mathbb{R}^+$ satisfying the following conditions for any polygonal regions **R** and **S**:
A0: $\mathbf{R} \cong \mathbf{S} \Rightarrow \alpha(\mathbf{R}) = \alpha(\mathbf{S})$;
A1: $\alpha(\mathbf{R} \cup \mathbf{S}) = \alpha(\mathbf{R}) + \alpha(\mathbf{S})$ iff Int **R** $\cap$ Int **S** $= \varnothing$;
A2: If **R** is a right triangular region with leg lengths b and h, then $\alpha(\mathbf{R}) = \frac{1}{2}bh$.

Definition: For any polygonal region **R**, $\alpha(\mathbf{R})$ is the *area of* **R**.

Remark: Note that Axiom 14 tells us that *every* polygonal region **R** has associated with it a unique *positive* real number called $\alpha(\mathbf{R})$. Notice that A1 says that the area of the union of two polygonal regions **R** and **S** (i.e., the area of the set of points in either one, the other, or both) is the sum of their areas provided that their interiors do not overlap. This should seem most reasonable to you if you think about what it means and sketch a few pictures to illustrate your thoughts on the matter.

Now, let's begin our study of area by proving a small, unsurprising theorem:

Theorem: The area of a rectangular region with width w and length l is lw.

4. Prove the theorem just above. (Hint: The rectangular region can be represented as the union of two right triangular regions with a common hypotenuse.)

Corollary: The area of a square region with side length x is x^2.

Remark: The above corollary is the rationale for calling the second power of x by the name "x squared."

Definition: Given $\triangle ABC$, the *altitude* (or height), denoted by h_A, of $\triangle ABC$ associated with the *base* (side) $\overline{BC}$ is the unique segment which connects A and a point of $\overleftrightarrow{BC}$ in such a way that $h_A \perp \overleftrightarrow{BC}$.

Remark: Note that $h_A \perp \overleftrightarrow{BC}$, but it is *not* necessarily the case that $h_A \perp \overline{BC}$. In fact, it can happen that $h_A \cap \overline{BC} = \varnothing$.
Example:

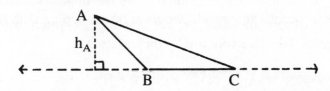

5. Make a sketch to indicate that any triangle, say $\triangle ABC$, has three altitudes h_A, h_B, and h_C which are not necessarily congruent to each other.

Remark: We shall follow the common abuse of language which allows the words "altitude" and "base" to have dual meanings. The "altitude" h_A of $\triangle ABC$ may be *either* the *segment* described in the definition above *or* the *length* of that segment. Similarly, the "base" associated with altitude h_A may be either the segment $\overline{BC}$ or the length BC. The intended meaning is usually crystal clear in context. Moreover, for the sake of convenience (and in keeping with tradition) we shall allow ourselves to speak of the area of a triangle, rectangle, parallelogram, etc., rather than of the area of the *region* having the given polygon as its boundary.

Now, let's see how we can derive a formula for the area of any triangle (i.e., any triangular region):

Consider the region **R** with boundary $\triangle ABC$ as shown in the diagram below:

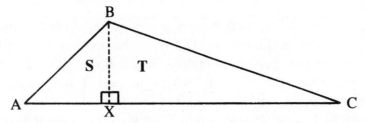

We can represent **R** as the union of two right triangular regions, **S** and **T**, by taking $\overline{BX}$ to be the unique perpendicular to $\overline{AC}$ from B, i.e., $\overline{BX}$ is the altitude h_B of $\triangle ABC$.

By Axiom 14,A1, we know $\alpha(\mathbf{R}) = \alpha(\mathbf{S}) + \alpha(\mathbf{T})$.
By Axiom 14,A2, $\alpha(\mathbf{S}) = \frac{1}{2}(AX)(BX)$,
$$\alpha(\mathbf{T}) = \frac{1}{2}(XC)(BX)$$
Thus,
$$\begin{aligned}\alpha(\mathbf{R}) &= \tfrac{1}{2}(AX)(BX) + \tfrac{1}{2}(XC)(BX)\\ &= \tfrac{1}{2}(AX + XC)(BX) = \tfrac{1}{2}(AC)(BX)\\ &= \tfrac{1}{2}bh.\end{aligned}$$

Hence, the area of $\triangle ABC$ is half the product of a base times the altitude associated with that base.

The formula derived above for the area of a triangle is surely familiar to you from some previous course in which you studied geometry intuitively. However, you probably haven't given much *thought* to the formula. In particular, since the three sides of a triangle and their associated altitudes are, in general, of different lengths, ask yourself how we know that the product $\frac{1}{2}bh$ is the *same number* for each of the three possible choices of base-height pairs! Were it not the same number for all three possible choices, we would be in *serious* trouble with our area axiom.

6. Can you explain what the serious trouble hinted at above might be? (Hint: If the three choices did not produce the same result, would α be a mapping with the desired properties?)

7. Prove: Any triangle must contain at least two acute angles.
(Hint: Use RAA; EAST may be helpful.)

Theorem: Suppose $\triangle ABC$ contains acute angles, $\angle A$ and $\angle B$. Then $h_C \cap \overset{\circ}{\overline{AB}} \neq \varnothing$.

Proof: Suppose $h_C \cap \overset{\circ}{\overline{AB}}\!^{\circ} = \emptyset$. Let $h_C \cap \overleftrightarrow{AB} = X$. If X is not in $\overset{\circ}{\overline{AB}}\!^{\circ}$, we have a contradiction (why? Hint: Draw a diagram; use WEAT). Thus, by RAA, $h_C \cap \overset{\circ}{\overline{AB}}\!^{\circ} \neq \emptyset$.

Q.E.D.

8. Answer the question in the proof above.

Theorem: The product ½bh is the same for all three choices of base-height pairs in any triangle.

Proof: Let $\triangle ABC$ be given and suppose (without loss of generality) that $\angle A$ and $\angle B$ are acute angles. (Why does this supposition not reduce the generality of the proof?) We shall prove that: $h_C \cdot (AB) = h_B \cdot (AC)$. Refer to the diagram below as you read on:

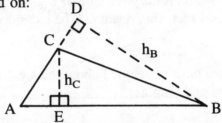

Whether $\angle C$ is obtuse (as shown), right, or acute, we have $\triangle ACE \sim \triangle ABD$. (Why? Hint: Sketch the two cases not shown in my diagram; deduce that the similarity is valid in all three instances.)
Thus, $AC/AB = CE/BD$ (why?). So, $(BD)(AC) = (CE)(AB)$;
i.e., $h_B \cdot (AC) = h_C \cdot (AB)$.

Q.E.D.

9. Answer the questions in the proof above.

There is a very special result for the area of an equilateral triangle:

Theorem: If $\triangle ABC$ is an equilateral triangle of side length s,
then $\alpha(\triangle ABC) = \sqrt{3} \cdot S^2/4$.

10. Prove the special result above. (Hint: Draw in an altitude and use 30-60-90 triangle facts to deduce the desired result.)

11. Prove: If two triangles have a pair of congruent sides and the altitudes associated with those sides are congruent, then the two triangles have the same area.

12. Prove: A median splits a triangle into two triangles having equal area.

13. Prove: The diagonals of a parallelogram form four triangles having the same area.

14. Prove: If two triangles have congruent bases (altitudes), then the ratio of their areas is the same as the ratio of their corresponding altitudes (bases).

Theorem: Suppose $\triangle ABC \sim \triangle DEF$ because $S(\triangle ABC) = \triangle DEF$ where S is a similarity mapping with scale factor k. Then, $\alpha(\triangle DEF) = k^2 \cdot \alpha(\triangle ABC)$.

Proof: $\alpha(\triangle ABC) = h_C \cdot AB$ and $\alpha(\triangle DEF) = h_F \cdot DE$.

$DE = k \cdot AB$ and $h_F = k \cdot h_C$ since they are corresponding parts of similar triangles. Thus,

$$\begin{aligned}\alpha(\triangle DEF) &= h_F \cdot DE = k \cdot h_C \cdot k \cdot AB \\ &= k^2 \cdot h_C \cdot AB \\ &= k^2 \cdot \alpha(\triangle ABC).\end{aligned}$$

Q.E.D.

Corollary: The ratio of the areas of similar triangles is the square of the ratio of *any* two corresponding segment lengths.

15. Explain why the corollary above is valid.

16. State the theorem and its corollary for similar n-gons. Try to explain why your new statements are valid. In fact, this result can be extended to any regions which have area.

We can use the results we have developed about the areas of triangular and rectangular regions to discover other area formulas:

Theorem: Let ABCD be a trapezoid. Then, $\alpha(ABCD) = \frac{1}{2} \cdot (b_1 + b_2) \cdot h$, where b_1 and b_2 are the lengths of the parallel bases of ABCD and h is the altitude of ABCD, i.e., the distance between the bases.

Proof: Consider the diagram below:

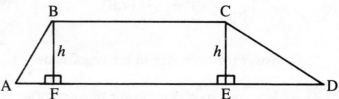

Let $\overline{BF}$ and $\overline{CE}$ be perpendicular to $\overline{AD}$. Then, $BF = CE = h$ and $BC = FE$ (why?).

Now, $\alpha(\triangle ABF) = \frac{1}{2} \cdot AF \cdot h$

$\alpha(\square BCEF) = BC \cdot h$

$\alpha(\triangle CDE) = \frac{1}{2} \cdot DE \cdot h$.

Moreover, we know that $\alpha(ABCD) = \alpha(\triangle ABF) + \alpha(\square BCEF) = \alpha(\triangle CDE)$ (why?). Thus,

$$\begin{aligned}\alpha(ABCD) &= \frac{1}{2} \cdot AF \cdot h + BC \cdot h + \frac{1}{2} \cdot DE \cdot h \\ &= \frac{1}{2} \cdot (AF \cdot h + 2 \cdot BC \cdot h + DE \cdot h) \\ &= \frac{1}{2} \cdot (AF + 2 \cdot BC + DE) \cdot h \\ &= \frac{1}{2} \cdot (BC + AF + BC + ED) \cdot h \\ &= \frac{1}{2} \cdot (BC + AF + FE + ED) \cdot h \\ &= \frac{1}{2} \cdot (BC + AD) \cdot h \quad \text{(why?)} \\ &= \frac{1}{2} \cdot (b_1 + b_2) \cdot h.\end{aligned}$$

Q.E.D.

17. Answer the questions in the proof above.

Theorem: Suppose ABCD is a parallelogram. Then α(ABCD) = b · h, where b is the length of any side and h is the distance between that side and the other side parallel to it.

Proof: Consider the diagram:

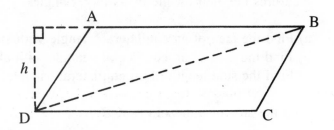

α(ABCD) = α($\triangle$ABD) + α($\triangle$CBD)
$\qquad$ = 2 · α($\triangle$ABD)   (why?)
$\qquad$ = 2 · ½ · AB · h   (why?)
$\qquad$ = AB · h
$\qquad$ = CD · h   (why?)
Similarly for the bases $\overline{AD}$ and $\overline{BC}$.

$\qquad\qquad\qquad\qquad\qquad\qquad\qquad\qquad$ Q.E.D.

18. Answer the questions in the proof above.

19. Explain an alternative method of deriving the formula for the area of a parallelogram by considering the diagram below:

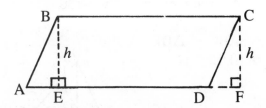

Theorem: The area of a rhombus is half the product of the lengths of its diagonals.

Proof: Let ABCD be a rhombus. Refer to the diagram below:

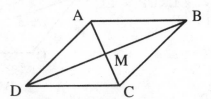

Recall that the diagonals of a rhombus are perpendicular bisectors of one another.
α($\square$ABCD) = α($\triangle$ADM) + α($\triangle$ABM) + α($\triangle$CDM) + α($\triangle$CBM)
$\qquad\qquad$ = ½ · DM · AM + ½ · MB · AM + ½ · DM · MC + ½ · MB · MC
$\qquad\qquad$ = ½ [(DM + MB) · AM + (DM + MB) · MC]
$\qquad\qquad$ = ½ [(DM + MB) · (AM + MC)]
$\qquad\qquad$ = ½ · DB · AC.

$\qquad\qquad\qquad\qquad\qquad\qquad\qquad\qquad$ Q.E.D.

20. One side of a rectangle is twice as long as another. Find the area of the rectangle if its perimeter is 24 meters.

21. Find the area of an isosceles triangle with base 30 and vertex angle measure 60.

22. Find the area of a rhombus with side length 8 if one of its smaller angles measures one-half of one of its larger angles.

23. a) Find the area of an equilateral triangle with side length 16.
    b) Find the area of an equilateral triangle with altitude 4.
    c) Find the side length of an equilateral triangle with area 36.

24. Find the area of trapezoid ABCD.

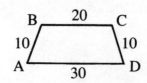

25. Given: $\overline{CF} \perp \overline{BD}$, $\overline{CF} \perp \overline{AE}$, AE = 48,
    CF = 30, GF = 20.
    Find the area of ABDE.

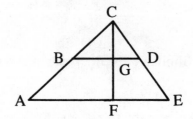

26. Find the area of an isosceles right triangle with hypotenuse 40.

27. Find the area of the triangle formed by the x-axis, the y-axis, and the line which is the graph of 3x + 2y = 30.

28. Given: △ABC ~ △DEF.
    Find: α(△DEF).

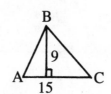 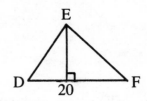

29. Find the area of a triangle with side lengths 13, 5, 12.

30. Given: $\overline{DO} \cong \overline{FL}$, $\angle D \cong \angle L$, $\overline{DP} \cong \overline{LI}$
    Prove: α(DOAP) = α(LFAI)

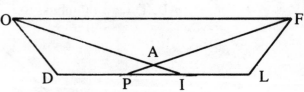

31. Given: D, E, F are midpoints.
    Prove: α(□ADEF) = ½α(△ABC).

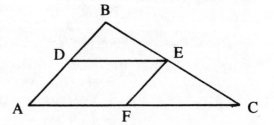

32. Find the area of the trapezoid illustrated below.

-234-

33. Given: HALF is a parallelogram, $\overleftrightarrow{HU}$ bisects $\angle H$, $\overleftrightarrow{LT}$ bisects $\angle L$.
Prove: α(HUTLF) = α(LTUHA).

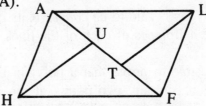

34. Suppose **S** is a square and **T** is an equilateral triangle such that **S** and **T** have the same perimeter. Which has the greater area? Explain.

Section 2

Definition: A polygon is said to be *convex* if its interior is completely contained in *one* of the halfplanes of each of the lines which contain a side of the polygon.

Remark: It is possible to prove that a polygon is convex iff the unique line segment which connects any two points of the interior of the polygon is completely contained in the interior of the polygon. Intuitively, a polygon is convex iff it has no "dents" in it.

1. Sketch a few examples of convex and non-convex polygons.

Definition: A convex polygon is said to be *regular* if its sides are all of the same length and its angles are all of the same measure.

2. Draw several examples of regular polygons and note what sort of symmetry each has. (Hint: Each should have either a cyclic or a dihedral symmetry group. How is the order of the symmetry group related to the number of sides of the regular polygon?)

Definition: A line segment having two non-adjacent vertices of a polygon as its endpoints is called a *diagonal* of the polygon.

3. Suppose P is a convex n-gon. State a formula in terms of n for:
   a. the number of distinct diagonals of P having a fixed endpoint at one of the vertices of P; call this number D.
   b. the total number of distinct diagonals of P; call this number T.
   (Hint: Compute the values of D and T for n = 3, 4, 5, 6, 7 . . . , and try to deduce formulas in terms of n which produce the values you find. Once you know the very simple formula for D, you can derive the formula for T by noticing that:
   i. each vertex is the endpoint of D distinct diagonals of P, and
   ii. if you add up the numbers of distinct diagonals of P at each vertex of P, you will wind up with precisely double the total number of distinct diagonals of P, since each diagonal has two endpoints.)

If you did exercise 3 correctly, you now know that an n-gon has D = n − 3 distinct diagonals at any one of its vertices and has T = n(n − 3)/2 distinct diagonals in all. (If you didn't get these values, go back and try to figure out where they came from.) In particular, a regular n-gon may be thought of as the boundary of a polygonal region composed of n − 2 triangular regions.

4. Sketch several regular n-gons (n = 3, 4, 5, 6, 7) and, by drawing in all the distinct diagonals from a given vertex, show that the claim in the last sentence before this exercise is a reasonable one.

Thus, since each triangle has an angle sum of 180, we have that:

> The sum of the angle measures of the interior angles of a regular n-gon is
> (n − 2) · 180.

5. Explain why the result above is valid.

Since all of the angles of a regular n-gon are congruent to one another, we have:

> The measure of each interior angle of a regular n-gon is (n – 2) · 180/n.
> The measure of each exterior angle of a regular n-gon is 360/n.

6. Prove the two claims above. (Hint: Recall that an exterior angle of a polygon is *supplementary* to an interior one.)

7. What is the sum of the measures of the exterior angles of a regular polygon? (Note: Count only *one* exterior angle at each vertex of the polygon.)

The symmetry of a regular n-gon might lead you to suspect that there is a unique circle containing the vertices of any regular n-gon.

8. (Extra Credit) Explain why there is such a circle as described above.

Remark: A circle such as described above is said to be *circumscribed* about the polygon which is said to be *inscribed* in the circle. The circle is called the *circumcircle* of the polygon.

Definition: The center and radius of the circumcircle of a regular n-gon are said to be the *center* and *radius* of the n-gon itself. The (perpendicular) distance from the center to any of the sides of the regular n-gon is called the *apothem* of the polygon.

Remark: By a common abuse of language, the word "apothem" may also denote a *segment* drawn from the center of the polygon and perpendicular to one of its sides.

9. Describe how one could, in theory, locate the center of a given n-gon. (Hint: Recall that the perpendicular bisector of any chord of a circle must contain the center of the circle.)

10. Explain why all apothems of a given regular n-gon are congruent. (Hint: Draw a picture!)

Definition: An angle with vertex at the center of a regular n-gon and having its sides passing through adjacent vertices of the n-gon is said to be a *central angle* of the n-gon.

11. Prove: All the central angles of a regular n-gon are congruent. What is the measure of each such angle? (Hint: Of course, your expression for the measure will be in terms of n.)

12. A *central triangle* of a regular n-gon is a triangle having the center and two adjacent

vertices of the n-gon as its vertices. Prove that all the central triangles of a regular n-gon are congruent to one another.

Since all n central triangles of a regular n-gon are congruent to one another, we can easily see that the area of the polygonal region determined by a regular n-gon is n times the area of one of its central triangles.

Let a be the apothem (length) of a regular n-gon, P, of side length e. Then:

$$\alpha(P) = n \cdot \frac{1}{2} \cdot e \cdot a$$
$$= \frac{1}{2} \cdot a \cdot n \cdot e$$
$$= \frac{1}{2} \cdot a \cdot \text{perimeter of P}$$

13. Compute the area of a regular polygon with perimeter 120 and apothem 12.

14. Find the area of a regular hexagon (6-gon) with radius 8.

15. Find the area of a square inscribed in a circle with radius 5; find the area of a square circumscribed around a circle with radius 5. (Hint: Each of the sides of the latter square must be tangent to the circle around which it is circumscribed.)

16. Find the measure of each interior angle of a regular nonagon (9-gon).

17. If each interior angle of a regular n-gon has measure 156, what is n?

18. Find the measure of a central angle of a regular octagon (8-gon).

19. If you know how, write a procedure in Logo, Pascal, or another computer language to draw a regular n-gon. The procedure should accept the input of n, the number of sides, and also of e, the edge length, of the n-gon.

20. A *tessellation* of the plane is a "covering" of the plane with shapes which fit together without gaps, and also cover the entire plane (in theory). A regular tesselation of the plane uses only regular polygons, all of the same type. for example, one can easily imagine a regular tessellation of the plane which only uses squares. (Think of all the floors you have seen paved with square tiles.) Many old bathrooms have floors which demonstrate that regular hexagons (6-gons) may be used as the shapes in a regular tessellation of the plane. What other regular polygons could be used as the shapes in a regular tessellation of the plane? Explain your answer. (Hint: There is only *one* other possibility! Your explanation should depend heavily on the measure of the interior angles of the polygons which work.)

21. (Extra Credit) A semi-regular tessellation of the plane is a tessellation which uses regular shapes of exactly two different types. Try to discover as many semi-regular tessellations of the plane as you can. (Hint: Once again, the solution depends upon the measures of the interior angles of the regular n-gons.)

Section 3

For the rest of this Unit, we shall significantly relax our standards of rigor. We are concluding our study of plane geometry, and now we shall let our well-cultivated intuitions be our guides.

First, let's try to extend our idea of perimeter to apply to circles. Consider a square inscribed in a circle.

1. Explain how one could construct (with only the classical tools, if possible,) such a square.

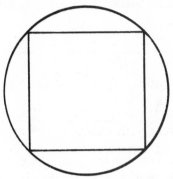

It should seem reasonable to you that the perimeter of such a square is less than the total distance around the circle, whatever that may mean. By bisecting each of the central angles of the square, we could obtain the central angles of an inscribed octagon as shown below:

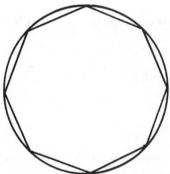

Once again, it should seem reasonable to you that the perimeter of the octagon is less than the total distance around the circle, but greater than the perimeter of the square with which we began.

2. Explain why the perimeter of the inscribed regular 8-gon described above is greater than that of the square. (Hint: The triangle inequality is helpful.)

It should seem obvious that if we were to repeat the process and get inscribed regular polygons with 16, 32, 64, 128, . . . sides, the perimeter of each such n-gon would be greater than that of the previous one, and yet less than the total distance around the circle. Moreover, it should also seem reasonable for us to think that the perimeters of the inscribed n-gons get closer and closer to the total distance around the circle. In some bizarre sense, it is intuitively "reasonable" to think of the circle itself as a regular n-gon with "infinitely many" sides and that the circle is being better and better approximated by the regular n-gons we inscribe within it.

The underlying idea in the approximation process above is that of *limit*. This idea is crucial in mathematics and deserves a small digression to make it as clear as possible to you at this stage of your mathematical growth.

Consider the following sequence of numbers:

$$1/2, \ 2/3, \ 3/4, \ 4/5, \ 5/6, \ 6/7, \ \ldots, \ n/(n + 1), \ \ldots$$

Each of these numbers is in the form $n/(n + 1)$ for $n = 1, 2, 3, \ldots$. Moreover, each of the numbers is greater than the one preceding it and yet less than 1. The numbers in the sequence are, however, getting closer and closer to 1 as n takes the values 1, 2, 3, ... (In fact, $n/(n + 1)$ is exactly $1/(n + 1)$ less than 1.) When n is very large, $n/(n + 1)$ gets very close to 1; so we say that 1 is the limit of the sequence, and denote this by writing:

$$\lim_{n \to \infty} \frac{n}{n + 1} = 1$$

Similarly, it should be clear to you that the sequence 0.3, 0.33, 0.333, 0.3333, 0.33333, . . . has 1/3 as its limit. Without realizing it, this is probably what you have always meant when you have blithely asserted that $1/3 = 0.33333333333333333$. . . . .

3. Students generally have no problem believing that:

$$1/3 = 0.33333333333333333333. \ . \ . = 0.\overline{3}$$
$$2/3 = 0.66666666666666666666. \ . \ . = 0.\overline{6}$$

Most, however, recoil in horror and disbelief (or at least find it highly counterintuitive) when asked to believe that:

$$3/3 = 0.99999999999999999999. \ . \ . = 0.\overline{9} = 1.$$

Do *you* have trouble grasping that $1 = 3/3 = 0.99999999999999999999$. . .? Why do you suppose this is so?

4. What is the limit of each of the following sequences? Explain.
   a. $1, \ 1/2, \ 1/4, \ 1/8, \ \ldots, \ 1/2^{n-1}, \ \ldots$
   b. $1/2, \ 4/5, \ 9/10, \ 16/17, \ \ldots, \ n^2/(n^2 + 1), \ \ldots$
   c. Use a calculator to investigate the behavior of the sequence
   $2, \ (1 + 1/2)^2, \ (1 + 1/3)^3, \ (1 + 1/4)^4, \ \ldots, \ (1 + 1/n)^n, \ \ldots$

Of course, some sequences of numbers do not have limits. E.g., each of the following sequences has no real number as its limit:

$$\text{a. } 1, 2, 3, 4, 5, 6, \ldots$$
$$\text{b. } 0, 1, 0, 1, 0, 1, \ldots$$

The first sequence lacks a limit because it is *unbounded*, i.e., for any number—no matter how great—there is a number in the sequence which is greater than that number.

The second sequence lacks a limit because it is *oscillating*, i.e., the values of the terms in the sequence are bouncing back and forth from 0 to 1.

5. What is the limit, if any, of each of the following sequences? Explain.
   a. 1, -1, 1/2, -1/2, 1/3, -1/3, 1/4, -1/4, . . .
   b. -1, -2, -3, -4, -5, -6, . . .
   c. 2, 2, 2, 2, 2, 2, 2, 2, 2, . . .
   d. 1, -1, 1, -1, 1, -1, 1, -1, 1, -1, 1, -1, . . .

Fortunately for our purposes, the sequence of numbers which represents the perimeters of the regular n-gons inscribed in a circle as described above is bounded (since each such perimeter is, for example, less than the perimeter of a square circumscribed around the circle) and does not oscillate, but rather steadily increases. It is a fact about real numbers (and a very deep fact, indeed) that:

A bounded, increasing sequence of real numbers has a real number as its limit.

We shall *define* the limit of the sequence of perimeters of inscribed regular n-gons to be the perimeter, i.e., the *circumference* of the circle. Moreover, it is intuitively clear that the limit of the apothems of the inscribed n-gons is the radius, r, of the circle.

Remark: We are glossing over a big difficulty here. We have no real reason to believe that we would get the same limit if we began the process with an inscribed equilateral triangle (instead of an inscribed square), and then repeatedly doubled the number of sides of the inscribed n-gons. You'll have to take my word for it when I say that it all works out.

Now, since all circles are similar to one another, it is also intuitively clear that the ratio of corresponding numbers (distances)

$$\frac{\text{Circumference}}{\text{Diameter}} = \frac{C}{D}$$

is the same for every circle. This famous ratio is given the name π, pi.

Definition: For any circle, $\pi = C/D$.

Corollary: $C = \pi D = \pi \cdot 2 \cdot r = 2 \cdot \pi \cdot r$, where r is the radius of the circle.

It should be intuitively clear that we can make the following assertion:
$\alpha(\text{circle}) = \lim_{n \to \infty} (\text{area inscribed regular n-gons})$

$= \lim_{n \to \infty} (\frac{1}{2} \cdot \text{apothem} \cdot \text{perimeter of n-gon})$

$= \frac{1}{2} \cdot r \cdot 2 \cdot \pi \cdot r$

$= \pi r^2$

Thus,

$\alpha(\text{circle}) = \pi r^2$, where r is the radius of the circle.

We can easily modify our formulas to enable us to find the area of certain special parts of circular regions.

Definition: A *sector* of a circular region is the intersection of a central angle and its interior with the circular region.

For example,

sector

The area of a sector with a central angle of measure m is $(m/360) \cdot \pi \cdot r^2$.

Definition: A *segment* of a circular region is a sector minus a central triangular region —except that we leave the part of the central triangle which is a chord of the circle.

Example:

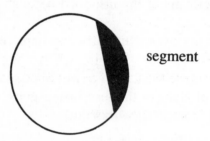

segment

The area of a segment which has a central angle of measure m is:
$(m/360) \cdot \pi \cdot r^2 - \alpha$(the central triangle which has the same central angle).

Finally, we can easily see that the *length* of an arc intercepted by a central angle of measure m is:
$$(m/360) \cdot C = (m/360) \cdot 2 \cdot \pi \cdot r = m\pi r/180$$

6. Suppose the area of a circle is 121π sq. cm.
    a. What is the circumference of this circle?
    b. What is the area of a 60° sector of this circle?
    c. What is the length of the arc of the sector in b.?
    d. What is the area of the segment determined by the sector in b.?

7. Find the area of a circle with circumference 48π.

8. Suppose the radius of a circle is doubled? What happens to the area of the circle? Is it doubled? Explain.

9. An *annulus* is the region between two concentric (having the same center) circles.
    a. Find the area of the annulus illustrated:

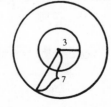

b. Given: $\overleftrightarrow{AB}$ is tangent to the inner circle at X; AB = 10.
Find: The area of the annulus formed by the two circles if the radii of the circles are integers. (Hint: Draw $\overline{OX}$ and $\overline{OA}$.)

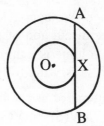

10. A square is inscribed in a circle of radius 10. Find the area of the region inside the circle but outside the square.

11. Find the area of the shaded region if ABCD is a square of side length 8 and each side of the square is a diameter of a semicircle as shown.

12. Each of the arcs in the diagram is a semicircle;
$\overline{DB} \perp \overline{AC}$ at B.
Prove: The area of the shaded region is $\pi(BD)^2/2$

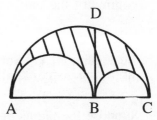

13. The Earth is about 93,000,000 miles from the Sun. Assume that the path of the Earth around the Sun is approximately a circle with the Sun at its center.
   a. Find the distance travelled by the Earth around the Sun in one full orbit (i.e., in one "year").
   b. Compute the average speed (in miles per hour) of the Earth as it goes around the Sun. Assume that a "year" is exactly 365 days long. Is the answer surprising?

14. Each of the arcs in the diagram is a semicircle. Find the area of the shaded region if AB = 16 and O is the midpoint of $\overline{AB}$.

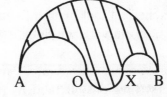

15. Suppose OAB is a 60° sector of ⊙O and AXB is a semicircle with diameter AB.
Find the area of the shaded region if the radius of ⊙O is 10.

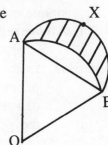

-243-

Section 4

In this section, we conclude our study of purely geometric concepts with a brief and highly intuitive discussion of the idea of volume as it relates to certain special solids.

Intuitively, volume is a third-dimensional analog of area. Thus, our intuitive notion of volume should satisfy the following conditions:

V0: The volume of any solid S, denoted by V(S), is a non-negative number.
V1: $S \cong T \Rightarrow V(S) = V(T)$
V2: $V(S \cup T) = V(S) + V(T)$ iff S and T have disjoint interiors.

Let's begin by considering the volume of a spherical region (ball).

Definition: A *sphere* S with center at O and radius r is the set of all points in space at a distance of r from O.

Definition: A *spherical region* with center at O and radius r is the set of all points in space at a distance of r or less from O.

Volume Formula 1: The volume of a spherical region with radius r is: $4\pi r^3/3$.

1. Assume that the Earth is a spherical region with a radius of 8000 miles. What is the volume of the Earth?

2. Assume that our Sun is a spherical region with a radius of 872,000 miles. What is the volume of the Sun? Approximately how many times greater than the volume of the Earth is the volume of the Sun?

3. Suppose the radius of a spherical region is doubled. Does the volume of the region double? If not, what happens to it? Explain. What if the radius were tripled, quad-rupled, etc.?

4. A spherical snowball melts uniformly so as to retain its spherical shape. If the radius of the snowball was originally 2 inches, what is the radius of the remaining ball after half of the original ball has melted away?

5. A spherical tank has a volume of 1,000,000 cubic feet. What is the radius of the sphere?

6. A spherical tank with a radius of 3 feet is to be covered with insulation which is to be uniformly 1 inch thick. What volume of insulation will be needed?

Intuitive Notion: A *prism*, P, consists of:
    i. Two regions, B_1 and B_2 (the *bases*) which are congruent to one another under a simple translation, T, in space, and
    ii. All line segments joining a point X of one base with its image T(X) in the other base.

Remarks: Prisms are usually named in terms of the shape of their bases: a triangular prism has two bases which are congruent triangular regions. Since the bases of a prism are "translates" of one another, they lie in parallel planes. Moreover, the perpendicular distance between these two parallel planes is called the *altitude* of the prism. Any plane between these two planes and parallel to them cuts the prism in a region (called a *cross-section*) which is congruent to the bases. Thus, all cross-sections of a prism are congruent to one another. A circular prism (i.e., a prism with circular regions for bases) is usually called a *cylinder*. Finally, if the altitude of a prism equals the distance between X and T(X) for a point of the base, we say that the prism is a *right* prism.

7. Sketch some examples of prisms. In particular, sketch a *right circular* prism.

Volume Formula 2: The volume of any prism P is given by:
$$V(P) = \alpha(B) \cdot h$$
where $\alpha(B)$ is the area of a base and h is the altitude of the prism.

8. Suppose C is a cube with edge length 5 cm.. What is the volume of C? If the edge length of C is doubled, what is the effect on the volume of the cube? Explain.

9. What is the volume of a tin can (right circular cylinder) which has a base of radius 15 cm. and a height of 30 cm.? If the base radius and height of the tin can are both doubled, what is the effect on the volume of the tin can? Explain.

10. Suppose B is a box (right rectangular prism) with length 10 in, width 6 in, and height 4 in. What is the volume of B? If the height, width, and length of B are all doubled, what is the effect on the volume of B? Explain.

11. Suppose a solid is subjected to a similarity transformation which doubles its size. What is the effect of such a transformation on the volume of the solid? Explain as well as you can.

12. Find the volume of a prism with height 10 whose bases are rhombi with diagonals of length 12 and 5.

13. Find the volume of a right triangular prism which has bases with side lengths 3, 4, 5, and a height of 8.

14. What are the approximate dimensions of the largest tin can (right circular cylinder) which can fit into a box which has a base 4 inches square and a height of 10 inches?

15. A ball of gold 6 inches in diameter is melted down and cast into discs 1 inch in diameter and 1/8 inch thick. How many such discs could be made from the ball?

Finally, we consider conical regions.

Intuitive Notion: A conical region C consists of:
  i. A plane region B (the *base*) and a point V (the *vertex*) not in the same plane as B, and
  ii. All closed line segments which join a point of B with V.

Remarks: We say that the *height* or *altitude* of a conical region is the perpendicular distance from V to the plane containing B. We usually visualize a cone as having a circular base whose center is the "foot" of the altitude of the cone. Cones may, however, have other shapes as shown below:

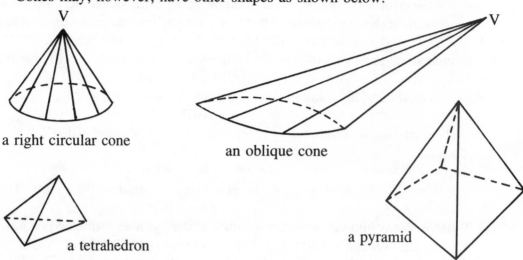

a right circular cone

an oblique cone

a tetrahedron

a pyramid

Volume Formula 3: the volume of any conical region C is given by:

$$V(C) = (1/3) \cdot \alpha(B) \cdot h$$

where $\alpha(B)$ is the area of the base of C and h is the height of C.

16. Find the volume of a conical reservoir whose surface is a circle of radius 30 feet and whose depth is 20 feet.

17. Find the volume of a pyramid (a cone with a square base) whose base is 100 yards square and whose height is 75 yards.

18. The volume of a right circular cone is 1800 cubic inches. What is the height of this cone if the radius of its base is 15 inches?

19. The height of a right circular cone is 12 cm. and the radius of its base is 8 cm.. A cylindrical hole of diameter 2 cm. is drilled through the exact center of the cone from top to bottom. What is the volume of the resulting solid?

20. A grain bin is illustrated below. What is its volume?

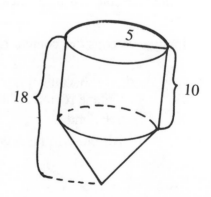

Unit IX—Review Topics

1. Definition of triangular region; polygon—vertices, edges, adjacent vertices and edges; boundary, perimeter, angle of polygon; names of various polygons; polygonal region— interior, boundary.
2. Area axiom—Axiom 14; definition of area.
3. The area of a rectangle is the product of its length and width; the area of a square is the square of its side length.
4. Definition of altitude and base of triangle.
5. The area of a triangle is half the product of its base and associated altitude; the area of an equilateral triangle with side length s is $\sqrt{3}s^2/4$.
6. If $\triangle ABC \sim \triangle DEF$, $\alpha(\triangle DEF) = k^2 \cdot \alpha(\triangle ABC)$ where k is the scale factor of the similarity.
7. $\alpha(\text{trapezoid}) = \frac{1}{2} \cdot (b_1 + b_2) \cdot h$
8. $\alpha(\text{parallelogram}) = b \cdot h$
9. $\alpha(\text{rhombus}) = \frac{1}{2} \cdot d_1 \cdot d_2$
10. Definition of a convex polygon, regular polygon, and diagonal of a polygon.
11. The angle sum of the interior angles of a convex n-gon is $(n - 2) \cdot 180$
12. Each interior angle of a regular convex n-gon measures $[(n - 2) \cdot 180]/n$
13. Each exterior angle of a convex regular n-gon measures $360/n$.
14. Definition of circumscribed circle; inscribed polygon; circumcircle; center, radius, and apothem of a regular n-gon.
15. The area of a convex regular n-gon is $\frac{1}{2} \cdot$ apothem $\cdot$ perimeter.
16. The idea of the limit of a sequence of real numbers; how limits can fail to exist; a bounded increasing sequence of real numbers has a real number as its limit.
17. Definition of circumference of a circle; circumference $= \pi \cdot D = 2 \cdot \pi \cdot r$.
18. The area of a circle with radius r is $\pi \cdot r^2$;
    the area of a sector with central angle of measure m is $m/360 \cdot \pi \cdot r^2$;
    the area of a segment with central angle of measure m is $\alpha(\text{sector}) - \alpha(\triangle)$;
    the length of arc intercepted by a central angle of measure m is $\pi mr/180$.
19. The basic intuitive properties of volume.
20. Definition of sphere, spherical region.
21. The volume of a sphere with radius r is $4\pi r^3/3$.
22. Definition of prism, bases, cross-section; cylinder; right prism.
23. The volume of a prism with base B and height h is $\alpha(B) \cdot h$.
24. Definition of cone, base, vertex, and altitude.
25. The volume of a cone with base B and height h is $1/3 \cdot \alpha(B) \cdot h$.

Unit X
Trigonometry

In this unit we shall complete a brief study of trigonometry (triangle measure). You are assumed to have a scientific calculator which you can use to compute the values of the trigonometric functions. The origins of trigonometry lie in the work of the ancient Greeks at Alexandria who studied astronomy for such purposes as time reckoning, making calendars, and navigation. The father of trigonometry was Hipparchus (flourished 161–126 BC) who made astronomical observations while living in Alexandria. Later development of trigonometry was spurred in part by keen interest in astrology, which created a need for extended knowledge of astronomy. The name trigonometry (which, although it comes from the Greek, was *not* used by the ancients) is an unfortunate one. It gives the impression that trigonometry is a subject limited almost entirely to the study of how to determine the sizes of the various parts of triangles about which one has obtained some data such as SAS. While this may once, 200 or more years ago, have been the principal "use" for trigonometry, it is most assuredly not so today. In fact, trigonometry and the functions associated with it play a crucial role in many areas of pure and applied mathematics and science. Thus, we shall begin our study of trigonometry in a *general* context, develop the so-called circular functions, and then give a very brief examination of their applications to triangles. Further applications must await your advanced study of both mathematics and science.

Consider a unit circle (i.e., a circle with radius 1) having its center at the origin of a coordinatized plane:

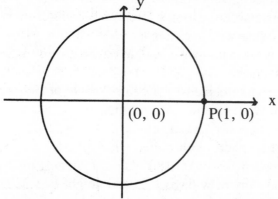

Recall that an equation for this circle is $x^2 + y^2 = 1$. The coordinates of any point (x, y) on this circle *must* satisfy the equation, e.g., (1, 0) and (0, 1) are on the circle as are (-1, 0) and (0, -1).

1. Test to see whether or not each of the following points is on the unit circle with center at the origin:
   a. (1/2, $\sqrt{3}/2$), (1/2, -1/2), (-1, 1/2), ($-\sqrt{2}/2$, $\sqrt{2}/2$).
   b. Sketch a graph indicating the location of each of the points in a. with respect to the unit circle.

2. Find the points of intersection of the unit circle with the lines y = x and y = -x by solving appropriate systems of equations. Sketch the graphs of the unit circle and both of these lines and label the points of intersection with their coordinates in *exact* (i.e., use radicals when necessary) form.

Let us imagine the rotation of the unit circle around the origin and focus our attention on the point P (1, 0) and its images.

Notation: R_θ is the isometry which rotates the plane around the origin through an angle of measure θ.

We shall extend our idea of angle measure in a natural, intuitive way, so that we may discuss angles which have *any* real number as their measure.

Definition: An angle is said to be in *standard position* if:
  i. Its vertex, O, is the origin, and
  ii. One side of $\angle$AOB, called the *initial* side, is the ray which is the non-negative x-axis.

Note that the initial side of an angle in standard position contains the point P (1, 0). Also note that the non-initial side of such an angle is called the *terminal* side; it is, of course, a ray with the origin as its vertex. We think of the terminal ray of the angle as containing the image $R_\theta(P)$ of the point P(1, 0) under the rotation R_θ. This image point is, obviously, located at the intersection of the unit circle and the terminal side of the angle in standard position.

We orient angles by agreeing that a rotation in the *counterclockwise* direction corresponds to a *positive* angle measure; accordingly, a rotation in the *clockwise* direction corresponds to a *negative* angle measure. Of course, we also agree that the identity map corresponds to a rotation through an angle of measure zero. Finally, we agree (in accordance with our old angle measure axiom) that a rotation through $\pm 180°$ corresponds to a half-turn around the origin. Thus, a rotation through $\pm 360°$ corresponds to a full turn around the origin (which yields the same effect on the plane as the identity map). Our use of these angle measures agrees with the ancient Babylonian and Greek tradition of dividing the circle into 360 equal parts—each corresponding to a central angle of 1°. The figures below should serve to clarify our *intuitive* extension of the ideas of angle and angle measure:

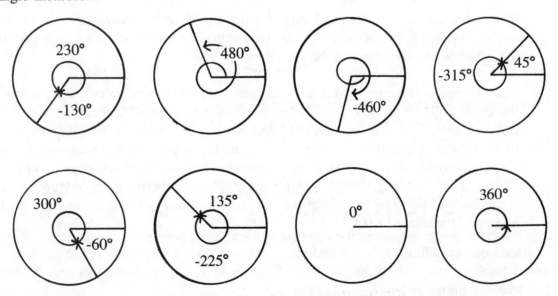

3. **Regard each member of the pairs of numbers below as being the measure of an angle in standard position. Explain why the two angles of each pair have the same terminal side:**

a. 60, -300
b. 120, 480
c. -30, 330
d. -200, -920
e. 20, 1100
f. 405, 4005

    g. Sketch a picture showing each of
       the pairs of angles above.

Recall that we are going to focus our attention on $R_\theta(P)$ for various θ and, in particular, on the *coordinates* of $R_\theta(P)$. Note that since R_θ is an *isometry*, $R_\theta(P)$ is *always* on the unit circle for any θ. Thus, the coordinates of $R_\theta(P)$ *must* satisfy the equation $x^2 + y^2 = 1$.

4.   What are the coordinates of $R_\theta(P)$ if $\mu\angle\theta =$

        a. 0
        b. 90
        c. 180
        d. 270
        e. -90
        f. -180
        g. -270
        h. 1000
        i. -900

    (If necessary, sketch pictures to help yourself find the answers.)

The coordinates of $R_\theta(P)$ are so important that they have special names:

$$R_\theta(P) = (\text{cosine } \theta, \text{ sine } \theta)$$

These coordinates are usually abbreviated as $(\cos\theta, \sin\theta)$. Your scientific calculator should have buttons labelled cos and sin which will compute the values of these coordinates for *any* angle θ. Set your calculator to measure angles in degrees and simply enter into the calculator the value of the angle measure and then press the appropriate key, sin or cos, to get the desired coordinate. E.g., if you enter 30 and press cos, the result is 0.866025404 (in fact it is *exactly* $\sqrt{3}/2$). Similarly, you can check that entering 30 and then pressing sin yields 0.5.

5.   Check that the values of cos and sin computed for 30 satisfy the equation of the unit circle. Sketch a graph of the unit circle and indicate on it the angle and point $R_{30}(P)$ for which we have computed the coordinates.

6.   Sketch a graph of the unit circle and indicate $R_{45}(P)$. Use your calculator to compute the coordinates of $R_{45}(P)$, i.e., compute $\cos(45)$ and $\sin(45)$. What do you find? Refer to exercise 2 and state the coordinates of $R_{45}(P)$ in *exact* radical form. Refer to exercise 3 and explain why each of the angles in each part of that exercise has the same cos and sin. Based on your observations, what would you expect to be true of $\cos\theta$ and $\cos(\theta + k \cdot 360)$? Of $\sin\theta$ and $\sin(\theta + k \cdot 360)$ for any integer k? I.e., what do you find to be true about the cos and sin of any two angles which differ by an integral multiple of 360?

Based on the definition of cos and sin which we saw above, it is easy to see that we could think of cos and sin as mappings from $\mathbb{R}$ to $\mathbb{R}$. These mappings are the basic *circular functions*.

7. a. Explain as best you can why the *image* of both sin and cos is the closed interval
        [-1,1]. Thus, both sin and cos map $\mathbb{R}$ *onto* [-1,1]. (Hint: Recall that $R_\theta(P)$ is
        always on the unit circle.)
    b. Explain why $(\cos \theta)^2 + (\sin \theta)^2 = 1$ for every θ.

Remark: One usually writes $\cos^2\theta + \sin^2\theta \equiv 1$ where $\equiv$ means that the equation is an
            identity, i.e., it is true for *every* possible value of θ.

   In exercise 6, you should have found that $\cos 45 = \sin 45 = \sqrt{2}/2$. There are very
few non-equivalent angles for which it is possible to compute the *exact* values of cos and
sin. Let's see how one may use some facts known about certain special triangles to
compute exact values for cos and sin. First, let's re-examine the case of $\theta = 45$. Consider
$R_{45}(P) = P'$ as illustrated below:

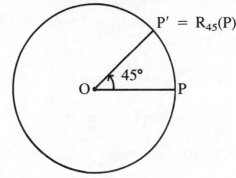

Draw the half-chord through P', perpendicular to the x-axis to get:

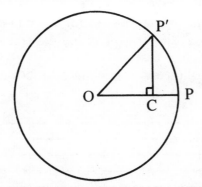

8. a. Explain why $\triangle OP'C$ is a 45-45-90 triangle (i.e., an isosceles right triangle) with
      hypotenuse 1.
   b. Explain why $OC = CP' = \sqrt{2}/2$.
   c. Explain why $P' = (\sqrt{2}/2, \sqrt{2}/2)$ and thus why $\cos 45 = \sin 45 = \sqrt{2}/2$.

            Now, consider $R_{30}(P) = P'$ as illustrated below:

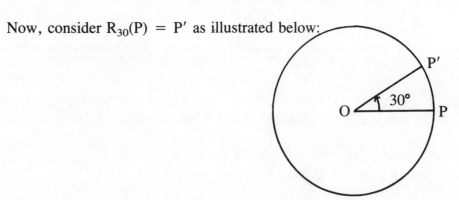

Doing the same sort of construction as we did for $R_{45}(P)$ yields:

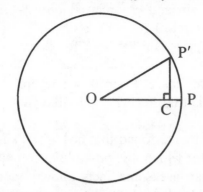

9. a. Explain why $\triangle OP'C$ is a 30-60-90 triangle with hypotenuse 1.
    b. Explain why $OC = \sqrt{3}/2$ and $CP' = 1/2$.
    c. Explain why $P' = (\sqrt{3}/2, 1/2)$ and thus why $\cos 30 = \sqrt{3}/2$ and $\sin 30 = 1/2$.

   Thus, we can compute the *exact* values of cos and sin for 30 and 45.

10. a. Draw a sketch of the unit circle and of the line p with equation $y = x$. Explain why $F_p(R_{30}(P)) = R_{60}(P)$.
     b. State the *exact* values of cos 60 and sin 60. (Hint: Recall that $F_p(x, y) = (y, x)$.)

11. Let p be the line $y = x$. Explain why $F_p(R_\theta(P)) = R_{90-\theta}(P)$ for any θ in [0,90]. (Hint: Draw a sketch!)
    Thus, explain why $\cos \theta = \sin (90 - \theta)$ for any θ in [0,90]. We see here the *reason* for the name *co*sine θ; *co*sine θ is precisely the sine of the *co*mplement of θ.

   So far, we know the following exact values for cos and sin:

θ	$\cos \theta$	$\sin \theta$
0	1	0
30	$\sqrt{3}/2$	1/2
45	$\sqrt{2}/2$	$\sqrt{2}/2$
60	1/2	$\sqrt{3}/2$
90	0	1
180	-1	0
270	0	-1
360	1	0

12. Draw a large sketch of the unit circle and label the point on it which corresponds to each entry in the table of exact values of cos and sin (look just above for the table).

13. Explain why $\cos 0 = \cos 360 = \cos 720 = \cos 1080 = \ldots$ and $\sin 0 = \sin 360 = \sin 720 = \sin 1080 = \ldots$

   Let's investigate a bit more carefully to clarify some relationships of circular functions to triangles. Consider the diagram below.

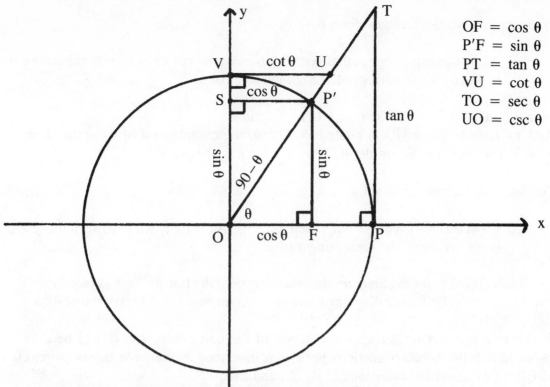

OF = cos θ
P'F = sin θ
PT = tan θ
VU = cot θ
TO = sec θ
UO = csc θ

By definition, we see that OF = cos θ and P'F = sin θ.

14. a. Explain why △OFP' ∼ △OPT.
   b. There is a stretch map S_k for which $S_k(△OFP') = △OPT$. How may k be expressed in terms of a circular function of θ?
   (Hint: Explain why k = OP/OF = OT/OP' = TP/P'F.)

Since △OFP' ∼ △OPT and since OF = cos θ while OP = 1, we can see from the previous exercise that for k = 1/cos θ we have $S_k(△OFP') = △OPT$.

Since the ratios of corresponding side lengths of similar triangles are all equal, we have: OP/OF = 1/cos θ = OT/OP' = OT/1 = OT

Since OT is a *secant* to the unit circle, we define 1/cos θ = OT = secant θ.

Definition: secant θ = 1/cos θ

Remark: Secant θ is usually abbreviated as sec θ.

Similarly, P'F/OF = TP/OP, i.e., sin θ/cos θ = TP/1 = TP.

Since $\overleftrightarrow{TP}$ is a tangent to the unit circle, we define TP = sin θ / cos θ = tangent θ.

Definition: tangent θ = sin θ / cos θ

Remark: Tangent θ is usually abbreviated tan θ.

Furthermore, VU/VO = SP'/SO, i.e., VU/1 = cos θ/sin θ.

Since $\overline{VU}$ is related to 90 − θ, the complement of θ, just as $\overline{TP}$ is related to θ, we define VU = cos θ/sin θ = cotangent θ.

Definition: cotangent θ = cos θ/sin θ.

Remark: As in naming cosine, cotangent θ (abbreviated cot θ) is so called because it is precisely the tangent of the complement of θ!

Finally, UO/VO = P'O/SO, i.e., UO/1 = 1/sin θ
so UO = 1/sin θ. Since $\overline{UO}$ is related to 90 − θ, the complement of θ, in the same way as $\overline{TO}$ is related to θ, we define UO = 1/sin θ = cosecant θ.

Definition: cosecant θ = 1/sin θ

Remark: Cosecant θ is usually abbreviated as csc θ. As before, we have seen that csc θ is the secant of the complement of θ.

15. a. Study △OPT in the big diagram above and explain why $(\tan \theta)^2 + 1 = (\sec \theta)^2$.
   b. Study △OVU in the big diagram above and explain why $1 + (\cot \theta)^2 = (\csc \theta)^2$.

If you examine and reflect upon a diagram of the unit circle, you should be able to understand that the circular functions behave as described in the table below (note: QI, QII, QIII, QIV stand for *quadrants* I, II, III, and IV):

```
        QII | QI
       -----+-----→
        QIII| QIV
```

	sin θ	cos θ	tan θ	cot θ	sec θ	csc θ
QI 0 ≤ θ ≤ 90	+ Increases from 0 to 1	+ Decreases from 1 to 0	+ Increases from 0 to +∞	+ Decreases from +∞ to 0	+ Increases from 1 to +∞	+ Decreases from +∞ to 1
QII 90 ≤ θ ≤ 180	+ Decreases from 1 to 0	- Decreases from 0 to -1	- Increases from -∞ to 0	- Decreases from 0 to -∞	- Increases from -∞ to -1	+ Increases from 1 to +∞
QIII 180 ≤ θ ≤ 270	- Decreases from 0 to -1	- Increases from -1 to 0	+ Increases from 0 to +∞	+ Decreases from +∞ to 0	- Decreases from -1 to -∞	- Increases from -∞ to -1
QIV 270 ≤ θ ≤ 360	- Increases from -1 to 0	+ Increases from 0 to 1	- Increases from -∞ to 0	- Decreases from 0 to -∞	+ Decreases from +∞ to 1	- Decreases from -1 to -∞

Using the basic formulas: $\sin^2\theta + \cos^2\theta = 1$
$$\tan^2\theta + 1 = \sec^2\theta$$
$$1 + \cot^2\theta = \csc^2\theta$$
we can solve problems such as the following:

Example: Suppose $\sin \theta = 2/3$ and $R_\theta(P)$ is in QII. Find the other five circular functions of θ.

Solution: Using $\sin^2 \theta + \cos^2 \theta = 1$, we get $\cos \theta = \pm\sqrt{1 - \sin^2 \theta}$
thus, since cos is negative in QII, we get:
$\cos \theta = -\sqrt{1 - 4/9} = -\sqrt{5/9} = -\sqrt{5}/3$.

Then, $\tan \theta = \sin \theta/\cos \theta = (2/3)/(-\sqrt{5}/3) = 2/-\sqrt{5} = -2\sqrt{5}/5$
$\cot \theta = 1/\tan \theta = -\sqrt{5}/2$
$\sec \theta = 1/\cos \theta = -3/\sqrt{5} = -3\sqrt{5}/5$
$\csc \theta = 1/\sin \theta = 3/2$.

16. Using the data below, find all of the circular functions of θ in each part:
   a. $\sin \theta = -12/13$ and $\tan \theta > 0$
   b. $\cos \theta = 8/17$ and $\sin \theta < 0$
   c. $\tan \theta = 1/2$ and $\cos \theta > 0$
   d. $\sec \theta = -5/3$ and $\sin \theta < 0$

   Careful examination of the complex diagram below will reveal to you that one may use the symmetry of the unit circle to discover many interesting relationships among the circular functions. In particular, you should be able to see why it is sufficient to know the values of the circular functions for the angles between 0 and 45 in order to deduce their values for *any* angle.

17. Carefully examine the diagram and explain *why* it is sufficient to know the values of the circular functions for angles from 0 to 45 in order to deduce their values for *any* angle.

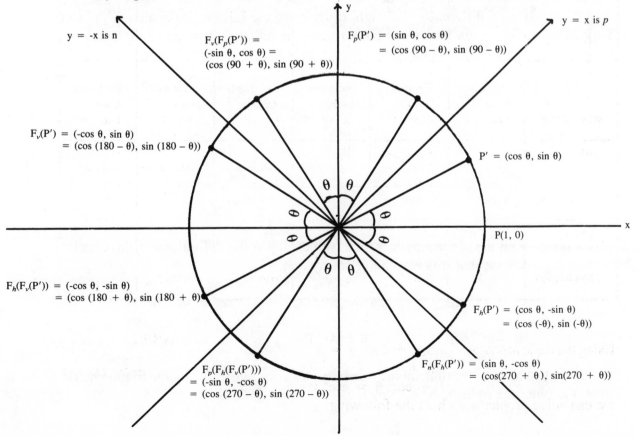

18. Let p be the line $y = x$; let n be the line $y = -x$; let h be the x-axis; and let v be the y-axis. Examine the diagram above and:

a. Use what you know about the effect of F_p to explain why
$$\sin \theta = \cos (90 - \theta) \text{ and}$$
$$\cos \theta = \sin (90 - \theta)$$

b. Use what you know about the effect of F_h to explain why
$$\cos (-\theta) = \cos \theta \text{ and}$$
$$\sin (-\theta) = -\sin \theta$$

c. Use what you know about the effect of F_v to explain why
$$\cos (90 + \theta) = -\sin \theta \text{ and}$$
$$\sin (90 + \theta) = \cos \theta$$

d. Use what you know about the effect of F_v to explain why
$$\cos (180 - \theta) = -\cos \theta \text{ and}$$
$$\sin (180 - \theta) = \sin \theta$$

e. Use the fact that $F_h \circ F_v = R_{180}$ to explain why
$$\cos (180 + \theta) = -\cos \theta \text{ and}$$
$$\sin (180 + \theta) = -\sin \theta$$

f. Use the fact that $F_p \circ F_h \circ F_v = R_{270}$ to explain why
$$\cos (270 - \theta) = -\sin \theta \text{ and}$$
$$\sin (270 - \theta) = -\cos \theta$$

g. Use the fact that $F_n \circ F_h = R_{270}$ to explain why
$$\cos (270 + \theta) = \sin \theta \text{ and}$$
$$\sin (270 + \theta) = -\cos \theta$$

Since any two right triangles containing an acute angle of measure θ are similar (why?), we may regard the so-called trigonometric functions (i.e., the circular functions restricted to acute angle measures) as being defined in terms of ratios of side lengths in such a triangle. It makes no difference what right triangle we use (and so we could use the sort of triangles we have seen in the unit circle) since the ratios of corresponding lengths in similar triangles are all the same. Consider the right triangle shown below:

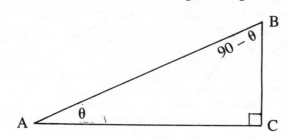

By analogy with the discussion in which we developed the definitions of the circular functions, we can see that it is reasonable to say that:

$$\cos \theta = AC/AB \qquad \tan \theta = BC/AC \qquad \sec \theta = AB/AC$$

$$\sin \theta = BC/AB \qquad \cot \theta = AC/BC \qquad \csc \theta = AB/BC$$

Let's look at an excellent mnemonic (memory) trick for remembering the trigonometric ratios. Consider the right triangle below:

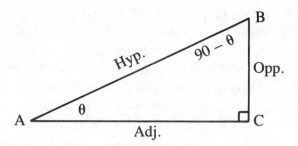

Since side $\overline{BC}$ is opposite $\angle\theta$, we label it Opp.
Since side $\overline{AC}$ is adjacent to $\angle\theta$, we label it Adj.
Since side $\overline{AB}$ is the hypotenuse of $\triangle ABC$, we label it Hyp.
Then,

$$\sin\theta = \text{Opp./Hyp} \qquad \tan\theta = \text{Opp./Adj.} \qquad \sec\theta = \text{Hyp./Adj.}$$

The easy way to remember this is to use the mnemonic SOHTOASHA (recall this by thinking Some Oaf Has Taken Orphan Annie's Sandy Hound Away) to see that Sine is O/H, that Tangent is O/A, and that Secant is H/A. Furthermore, you may use the "magic" hexagon below as a mnemonic to remind you that the functions at opposite ends of its diagonals are reciprocals of one another.

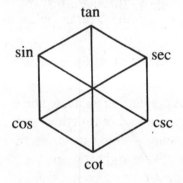

19. In each of the following, verify that the triangle indicated is really a right triangle and then compute all six of the circular (trigonometric) functions (sin, cos, tan, cot, sec, csc) for *each* of the acute angles:

a)
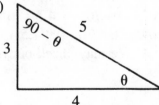

b)
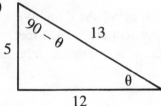

c)
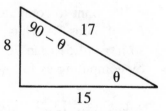

Consider the right triangle

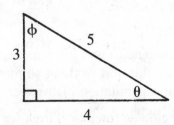

You should have found in exercise 19a that sin φ = 4/5 = 0.8. How can we find the angle measure of φ? Your calculator should have a button labelled $\sin^{-1}$, the *inverse* of the sin mapping. We can use $\sin^{-1}$ to find the measure of φ as follows:

Enter 0.8 into your calculator and then press $\sin^{-1}$. The result will be the *degree measure* of φ (assuming your calculator is set to measure angles in *degrees*—refer to the manual to see how to set it to do so). Why does this work? Because $\sin^{-1}$ is the *inverse* of the sin function, i.e., it *undoes* what the sin does. Thus, $\sin^{-1}(\sin φ) = φ$ and $\sin(\sin^{-1} φ) = φ$. In the example above, $\sin^{-1}(0.8)$ is approximately 53.13 degrees.

Similarly, in the exercise we found that sin (90 – φ) = cos φ = 3/5 = 0.6. Thus, we could use the $\sin^{-1}$ function to find 90 – φ or the $\cos^{-1}$ function to find φ. Using the $\sin^{-1}$ function, we find 90 – φ to be approximately 36.87 degrees, as we had expected it to be as soon as we had found φ. Notice that we may check our work by observing that 53.13 + 36.87 = 90.00.

20. Use your calculator as described in the example above to compute the measure of each of the acute angles in exercise 19 parts b. and c.

Let's look at some typical applications of trigonometric functions to right triangles.:
A ladder leaning against a wall makes an angle of 70° with the floor. If the foot of the latter is 4.5 feet from the base of the wall, how long is the ladder? How far up the wall is the tip of the ladder? Consider the diagram below as you read about the solution:

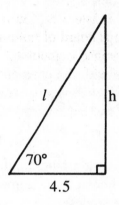

We want to compute *l* and h using the data. We know that cos 70° = 4.5/*l* so *l* = 4.5/cos 70. Thus, *l* is approximately 13.2 feet. Moreover, tan 70 = h/4.5; so h = (4.5) · tan 70. Hence, h is approximately 12.4 feet. We may check our results by computing as follows:

$$\cos^{-1}(4.5/13.2) \approx 70.1° \qquad\qquad \tan^{-1}(12.4/4.5) \approx 70.1°$$

Thus, within the limits of error produced by rounding off, our answers for *l* and h are acceptable.

Remarks: Notice that we computed *l* and h independent of one another. It is always a good practice to do this sort of thing so that any error in computing the first will not affect our computation of the second. Note that we can use *inverse* trigonometric functions to check our answers. Finally, note that we solved for *l* and h by selecting a simple trigonometric equation in which the item desired was the only unknown (so that we could solve directly for it).

21. A rocket carrying a space shuttle rises vertically from its launch pad while being tracked by a radar device located 1000 yards away from the pad. What is the altitude of the rocket and how far is it from the radar site when its angle of elevation is 40°? (Round to the nearest yard.) (Note: The angle of elevation of an object is the angle between the horizontal and the line of "vision" of the "observer.")

22. Find the angle of elevation to the Sun when the shadow of a 110 foot tall monument is 50 feet long. (Round to the nearest degree.) (Hint: You will have to use an inverse function!)

23. How tall is the tallest fence you could climb over with a 12 foot ladder, if the angle between the ladder and the ground must not exceed 80°? (Assume that the very tip of the ladder rests at the top of the wall.)

24. A flagpole which is 75 feet tall casts a shadow 30 feet long at a certain time. If the Sun rose at 6:50 am and is directly overhead at noon, what is that time? (Round to the nearest minute.)

25. If tan θ = 2 and θ is an angle of a triangle, find sin θ and cos θ. (Hint: You will have to use an inverse function. Round your answer to 3 decimal places.)

26. While hacking your way through a dense jungle, you come to a large clearing and look up toward a vertical cliff in the distance. You can see the entrance to a cave which you believe contains a fabulous hoard of gold and jewels! You estimate that the angle of elevation of the cave entrance is about 40°. You hurry 100 steps straight toward the cliff face directly in line with the cave entrance and estimate the angle of elevation of the cave entrance from your new location to be about 50°. Assuming your steps are approximately 1 meter long, about how far will you have to climb up the cliff to get to the cave?

Section 2

When defining angle measure, it is standard in advanced mathematics to use a unit of measure *different* from the degree, called a radian. This unit is so named because it is closely related to the size of the radius of the circle whose center is the vertex of the angle being measured. By definition, a central angle of one radian intercepts an arc of the circle with length equal to the radius of the circle. Since the total arc length (i.e., the circumference) of a circle is $2\pi r$, we can see that:

$$2\pi \text{ radians} = 360 \text{ degrees}$$

Remark: When measuring angles in radians, it is usual to say, for example, that an angle has measure $\pi/4$ rather than $\pi/4$ *radians*; i.e., we usually don't include the *unit* of measure for angles when using radian measure (we have often omitted the degree unit when discussing the measure of angles prior to this). This is a universal standard in mathematics when using radian measure.

1. Using your calculator, find the approximate degree measure equivalent to 1 radian. Then convert each of the following degree measures into an equivalent radian measure:

   a. 0°   b. 30°   c. 45°   d. 60°
   e. 90°   f. 120°   g. 135°   h. 150°
   i. 180°   j. 210°   k. 225°   l. 240°
   m. 270°   n. 300°   o. 315°   p. 330°

Your calculator is probably equipped to compute circular functions of angles measured in either degrees or radians (and probably also in grads, which we won't discuss at all).

2. Experiment with your calculator (if necessary) until you are thoroughly familiar with operating it in either degrees or radians. Then use your calculator to compute and make a table to record the values of the sine of each of the angles in exercise 1. E.g.,

x	sin x
0	0.0
$\pi/6$	0.5
$\pi/4$	0.707. . .
.	.
.	.
.	.

Using the table of values computed above, carefully sketch the graph of the function $y = \sin x$ for x in the closed interval $[0, 2\pi]$; use graph paper for this project. Based on the fact that the sine function is *periodic* (i.e., repeats its values over and over again) with a *period* of 2π, extend your sketch to cover at least the values of x in the closed interval $[-4\pi, 4\pi]$ and indicate that the graph extends indefinitely in the same pattern. (When we say that the *period* of the sine function is 2π, we mean that the graph of the function on any interval of length 2π is endlessly repeated—think of the graph as having translational symmetry where the length of the motif is 2π.)

Repeat the previous parts of this exercise replacing sine by cosine and sketch its graph on the same axes, but in a different color. Compare the graphs. What do you notice? It should be apparent to you that the graphs of $y = \sin x$ and $y = \cos x$ are congruent to one another. What very simple transformation maps the graph of one onto the other? (Hint: $\sin(x - \pi/2) = \cos x$.)

3. We saw that $\sin(-x) = -\sin x$ and $\cos(-x) = \cos x$. These conditions imply something very important about the symmetry of the graphs of sin and cos. Try to describe the allowable symmetry motions for these graphs. (Hint: A half-turn about the origin carries (x, y) to $(-x, -y)$; reflection through the y-axis carries (x, y) to $(-x, y)$.)

4. Use your calculator to compute enough values to enable you to sketch reasonably accurate graphs of the tangent, cotangent, secant, and cosecant functions (i.e., sketch $y = \tan x$, etc.). (Hint: Recall the magic hexagon which tells you how to compute some of these functions as reciprocals of others.)

For those values of x which produce error messages on your calculator, use nearby values of x to deduce the behavior or the functions for x close to the values where they are undefined. E.g., $\tan \pi/2$ is undefined (since $\cos \pi/2 = 0$), so use values of x very close to $\pi/2$ to determine the behavior of the tangent function in a small "neighborhood" of $\pi/2$. (Try values of x such as $.49\pi$, $.499\pi$, $.4999\pi$, $.51\pi$, $.501\pi$, $.5001\pi$, etc.) Do this before you read on. Then look below to see if your graphs agree with the graphs here.

Your graphs of the circular functions should have looked like the following:

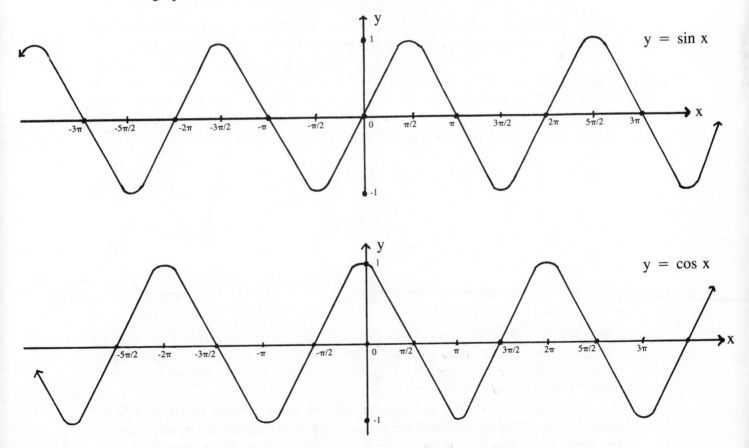

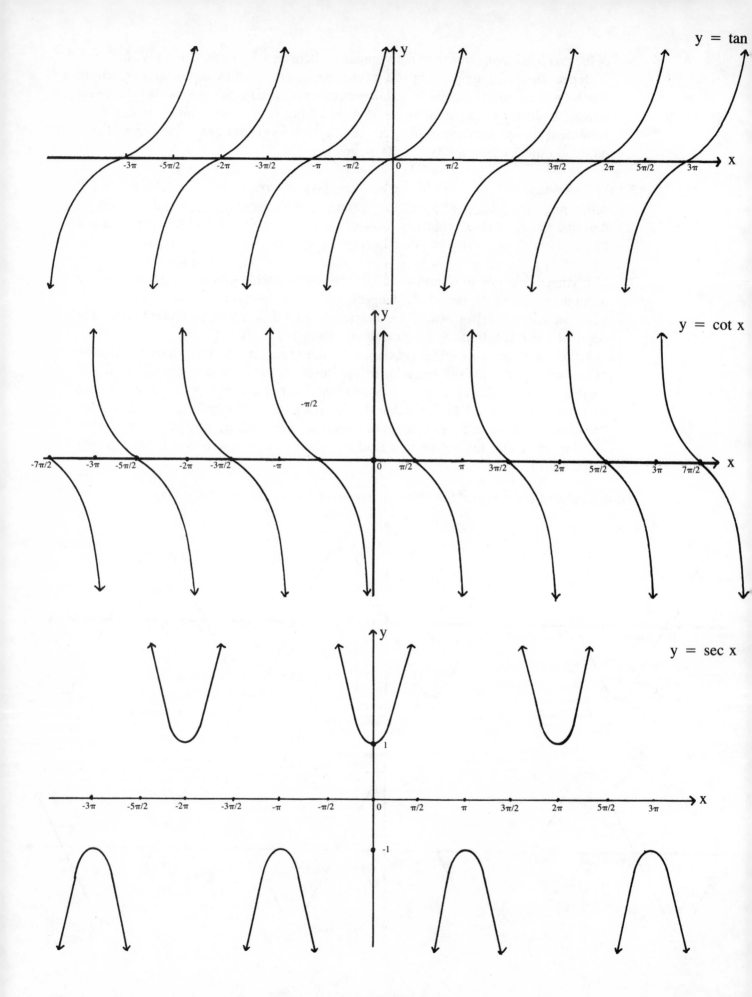

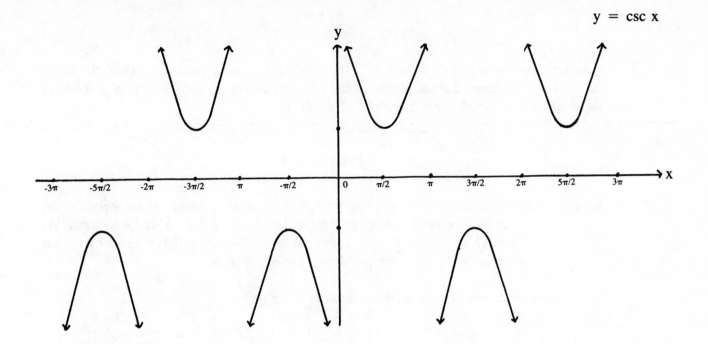

$$y = \csc x$$

Section 3

In this section we shall consider what is called a *general sinusoidal* (like the sine) *curve*. Since we know that the graphs of the sine and cosine are congruent to one another, we shall limit our study here to graphs of the form:

$$y = A + B \cos (Cx + D)$$

Remark: We shall be considering the graphs of sine and cosine simultaneously. In particular, we shall seek to determine the effect of the *real coefficients* A, B, C, and D on the graph of a general sinusoidal function. Let's begin by taking on the easiest part of the problem—the effect of A.

1. Sketch the graph of each of the following functions:
   a. $y = 1 + \cos x$ b. $y = 4 + \cos x$ c. $y = -2 + \cos x$
   d. $y = -8 + \cos x$ e. $y = 3 + \cos x$ f. $y = -5 + \cos x$
   g. Explain as best you can why the effect of using the various values of A given above is to *translate* the graph of $y = \cos x$ either straight up or straight down, depending on whether A is positive or negative.

In exercise 1, you should have obtained sinusoidal graphs which "wiggled" up and down along the line $y = A$.

Definition: The line $y = A$ is called the *sinusoidal axis* of the general sinusoidal curve
$$y = A + B \cos (Cx + D)$$

Now, let's consider the effect of B:

2. Sketch the graph of each of the following curves:
   a. $y = 2 \cos x$ b. $y = 0.5 \cos x$ c. $y = 10 \cos x$
   d. $y = -2 \cos x$ e. $y = -0.5 \cos x$ f. $y = -10 \cos x$
   g. Explain as best you can why the effect of using the various values of B given above is to *stretch* or *shrink* the graph of $y = \cos x$ in a vertical direction only; why do negative values of B reflect the graph in the x-axis as well as stretch or shrink it in the vertical direction? What are the largest and smallest values of y for each of the functions above? (I.e., what are the maximum and minimum values of y for each function?) What is the scale factor of the vertical stretch or shrink produced by B in $y = B \cos x$?

In exercise 2, you should have obtained sinusoidal graphs which "wiggled" along the sinusoidal axis and which had highest and lowest points (called *crests* and *troughs*) with y-coordinates $|B|$ and $-|B|$ respectively.

Definition: The *amplitude* of the general sinusoidal curve $y = A + B \cos (Cx + D)$ is $|B|$.

3. a. Sketch the graph of y = 3 + 2 cos x
   b. What is the sinusoidal axis of y = 3 + 2 cos x?
   c. What is the amplitude of y = 3 + 2 cos x?

There is an interplay between the effects of C and D in the general sinusoidal curve; in particular, C has an effect on the change produced by D. We shall consider C and D separately and then ponder the interplay between them. First, let's consider C:

4. Sketch the graph of each of the following functions:
   a. y = cos (2x)   b. y = cos (0.5x)   c. y = cos (3x)   d. y = cos (x/3)
   e. Explain as best you can why the effect of using the various values of C given above is to stretch or shrink the graph of y = cos x in the horizontal direction only. Which values of C stretch? Which shrink?
   f. What is the period of each of the functions above? (Hint: Recall that the period of cos is 2π.)
   g. So, what is the effect of C on the period of the function y = cos (Cx)?

In exercise 4, you should have found that your graphs were sinusoidal with a period less than 2π if C > 1, but with a period greater than 2π if 0 < C < 1.

Definition: The *period* of the general sinusoidal function y = A + B cos (Cx + D) is:
$$2\pi/|C|$$

---

5.   Sketch the graph of each of the following functions:
   a. y = cos (x + π/4)   b. y = cos (x – π/4)
   c. y = cos (x + π)   d. y = cos (x – π)
   e. Explain as best you can why the effect of using the various values of D given above is to translate the graph of y = cos x to the right or left by a distance of |D| . Which values of D translate the graph to the right? Which to the left?

   The distance which the graph is translated right or left (as in exercise 5) is called the *phase shift*. However, before we can define the phase shift of a general sinusoidal curve, we must ponder the interplay between C and D.

6.   Sketch the graph of y = cos (3x + π).

In exercise 6, you should have obtained a sinusoidal curve with:
                    sinusoidal axis : y = 0
                    amplitude   : 1
                    period   : 2π/3
At first glance, you probably expected the curve in exercise 6 to have a phase shift of π to the left. Your graph, however, should have revealed that there was, in fact, a phase shift of π/3 to the left. This unexpected outcome is due to the interplay of C and D.

7.   Sketch the graph of y = 3 + 2 cos (3x + π). What are the sinusoidal axis, amplitude, period, and phase shift of this function?

8. Sketch the graph of y = -2 + 3 cos (4x – π). What are the sinusoidal axis, amplitude, period, and phase shift of this function?

We have considered *only positive values of C so far*; we shall continue to do so since cos (-x) = cos x. Thus, the graphs of y = A + B cos (Cx + D) and y = A + B cos (-Cx-D) are identical. Hence, if we were considering y = 3 + 2 cos (-3x + π), we could convert to y = 3 + 2 cos (3x – π) and get the very same graph.

9. Explain as best you can what effect C is on D in producing the phase shift of a general sinusoidal curve.

Definition: The *phase shift* of the general sinusoidal curve y = A + B cos (Cx + D) has magnitude (size) |D|/C. It is a shift to the right if D < 0 or to the left if D > 0.

It is most helpful to keep the following summary of facts in mind when you have to graph a general sinusoidal curve y = A + B cos (Cx + D):
1. The sinusoidal axis is y = A; this line is the axis of the glide reflection which is a symmetry motion for the graph.
2. The amplitude is |B|; this is the maximum distance which the curve rises above or falls below its sinusoidal axis.
3. The period is 2π/C; this is the length of the motif of the basic translation which is a symmetry motion for the graph.
4. The phase shift is |D|/C—to the right if D < 0, to the left if D > 0.
5. The crests or troughs of the curve occur at the *midpoint* of the motif of the graph.
6. The curve crosses its sinusoidal axis at the points 1/4 and 3/4 of the distance from the left endpoint of the motif.

Example: Sketch the graph of y = 10 + 3 cos (2x – π)
1. The sinuisoidal axis is	: y = 10
2. The amplitude is	: 3
3. The period is	: 2π/2 = π
4. The phase shift is	: π/2 to the right
5. The curve crests at	: π/2 and 3π/2
The curve troughs at	: π
6. The curve crosses its sinusoidal axis at	: π/4 and 3π/4
7. The crests are	: 3 units above y = 10
The troughs are	: 3 units below y = 10

So, we can sketch *one period* of this function as below:

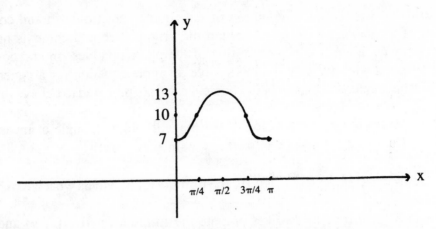

10. Sketch at least one full period of each of the following curves; in each part, state the information about the curve as illustrated in the example above:

   a. $y = 3 + 5 \cos (2x - \pi)$

   b. $-7 - 4 \cos (-3x + \pi)$

   c. $y = 8 + 10 \cos (x/2 - \pi/4)$

   d. $y = -4 - 6 \cos (2x/3 + \pi/3)$

11. Write a general sinusoidal equation for each of the curves sketched below:

   a)

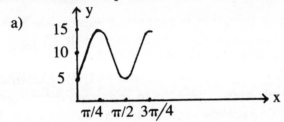

   b)

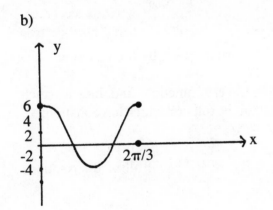

   c)

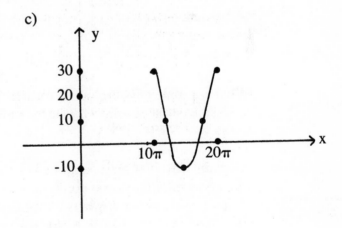

Section 4

Now that we know the definition of the circular functions sin and cos in terms of the result of a rotation of the plane around the origin, it should come as no surprise to you that the general equation for a rotation of the plane involves sin and cos functions. This is the reason why we were unable to give a simple equation for a general rotation when we first encountered the idea. Now, however, we are prepared to believe the following:

Let $R_\theta: \mathbb{R}^2 \to \mathbb{R}^2$ be the rotation of the plane through an angle of measure θ around the origin. Then, $R_\theta(x, y) = (x \cdot \cos\theta - y \cdot \sin\theta, x \cdot \sin\theta + y \cdot \cos\theta)$.

1. Show that if $(x, y) = P = (1, 0)$, the formula for R_θ yields what we would expect.

2. Let $\theta = \pi$ (i.e., $+180°$). Compute the formula for $R_{180}(x, y)$ and show that your answer agrees with what one would have expected for a half-turn around the origin (refer back to the material on half-turns if necessary).

   More generally, the formula for a rotation of the plane through an angle of measure θ around the point (h, k) is:
   $$(x, y) \rightsquigarrow ((x - h)\cos\theta - (y - k)\sin\theta + h, (x - h)\sin\theta + (y - k)\cos\theta + k)$$

3. Verify that the formula above gives the expected result when $\theta = 180°$. (Note: the formula should agree with that for a half-turn around (h, k).)

4. Let $\triangle ABC$ have vertices A(2, 2), B(6, 4), and C(4, 8). Sketch $\triangle ABC$. Use your calculator and the formula above to compute and graph the image of $\triangle ABC$ under the following rotations of the plane around the origin:

   a. R_{45} b. R_{90} c. R_{-60}

   Write the *exact* formula for each rotation first.

5. Suppose R_θ is a rotation of the plane around the origin given by the equation:
   $$(x, y) \rightsquigarrow (-\sqrt{3}x/2 - y/2, x/2 - \sqrt{3}y/2).$$
   What are some possible values for θ? (Hint: Use inverse functions and draw a sketch to visualize what is going on.) Do the same thing for the rotation which has equation:
   $$(x, y) \rightsquigarrow (-\sqrt{2}x/2 + \sqrt{2}y/2, -\sqrt{2}x/2 - \sqrt{2}y/2).$$

6. a. Explain why it is reasonable to say that $R_\theta \circ R_\phi = R_{\theta + \phi}$ if all of the rotations are centered at the same point.

   b. In particular, if the origin is the center,
   $R_{\theta + \phi}((1, 0)) = (\cos(\theta + \phi), \sin(\theta + \phi))$ by definition.
          i. Is $\cos(\theta + \phi) = \cos\theta + \cos\phi$?
          ii. Is $\sin(\theta + \phi) = \sin\theta + \sin\phi$?
   (Hint: An easy way to check is to use specific values of θ and ϕ, e.g., $\theta = \phi = \pi/4$.)

   Your solution to the last parts of the exercise above should have convinced you that things are never so simple as we might wish them to be. In fact, using the general formula for a rotation of the plane through an angle of measure around the origin, i.e.,
   $$R_\theta(x, y) = (x\cos\theta - y\sin\theta, x\sin\theta + y\cos\theta)$$
   we can easily deduce the correct formulas for $\cos(\theta + \phi)$ and $\sin(\theta + \phi)$.

Recall that: $(\cos(\theta + \phi), \sin(\theta + \phi)) = R_{\theta + \phi}(1, 0) = R_\theta \circ R_\phi(1, 0)$

$\quad = R_\theta(\cos\phi, \sin\phi)$

$\quad = (\cos\phi\cos\theta - \sin\phi\sin\theta, \cos\phi\sin\theta + \sin\phi\cos\theta).$

7. Why is the last equality above valid?

    Thus:

$$\begin{array}{l} \cos(\theta + \phi) = \cos\phi\cos\theta - \sin\phi\sin\theta \\ \sin(\theta + \phi) = \cos\phi\sin\theta + \sin\phi\cos\theta \end{array}$$

8. Using the formulas above, derive formulas for $\cos(\theta - \phi)$ and for $\sin(\theta - \phi)$.
    (Hint: Replace ϕ by $-\phi$.)

9. Using the formulas above, show that:
   a. i. $\cos 2\theta = \cos^2\theta - \sin^2\theta$
      ii. $\cos 2\theta = 1 - 2\sin^2\theta$
      iii. $\cos 2\theta = 2\cos^2\theta - 1$
   b. $\sin 2\theta = 2\sin\theta\cos\theta$ (Hint: Let $\phi = \theta$; use $\sin^2\theta + \cos^2\theta = 1$ where appropriate.)
   c. Solve the equation in a.ii. for $\sin^2\theta$ in terms of $\cos 2\theta$.
   d. Solve the equation in a.iii. for $\cos^2\theta$ in terms of $\cos 2\theta$.
   e. Substitute $\theta/2$ for θ in the equations obtained in each of c. and d. to obtain the so-called half-angle formulas:

   $\cos \theta/2 = $ _____ and

   $\sin \theta/2 = $ _____.

Remark: The formulas established above are particularly useful in simplifying certain problems encountered in calculus (specifically in integrating powers and products of sin and cos). They were also used, long ago, to ease the computation of such values as $\cos(\pi/4 + \pi/3)$ and $\sin 15°$, for which one once had to use complicated tables of trigonometric function values. Such mindless drudgery is best left to drones—it has all been left behind us since we now have good, cheap calculators to do the donkey work, while we devote ourselves to what is human in mathematics.

10. Compute the *exact* value of $\cos(\pi/4 + \pi/3)$ using the formula for $\cos(\theta + \phi)$, and the *exact* values for sin and cos of $\pi/4$ and $\pi/3$. Use your calculator to approximate the exact value by approximating the radicals involved. Of course, $\cos(\pi/4 + \pi/3) = \cos(45 + 60) = \cos 105$. Compute $\cos 105$ using your calculator. Does your answer agree with the approximate value you got above?

Section 5

In this section, we shall conclude our study of trigonometry by developing a few tools for solving triangles (i.e., for finding the lengths of their sides, the measures of their angles, etc.) about which we know a few crucial facts.

For example, suppose we know the lengths of two sides of a triangle and also the measure of the angle included between them, i.e., we know SAS. Since all triangles satisfying the given are congruent to one another (by SAS), it seems reasonable to suppose that we should be able to "solve" such a triangle. We shall first develop a tool designed to enable us to find the length of the third side of a triangle for which we have the data SAS. Suppose the two known side lengths are b and c while the known included angle has measure θ. Any triangle satisfying the data would have to look something like this:

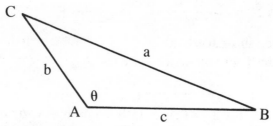

To develop a formula for a, the unknown side length, we impose a coordinate system on the plane containing $\triangle ABC$ so that we get:

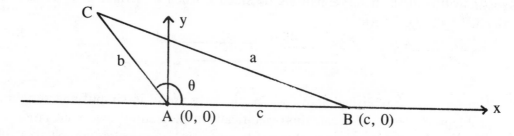

1. Verify that the coordinates of C are (b cos θ, b sin θ). (Hint: The similarity $S_{A, b}$ with scale factor b and center A maps $R_{\theta}(P)$ onto C. Recall that P is (1, 0). Why? So what?)

Thus, by the Euclidean distance formula we get:
$$\begin{aligned}
a^2 \quad &= (c - b \cos \theta)^2 + (0 - b \sin \theta)^2 \\
&= c^2 - 2bc \cos \theta + b^2\cos^2 \theta + b^2\sin^2 \theta \\
&= c^2 - 2bc \cos \theta + b^2(\cos^2 \theta + \sin^2 \theta) \\
&= c^2 - 2bc \cos \theta + b^2 \cdot 1
\end{aligned}$$
So, $a^2 = b^2 + c^2 - 2bc \cos \theta$

There are three formulas like this which are collectively known as:

> ### The Law of Cosines
>
> $$a^2 = b^2 + c^2 - 2 \, bc \cos A$$
> $$b^2 = a^2 + c^2 - 2 \, ac \cos B$$
> $$c^2 = a^2 + b^2 - 2 \, ab \cos C$$

2. Verify that the Law of Cosines is a generalized form of the Pythagorean theorem by testing what the resulting formula is like if $\mu\angle C = 90$.

3. In each of the following , compute the length of the missing side of $\triangle$ ABC:
    a. $b = 6$, $c = 8$, $\mu\angle A = 72$
    b. $b = 3$, $a = 7$, $\mu\angle C = 28$
    c. $c = 3.2$, $a = 6.8$, $\mu\angle B = 42.5$

We can also use the Law of Cosines to compute the measures of the angles of a triangle about which we have the data SSS. Suppose we know a,b, and c. We can solve the equations in the Law of Cosines to get:

$$\cos A = \frac{a^2 - b^2 - c^2}{-2bc} = \frac{-a^2 + b^2 + c^2}{2bc}$$

Thus, A is the angle whose cosine is $(-a^2 + b^2 + c^2)/2bc$; hence, A may be found by using the $\cos^{-1}$ function on your calculator after you have entered the value

$$\frac{-a^2 + b^2 + c^2}{2bc}$$

Suppose $a = 5, b = 6, c = 7$. Then $(-a^2 + b^2 + c^2)/2bc = (-25 + 36 + 49)/84 = 5/7$
Using the calculator, we find $A = \cos^{-1} 5/7 \approx 44.42°$.
Similarly, we may compute the other two angles of the triangle by saying:

$$\cos B = \frac{-b^2 + a^2 + c^2}{2ac} = \frac{-36 + 25 + 49}{70} \approx 0.5428. . .$$

Using the calculator, we get $B = \cos^{-1} (0.5428. . .) \approx 57.12°$.

Finally, $\cos C = \frac{-c^2 + a^2 + b^2}{2ab} = \frac{-49 + 25 + 36}{60} = 1/5 = 0.2$
Thus, $C = \cos^{-1} (0.2) \approx 78.46°$.

If we check our work, we first notice that ASIT is satisfied (i.e., the measures of the angles are in the same order as the side lengths opposite). Secondly, we note that the angle sum of our computed values is: $44.42 + 57.12 + 78.46 = 180.00$. This is enough to give us great confidence in the accuracy of our answer.

4. Compute the measure of each of the angles in a triangle defined by the SSS data in each of the following:
    a. $a = 2, b = 3, c = 4$.
    b. $a = 4.5, b = 3.2, c = 5.8$.

You will probably recall (see Unit IX on the area of triangles) that the area of a triangle may be computed by using the formula:
Area = $\frac{1}{2} \cdot b \cdot h$,
where b is the length of a side (base) of the triangle and h is the associated altitude (height). We shall now develop a formula useful for finding the area of a triangle about which we know SAS. Suppose we know b, c, and θ (as in the Law of Cosines) in a triangle such as the one shown below:

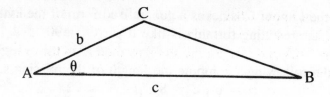

As before, we impose a coordinate system on the plane containing $\triangle ABC$ to get the result illustrated below:

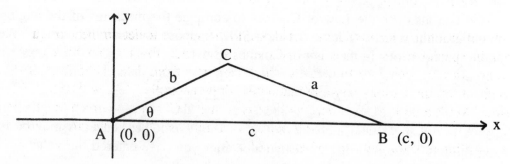

We can see that the coordinates of C are $(b \cos \theta, b \sin \theta)$. But then $h = b \cdot \sin \theta$. Thus, $\alpha(\triangle ABC) = \frac{1}{2} \cdot c \cdot b \sin \theta = \frac{1}{2} bc \sin A$
Similarly, $\alpha(\triangle ABC) = \frac{1}{2} ac \sin B = \frac{1}{2} ab \sin C$.

5.   Find the area of $\triangle ABC$ for each of the triangles in exercises 3 and 4.

Finally, we can use the formulas for area which we developed above to derive the very useful Law of Sines. Since we know that
$$\alpha(\triangle ABC) = \tfrac{1}{2} bc \sin A = \tfrac{1}{2} ac \sin B = \tfrac{1}{2} ab \sin C,$$
we can divide by $\frac{1}{2}abc$ to get:

Law of Sines
$$\frac{\text{Sin } A}{a} = \frac{\text{Sin } B}{b} = \frac{\text{Sin } C}{c}$$

We can use the Law of Sines to solve triangles for which we have the data ASA or SAA—and, if we are very careful, SSA.

Example: Suppose we know SAA, say $a = 10$, $\mu\angle A = 45$, $\mu\angle B = 50$. How could we find the other side lengths? We could use:
$$\frac{\sin A}{a} = \frac{\sin B}{b} \text{ as } \frac{\sin 45}{10} = \frac{\sin 50}{b} \quad \text{Thus, } b = \frac{10 \sin 50}{\sin 45} \approx 10.83.$$

We compute $\mu\angle C = 180 - (45 + 50) = 85$.

Thus, since $\dfrac{\sin A}{a} = \dfrac{\sin C}{c}$, we get $c = \dfrac{10 \sin 85}{\sin 45} \approx 13.00$.

Now, suppose we know ASA, say $\mu\angle A = 30$, $c = 12.8$, and $\mu\angle B = 42.5$. Then $\mu\angle C = 180 - (30 + 42.5) = 107.5$.

Thus, we know SAA and can use the *same* method as in the example above to compute the other two side lengths.

6. a. Compute the other two side lengths mentioned above.
   b. Solve the triangle satisfying the data in each of the following:
       i. $\mu\angle A = 23$, $b = 16.5$, $\mu\angle C = 50$.
       ii. $\mu\angle A = 68$, $\mu\angle C = 42$, $c = 100$.

You will doubtless recall that the data SSA do *not* suffice to determine a unique triangle except in special cases (which is why there is no such thing as an SSA congruence theorem). In fact, there are four cases which can arise from data of the form SSA:

To check on the various possible outcomes, draw an angle, $\angle A$, with the given angle measure. Mark a point, C, on one ray of $\angle A$ so that $AC = b$, the given length. Put the steel point of your compass, set for a radius $= a$, on C and swing an arc to see whether there is an intersection with the other ray of $\angle A$.

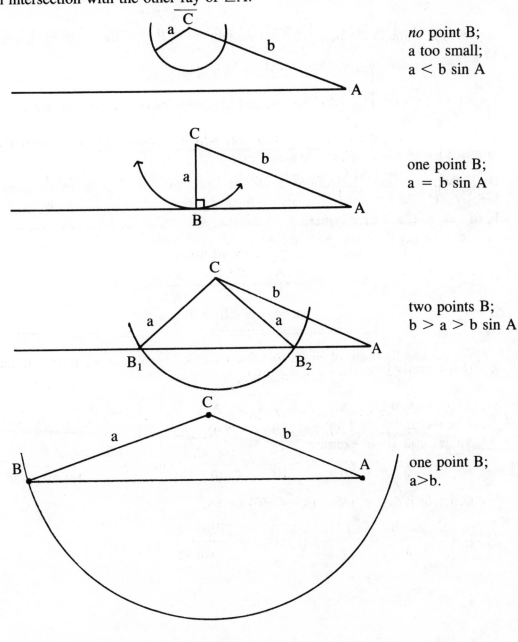

no point B;
a too small;
$a < b \sin A$

one point B;
$a = b \sin A$

two points B;
$b > a > b \sin A$

one point B;
$a > b$.

-273-

7. Solve the triangle (if any) which satisfies the data in each of the following:
    a. b = 5, a = 2, μ∠A = 27
    b. b = 5, a = 2.26995, μ∠A = 27
    c. b = 5, a = 4, μ∠A = 27
    d. b = 5, a = 6, μ∠A = 27

It would be a shame to stop our study of trigonometry without examining just one more slick trick using transformations. We shall rediscover the Law of Sines and yet another Law (which seems to have no special name) as a result. Suppose we know the data a, b, and μ∠A in △ABC, and impose a coordinate system on the plane containing △ABC to get the following:

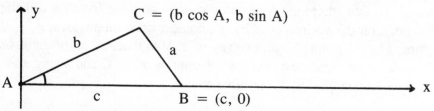

Reflect the plane in the perpendicular bisector of $\overline{AB}$ (i.e., in the vertical line x = c/2) to get

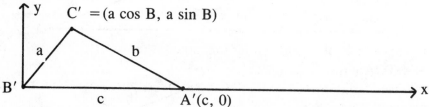

By known facts about reflections in vertical lines, the expressions for the second coordinates of C and C′ must be equal. Thus, we have b sin A = a sin B. Recall that $F_m(u, v) = (2a - u, v)$ where m is the line x = a. Since m is (in this case) the line x = c/2 we get $F_m(b \cos A, b \sin A) = (c - b \cdot \cos A, b \sin A)$. Therefore,
$$a \cos B = c - b \cos A, \text{ i.e.,}$$

$$\boxed{c = a \cos B + b \cos A}$$

What a pretty little result!

8. Suppose you know a = 5, b = 4, μ∠A = 34.58$\overline{3}$, μ∠B = 27.
    Use the un-named Law above to compute c; then check to make sure it's one of the values you got in exercise 7.

-274-

Unit X—Review Topics

1. Unit circle, angle in standard position—initial and terminal sides; orientation of angles—positive direction is counterclockwise, negative direction is clockwise.

2. R_θ, $P = (1, 0)$, $R_\theta(P) = (\cos\theta, \sin\theta)$, circular functions, how to use a calculator to compute cos, sin, tan, etc.

3. Values of circular functions for $0, 30, 45, 60, 90, \ldots$

4. tan, cot, sec, csc.

5. Global behavior of circular functions.

6. Basic identities:
$$\sin^2\theta + \cos^2\theta \equiv 1$$
$$\tan^2\theta + 1 \equiv \sec^2\theta$$
$$1 + \cot^2\theta \equiv \csc^2\theta$$

7. Relationships between circular functions which follow from the symmetry of the unit circle:

$$\cos(90-\theta) = \sin\theta \qquad\qquad \cos(90+\theta) = -\sin\theta$$
$$\sin(90-\theta) = \cos\theta \qquad\qquad \sin(90+\theta) = \cos\theta$$
$$\cos(-\theta) = \cos\theta \qquad\qquad \cos(180+\theta) = -\cos\theta$$
$$\sin(-\theta) = -\sin\theta \qquad\qquad \sin(180+\theta) = -\sin\theta$$

Etc.

8. Interpretation of trigonometric functions as ratios of side lengths in a right triangle; SOHTOASHA; magic hexagon.

9. Inverse trigonometric functions; how to use them and how to use a calculator to compute their values.

10. Applications of trigonometric and inverse trigonometric functions to triangle problems.

11. Radian measure of angles; 2π radians $= 360°$; how to use radians on a calculator.

12. Periodic functions, period of a function.

13. Graphs—symmetry and other properties—of each of the six circular functions.

14. General sinusoidal curves; effect of each real coefficient; sinusoidal axis, amplitude, period, phase shift; sketching graphs of general sinusoidal curves; deriving an equation for a general sinusoidal curve from its graph.

15. Formula for $R_\theta(x, y)$ centered at $(0, 0)$ is $(x\cos\theta - y\sin\theta, x\sin\theta + y\cos\theta)$.

16. $\cos(\theta + \phi) = \cos\theta\cos\phi - \sin\theta\sin\phi$
    $\sin(\theta + \phi) = \cos\phi\sin\theta + \sin\phi\cos\theta$

17. $\cos 2\theta = \cos^2\theta - \sin^2\theta$
    $\qquad\quad = 1 - 2\sin^2\theta$
    $\qquad\quad = 2\cos^2\theta - 1$
    $\sin 2\theta = 2\sin\theta\cos\theta$

18. Law of Cosines (used with SAS, SSS as data)
$$a^2 = b^2 + c^2 - 2\cdot b\cdot c\cdot\cos A$$
$$b^2 = a^2 + c^2 - 2\cdot a\cdot c\cdot\cos B$$
$$c^2 = a^2 + b^2 - 2\cdot a\cdot b\cdot\cos C$$

19. $\alpha(\triangle ABC) = \tfrac{1}{2}\cdot b\cdot c\cdot\sin A = \tfrac{1}{2}\cdot a\cdot c\cdot\sin B = \tfrac{1}{2}\cdot a\cdot b\cdot\sin C$

20. Law of Sines (used with ASA, SAA, and sometimes SSA as data):
$$\frac{\sin A}{a} = \frac{\sin B}{b} = \frac{\sin C}{c}$$

21. $c = a \cos B + b \cos A$
$a = b \cos C + c \cos B$
$b = a \cos C + c \cos A$

Epilog—Quo Vadis?

> How can I know what I think 'til I see what I say?"
> –Lewis Carroll–

Well, we've nearly reached the end of our long journey through the realm of geometry. So, the question arises—*quo vadis?*—where are you going now?

There are several paths which you could follow. Most of you will probably enroll next in either an advanced algebra or a pre-calculus class (assuming you are in high school). In either case, but especially in pre-calculus, you will find many of the ideas and topics you have learned (e.g., symmetry, groups, functions, and transformations) to be most useful and helpful—particularly the general ideas about functions or mappings.

If you are in a situation where any of the following are available, there are other major options which you are by now well prepared to pursue:

1. We have only barely scratched the surface of the study of groups, not to mention the study of such algebraic objects as rings, fields, vector spaces, etc. with richer structure. You could easily and profitably expand your knowledge of these areas since an algebraic flavor permeates much of modern mathematics and computing; an excellent resource for pursuing study in groups at an elementary level is: *The Fascination of Groups* by F.J. Budden (Camb. U. Press, 1972). For more advanced study of algebraic structures, refer to *A First Course in Abstract Algebra* (by J.B. Fraleigh; Addison-Wesley. Try to get the *latest* edition of this one.)

2. There remains an enormous amount of advanced geometry to be explored. In particular, you could extend your grasp of transformation geometry as well as analytic and synthetic geometry—both Euclidean and non-Euclidean. Your further study in geometry could retain a very strong algebraic flavor, especially if you were to pursue a vector-oriented approach and move toward studying geometry in the setting of linear algebra and vector spaces. Along such lines, you could look into *Transformation Geometry: An Introduction to Symmetry* (by G.E. Martin; Springer-Verlag, 1982) to forge on in transformational geometry. A good, readable exposition of a vector approach to geometry can be found in *Geometry, Algebra, and Trigonometry by Vector Methods* (by A.H. Copeland, Sr., The Macmillan Company, 1962). A wonderful, very thorough treatment of geometry via vectors and linear algebra is given in *A Vector Approach to Euclidean Geometry* (2 vols., by H.E. Vaughn and S. Szabo, The Macmillan Company, 1971). Finally, you will find all you ever wanted to know about symmetry in *Symmetry in Science and Art* (by A.V. Shubnikov and V.A. Koptsik; Plenum Press, 1974).

3. Your knowledge of trigonometry needs significant improvement, in a context which continues the introductory stress on circular functions, and which illustrates applications to topics other than routine (and routinely *boring!*) "triangle solving." You can find a *superb* elementary treatment of both advanced algebra and trigonometry in *Algebra and Trigonometry: Functions and Applications* (by P.A. Foerster; Addison-Wesley, 1980).

4. Finally, you should not overlook an outstandingly good and very readable (even fun to browse!) text: *Geometric Symmetry* (by E.H. Lockwood and R.H. Macmillan, Camb. U. Press, 1978).

Whatever path you choose to follow, I hope this book will have helped you develop both a robust spirit of mathematical thinking (my chief aim), and a rich storehouse of ideas which can be used as parts of the foundation as you structure the multitude of ideas you will encounter—no matter what you may go on to do.

Ave atque vale!

Index